이 책을 검토해 주신 선생님

강원
권대황 팀즈영어학원
권미현 리드영어
기은진 전문과외
김광희 한샘학원
김나은 나은영어
김세정 브릿지영어학원
김양수 스파르타코치미
김정은 김정은영어학원
김준성 구쌤학원
남상근 브릿지영어학원
노홍석 Red Stone Academy
박슬기 최상위수학마루슬기로운영어생활
박은진 삼육어학원
박정선 잉글리쉬클럽
백희영 이상학원
안서아 숲어학원
오은아 레이첼잉글리시학원
윤아영 전문과외
이금석 케이유이에스비
이성규 브릿지영어학원
이정혜 전문과외
전수지 에리카영어학원
정정화 구쌤학원
정정환 푸른입시학원
조연희 전문과외
천슬기 브릿지영어학원
최가영 전문과외
최수남 강릉영수배움교실
최현주 최샘영어
표유현 쉼표영어

경기
갈현주 GTC영어
강나리 필업단과전문학원
강석종 씨드학원 2관
강소윤 다른영어학원
강신혜 에이블중고등영어학원
강연수 안양외국어고등학교
강예진 YJ영어의정원
강유림 이지영어학원
강준수 미래인재학원
강춘화 양주 최고다학원
강태경 연세나로학원
강현숙 파주 토피아어학원 교하 캠퍼스
고승환 11월의 로렐
고승희 미래연학원
고윤재 연세학원
고현정 에이블영어
고혜경 Go쌤's 에듀
고혜리 최강영수학원
공윤진 한광중학교
곽억훈 최강영어
구대만 대입명문 트리비움 구쌤 합격영어
구혜령 젤라쿠 잉글리쉬
구혜영 구스영어보습학원
권수현 나홀로영어학원
권순상 사과나무학원
권인혜 전문과외
권정현 수잔잉글리쉬학원
권종혁 고등바른공부학원
권지영 트레져스영어학원
권해나 입시에날개

권향숙 에이블플러스영어교습소
기종훈 마하수능영어전문학원
길대현 길쌤 입시영어
김경영 청람학원
김광수 더배움 잉글리쉬
김규은 분당소피아영어학원
김기선 위너스일등급학원
김기영 서강학원
김남건 연세나로학원 수원본점
김문희 수만휘기숙학원
김미영 시너지영어수학학원
김미원 한진연 입시전략연구소 수원센터
김미희 J&W 학원
김민기 빨리강해지는학원
김민선 HC영수전문학원
김민영 남동탄 레이크에듀영어
김민정 이화영어
김민정 분당영덕여자고등학교
김병희 B&J 과외
김보람 JM학원
김상겸 물푸레스쿨
김설 한올입시학원
김성민 전문과외
김성한 양명고등학교
김세종 데이비드영어교습소
김숙영 더오름학원
김승민 룩스영어학원
김승호 명품M수학영어 학원
김승훈 장선생영어학원
김신태 원탑영어
김연남 Trooper English
김영아 김영아개인과외
김영희 파주운정 제니스학원
김완혁 단칼영어학원
김우성 남양 아토즈영어학원
김원동 미래인학원
김유진 하이노크 영어학원
김윤식 낙생고등학교
김윤아 코리안파인
김은지 양서고등학교
김은희 이든영어
김의식 에스엔티입시전문학원
김인호 맵학원
김정은 조이력 영어학원
김정택 솔터고등학교
김지원 대치탑영어학원
김지현 이지프레임 영어학원
김진희 우솔학원
김창홍 영품영어
김태준 이지고등영어
김하늘 훈선생영어학원
김한나 스카이 영수학원
김한빛 지니리영어학원
김현정 배곧 탑클래스 영수학원
김형원 전문과외
김혜진 모산센터 공터영어 공부방
김효진 옥정동 샤인학원
김후중 더플랜영어학원
나병찬 에스라이팅 영어학원
나애경 잉쥴리쉬
나태연 Welcome to English(WE) 영어교습소
남인철 배움의숲학원
남지원 용인필탑학원
남현경 정상어학원

남현제 강남글로벌입시학원
노연웅 알찬교육학원
노영임 하이영어
노영현 정상학원 광주경안분원
류동현 G EDU
류지은 SLB입시학원
마지영 전문과외
마헌정 인스쿨학원
맹대운 삼성영어 광교1교실
문슬기 문쌤전문과외
문은영 삼성영어쎈수학 은계학원
문장균 스카이학원
민수진 위드민 영어
박경란 영통강남학원
박경태 IMI영어학원
박계리 글로리영어교습소
박상근 DK영수학원
박상유 콕수학오드리영어보습학원
박서현 박서현영어
박선이 썬영어
박성식 경화여자English Business고등학교
박세영 쎄이학원
박세윤 이화인학원
박소연 부천 청명학원
박소영 이엘아이에스어학원
박수인 용인필탑학원
박수정 잉글리시아이 케이트학원
박숙현 에이사이드 입시학원
박연주 전문과외
박영심 전문과외
박영철 이즈원 영어수학 전문학원
박영훈 권선대성종합학원
박윤성 제일학원
박은경 서영영어
박은빈 오산 교일학원
박재은 서윤희영어학원
박정은 하늘English
박정현 JH 스파르타 영어학원
박정훈 안양외국어고등학교
박주연 전문과외
박준근 연세나로학원
박준호 필탑학원
박지연 시작
박지원 전문과외
박찬일 양명고등학교
박천형 한빛에듀
박지욱 Park's Room English
박현선 안양외국어고등학교
박혜리 조은샘 학원
박혜원 이투스247 수원시청점 학원
박효정 용인필탑학원
반인애 리딩유영어
방난효 명문필학원
방선아 가온영어
배가람 수만휘기숙학원
배이슬 에이블 학원
배종서 광명북고등학교
백승민 윈영어학원
백유안 전문과외
백은진 솔로몬학원
백재원 앤써학원
백지연 다산미래학원
서기동 베리타스 영어 학원
서다혜 Cloe English

서상... 안양외국어고등학교
손선화 더웨이영어교습소
손영은 팁탑잉글리쉬
손영준 파주열린학원
손유리 하비투스 영어
송의식 교일학원
송재용 대치명인학원
송주영 위상학원
송희승 전문과외
신승철 일탑영어학원
신원지 지니어스 영어
신윤주 전문과외
신혜원 해밀영어
신희진 스터디올킬학원
심소미 쎈수학영어학원_봉담
심종원 윤선생영어 이천하내해원
안명은 아우룸영어
안상현 프라미스자이영어학원
안수민 전문과외
안수예 전문과외
안지민 이엔영어학원
안지원 프렌글리시 은여울캠퍼스
양선화 성문고등학교
양시내 알지영수학원
양창현 조셉입시학원
양효근 더키(TheKEY)영어학원
엄한수 양명고등학교
여호수아 한샘학원 덕정캠퍼스
오국화 이랩스영어학원
오민희 미니오영어
오영철 광주비상에듀
오주향 대치힐영어학원
오준우 유투엠X로제타스톤
오현숙 천천메카학원
왕형규 이름영어
유경민 송현학원
유민재 백영고등학교
유복순 전문과외
유연이 큐이엠
유예지 삼성영어 한내학원
유옥경 만점영어
유지아 CINDY'S ENGLISH
유지현 ERC 유쌤영어 교습소
유효선 앨리스영어학원
윤경미 윙스영어
윤석호 야탑고등학교
윤숙현 광덕고등학교
윤연정 Tr.Annie's Library
윤정원 플랜어학원
윤정희 수어람학원
윤지후 오산 락수학 앤 윤영어
윤창의 이룸교육
윤형태 HAAS(하스)영어학원
윤혜선 아이비스 영어학원
윤혜영 이루다영어수학학원
이가림 전문과외
이강훈 이수학원
이경희 고려대아카데미

이지우 수원 레볼리쉬 어학원
엔터스카이학원
전문과외
철산에스라이팅영어학원
김수영보습학원
열린학원
꿈의 발걸음 학원
이민재 제리킹영어학원
이보라 디오영어
이보라 이쌤영어교습소
이상록 PRM
이상규 진짜공부입시학원
이상윤 한샘학원
이서윤 계몽학원
이선미 정현영어학원
이세미 유타스학원
이수정 이그잼포유
이수정 믿음영어전문과외
이슬희 입시코드학원
이승은 공터영어동탄호수센터학원
이예녹 위너비투비영어
이연경 비욘드 영어학원
이연경 제니학원
이영민 상승공감학원
이용우 한소망비전학원
이은영 가람학원
이은주 지에듀
이은주 귀인중학교
이은혜 리체움영어학원
이인철 루틴입시학원
이재협 사차원학원
이준 맨투맨학원
이지우 이지우영어학원
이지원 에듀플러스 학원
이지은 DYB 최선고등관
이지혜 공부방
이지혜 리케이온 어학원
이지효 스탠스영어교습소
이진성 용인필탑학원
이진주 아이원해법영어
이창석 넛지영어학원
이충기 영어나무
이태균 권선로제타스톤영어학원
이하원 전문과외
이한솔 위너스영어
이해진 파란영어학원
이현우 부천 신사고 영어학원
이효진 확인영어수학
임광영 러쎌기숙학원
임수경 전문과외
임수정 로고스아카데미
임승훈 다니엘학교
임연주 하이디드림팀
임은지 전문과외
임은희 Eunice English
임지현 현쌤영어
임창민 김포 우리학원
임창완 백영고등학교
임효진 폭스영어입시전문학원
장미래 안성종로엠
장민석 일킴훈련소입시학원
장슬기 폭스영어학원
장아련 목동J영어학원
장유리 더바른영어학원

장준성	링구아어학원	편광범	야탑고등학교	이문식	리더스 아카데미학원	이상열	이상렬입시단과학원	**대구**	
장현정	헤리티지영수학원	표호진	아너스영어전문학원	이수길	명성영수학원	이소연	전문과외	구교찬	새롬영어
장혜진	용인필탑학원	하사랑	덕계한샘학원	이연홍	리즈(Rhee's) 영어연구소	이주연	Rachel's English	구범모	굿샘영어학원
장호진	홍수학영어입시학원	하수용	시흥 대성학원	이윤섭	창원경일여자고등학교	이지연	전문과외	구수진	전문과외
장효선	영어의품격	한순현	동탄 SKY 비상학원	이인아	인잉글리쉬학원	장미	잉글리시아이 원리학원	구현정	헬렌영어학원
전성준	이든학원	한예진	필탑학원	임진희	어썸영어학원	장정원	옥스포드영어학원	권보현	씨즈더이어학원
전성훈	훈선생영어학원	함수향	진심팩토리인재양성소	장경출	야꼼영수학원	전영아	문일학원	권익재	제이슨영어교습소
전수빈	전문과외	현윤아	중동그린타운해법영어교습소	장은정	케이트어학원	정소연	YBM퍼펙트잉글리쉬	권하련	아너스이엠에스학원
전우정	안T영어학원	홍승완	전문과외	장재훈	메르센학원	정원갑	구미여자고등학교	김근아	블루힐영어학원
전주원	필업단과전문학원	홍은화	라라영어수학 학원	정상락	비상잉글리시아이 영어교습소	정현수	엠베스트se위닝학원	김기목	목샘영어교습소
전지애	고양국제고등학교	홍정우	정현영어학원	정수연	Got Them	정호정	인지니어스	김나래	더베스트영어학원
전지혜	위슬런학원	홍호영	닉고등입시학원	정수정	지탑영어	조효근	수학만영어도학원	김미나	전문과외
전호준	채움영어	홍희섭	조이 영어공부방	정희성	원스텝영수학원	최경주	전문과외	김민재	열공영강 영어수학학원
정규빈	대치다다학원	홍희진	청평 한샘 학원	최승관	창선고등학교	최미선	3030영어망청포은러닝센터	김병후	LU영어
정다움	카인드학원	황다연	The study 꿈자람	최지영	시퀀스영수학원	허우열	탑세븐입시	김상완	YEP영어학원
정다은	전문과외	황명덕	옥정 엠베스트	최현정	토킹스타영어학원			김수미	스펙마스터
정미란	티앤씨학원	황서윤	공부방	최환준	Jun English	**광주**		김연경	유니엠어
정병채	탁클래스영어수학학원	황은진	더에듀영어수학학원	최효정	인에이블영수학원	강나검	스위치영어수학	김유환	대구 유신학원
정선영	전문과외	황일선	M&E	하동권	네오시스템영어학원	곽해림	AMG 영어학원	김윤정	독쭘영어
정선영	코어플러스영어학원			하수미	진동삼성영수학원	김도엽	스카이영어학원	김은혜	고등어학원 중등관
정성은	JK영어수학전문학원	**경남**		한지용	성민국영어학원	김도영	KOUM ENGLISH	김정혜	제니퍼영어 교습소
정성태	에이든영어학원	강진원	T.O.P 에듀학원	허민정	허달영어	김동익	전문과외	김종석	에이블영수학원
정소연	이투스 전홍철 연구실	고성관	T.O.P 에듀학원			김명재	범지연영어학원	김준석	NOTION영어
정연우	최강학원	권승구	더케이영어학원	**경북**		김병남	일등급수학위즈덤영어학원	김지영	김지영영어
정연욱	인크쌤영어학원	권승미	전문과외	강민표	현일고등학교	김상연	우리어학원	김진호	강성영어
정영선	시퀀스학원	권장미	인서울영어학원	강선우	EiE 고려대 국제 어학원	김서현	전문과외	김철우	메라키 영어 교습소
정영훈	BS반석학원	권지현	우리모두의 영수학원	강유진	지니쌤영어	김수인	모조잉글리쉬	김하나	전문과외
정유진	전문과외	김계영	성신학원	강은석	은석학원	김유경	프라임 아카데미	김현정	도우영수학원
정지연	공부의정석 학원	김국희	새라영어학원	강혜성	EiE 고려대 국제 어학원	김유진	위트니영어유타학원	김호연	KK 수학 영어
정지영	이지학원	김루	상승영수전문학원	고일영	영어의비법학원	김인화	김인화영어학원	김희정	이선생영어학원
정하경	에듀플렉스	김민경	창선고등학교	김광현	전문과외	김재곤	김재곤 중고등영어학원	나기원	문강월성점
정희찬	파란영어학원	김민기	민쌤영어	김귀숙	퀸영어교습소	김한결	상무외대어학원	노태경	윙스잉글리쉬
제정미	제이영어	김선우	진성학원	김규남	경상북도 영양교육지원청	김효은	청담아카데미학원	문창숙	지앤비(GnB)스페셜입시학원
조대웅	전문과외	김신영	김가영어학원	김도량	다이너마이트잉글리쉬	김효정	광주 메이드영어학원	민승규	민승규영어학원
조병희	이철영어학원	김신현	세종학원	김도영	김도영영어	문장엽	엠제이영어수학전문학원	박고은	스테듀입시학원
조승규	제이앤와이 어학원	김용진	다락방 남양지점 학원	김민정	잇올초이스	박동훈	유캔영어	박라율	열공열강영어수학학원
조용원	이티엘영어교습소	김주은	동상교일학원	김상호	전문과외	박정준	동아여자고등학교	박민지	소나무학원
조원웅	클라비스 영어	김준	가우스 sme 전문학원	김윤채	포카학원	박주형	본선동 한수위 국어 영어	박연희	좀다른영어
조은쌤	조은쌤장쌤영어학원	김지윤	에듀퍼스트	김으뜸	EIE어학원 옥계캠퍼스	박혜지	YBM잉글루 최강학원	박예지	전문과외
조재만	가평한샘기숙학원	김지은	HNC영어전문학원	김정선	바투하이영어	배연주	본영수학원	박지환	전문과외
조정휘	유하이에듀 학원	김진영	연세어학원	김주훈	공터 영어학원	봉병주	철수와영수	박희숙	열공열강영어수학학원
조준모	에스라이팅	김형돌	통영여자고등학교	김지현	토피아 영어 교습소	손아미	공감스터디학원	방성모	방성모영어학원
조춘화	뮤엠영어발곡학원	김화선	마산중앙고등학교	김지훈	전문과외	신지수	온에어영어학원	백소양	태학영어학원
조현지	전문과외	남유림	이루다영어교습소	김현우	창녕 대성고등학교	양신애	오름국어영어학원	백재민	에소테리카 영어학원
조혜원	The 131	노경지	전문과외	김형표	표쌤영어학원	오승리	이지스터디	서상진	대진고등학교
주지은	JIEUN ENGLISH CLASS	노수진	인피니티영수전문학원	문상현	에이원영어	오평안	지산한길어학원	서정인	서울입시학원
진남월	영어종결센터신봉학원	박민정	더클래스수학영어학원	문홍민	메디컬영어학원	우진일	블루페스 영어학원	신경순	전문과외
차안나	아이비스 영어학원	박선영	전문과외	박경애	포항대성초이스학원	유현주	U's유즈영어교습소	신정식	넛지영어교습소
채희수	전문과외	박성용	박성용입시전문학원	박계민	영광중학교	윤은주	아이비영어교실	신혜경	외대어학원
채희연	전문과외	박신영	GH영수전문학원	박규정	베네치아 영어 교습소	이민정	롱맨어학원	심경아	Shim's English
최광현	포인트학원	박영하	네오시스템영어학원	박령이	한뜻입시학원	이소민	더클래스영어전문학원	안다영	일라영어학원
최명지	이천 청솔기숙	박재형	인투잉글리쉬어학원	박보성	문화고등학교	이영조	전문과외	엄재경	하이엔드영어학원
최민석	탑클래스기숙학원	박정아	전문과외	박예진	선주고등학교	이진희	이마스터	오선연	전문과외
최상이	엄마영어아빠수학학원	박제선	주식회사김은정교육그룹	박지수	포스코교육재단	이현창	진월유앤아이어학원	원현지	원샘영어교습소
최성원	패스파인더	박준권	박준권 개인과외	배세왕	BK영수전문학원	전솔	서강고등학교	위은령	대구 브릿지영어
최세열	JS수학영어학원	배승빈	에스영어전문학원	성룡	미르어학원	정세윤	아름드리학원	유소영	YH영어교습소
최영임	국립중앙청소년디딤센터	배종원	마산무학여자고등학교	손누리	이든샘영수학원	정지선	이지스터디	윤원채	원잉글리쉬영어교습소
최유나	전문과외	배찬희	라하잉글리시신진주역점	손희경	성균관아카데미 과학영어학원	최연숙	엠베스트se공부학원	윤이강	카르페디엠 영어수학학원
최은진	고래영어학원	신형섭	크림슨어학원	유영선	아이비티주니어	최현욱	최현욱 영어학원	이근성	헬렌영어학원
최은희	공부에 강한 아이들	심동현	The오름 영수학원	유진욱	공부의힘 영수학원	최혜란	토킹클럽영어학원	이동현	쌤마스터입시학원
최인선	캐써린쌤의슈가영어교습소	안혜경	T.O.P Edu학원	윤재호	이상렬단과학원	한기석	이(E)영어교습소	이샛별	데카어학원
최창식	조나단영어보습학원	양경화	봄영어	이강정	이룸단과학원	한방엽	신통학원	이소민	프라임영어학원
최희연	채움영어학원	양기영	다니엘어학원	이리나	제일영어놀이터	현동욱	박철영어학원	이수연	하이어영어
최희정	SJ클쌤영어	원임미	링구아어학원	이민정	레이먼원어민어학원	황선미	함께가는영어	이수희	이온영어
		유인희	보듬영어과외교실	이보라	전문과외				

이승민	전문과외	이원성	파스칼베스티안학원	이유림	유림영어교습소	김영미	WIN영어	성수하	전문과외
이승재	파머스어학원 침산캠퍼스	이유나	전문과외	이윤호	메트로 영어	김영삼	중계YS영어	성언형	대치AOP
이승현	대구 학문당입시학원	이재근	이재근영어수학학원	이은정	영어를ON하다	김윤선	쎌영어	송상종	에듀플러스 학원
이승희	독쫑영어학원	이진경	이룸학원	이재우	무한꿈터 동래캠퍼스	김은진	ACE영어 교습소	송근근	기정학원
이애진	한솔영어수학이쌤파워학원	이홍원	모티브에듀학원	이정윤	아벨영어	김종윤	가온에듀	송정은	이은재어학원
이정인	계성고등학교	장혜진	피어오름영어	이지은	Izzy English	김종현	김종현영어	송현우	양서중학교
이진영	전문과외	정동녘	에스오에스학원	이지현	Serena영어	김주혜	라온학원	송혜민	전문과외
이현욱	이헌욱 영어학원	정동원	대성외국어	이진선	전문과외	김지영	강서고등학교	신경훈	제프영어
임형주	사범대단과학원	정라라	영어문화원 정라라 영어교습소	이혜정	로엠어학원	김진돈	중계세일학원	신동주	공감학원
장현진	고려대EIE어학원 현풍캠퍼스	정윤희	Alex's English	이희정	로뎀영어 E&F English	김채원	정이조 영어학원	신연우	전문과외
전윤애	전문과외	정혜수	쌜리영어	장민지	탑클래스영어학원	김하나	전문과외	신정애	당산점 와와학습코칭학원
정대용	유신학원	조영재	카이젠교육	전정은	전문과외	김현지	목동 하이스트 본원	신호현	아로새김
정승덕	JSD English	조현	시나브로학원	정영훈	J&C 영어전문학원	김형준	미래탐구 오목관	신희경	신쌤영어
정용희	에스피영어학원	진정원	코너스톤엘 상대학원	조은상	드림엔영어	김혜림	대치 청담어학원	심건희	전문과외
조성애	조성애세움영어수학학원	채송은	위캔영어학원	조정훈	고려화 고등영어전문	김혜영	스터디원	심나현	성북메가스터디
조혜선	연쌤영수학원	최성호	에이스영어 교습소	채지영	리드앤톡영어도서관학원	나선아	전문과외	심미철	수능영어플러스+
주현자	E.T Betty	최현우	엠베스트SE엘리트학원	최우성	초이English&Pass	나영은	강남청솔기숙학원	심민혜	신일류수학학원
채유란	전문과외	한형식	서대전여자고등학교	최이내	일광IGSE 어학원	노은경	이은재어학원	심은지	연세YT어학원
최효진	너를 위한 영어			탁아진	에이블영어	노재순	씨투엠학원	안나연	전문과외
하해준	일라영어학원	**부산**		하현진	브릿츠영어	노종주	전문과외	안미영	스카이플러스학원
한정아	능인고등학교	고경원	남구감만한맥학원	한구상	전문과외	도선혜	중계동 영어 공부방	안성연	안스잉글리시학원
홍지수	홍글리시영어	김달용	Able 영어교습소	한영희	미래탐구	류기동	기동찬 영어학원	안웅희	이엔엠 영수전문학
황윤슬	사적인영어	김대영	나무와숲영어교습소	홍지안	에이블 어학원	맹혜선	휘경여자고등학교	안일훈	안일훈영어교습소
		김도담	도담한영어교실			명가은	명가은 영어학원	안현우	지니영어학원
대전		김도윤	코어영어교습소	**서울**		문명기	문명기영어학원	양세희	양세희수능영어학원
Tony Park	Tony Park English	김동혁	코어국영수전문학원	Diana	위례광장 해법영어	문민아	다른학원	양하나	목동 씨앤씨
강태헌	끊어읽기영어	김동휘	장정호 영어전문학원	Simon뱅	에이플교육	문영선	키맨학원	어홍주	이-베스트 영어학원
고우리	브릭스 영어학원	김미혜	더멘토영어	가혜림	목동종로학원	문지현	목동CNC	엄태열	대치 차오름학원
곽연우	유성고등학교	김병택	탑으로가는영어	강동수	일산학원	문진완	대원고등학교	염석민	은평지1230
권현이	디디쌤영어	김성미	다올영어	강민정	네오 과학학원	박광운	전문과외	오은경	전문과외
길민주	전문과외	김소연	전문과외	강성호	대원고등학교	박귀남	Stina+ English	용혜영	SWEET ENGLISH 영어전문 공부방
김경이	영어서당학원	김재경	탑클래스영어학원	강예린	TG 영어전문학원	박기철	한진연 입시전략연구소	우승희	우승희영어학원
김근범	딱쌤영어	김정화	센텀영어교습소	강인환	스터디코치영어전문학원	박남규	알짜영어교습소	위정훈	앤트스터디 명품 대입관 학원
김기형	관저진학학원	김지애	전문과외	강정훈	더(the)상승학원	박미애	명문지혜학원	유수연	인헌중학교
김수연	둔산 엠폴리어학원	김진아	의문을열다	공진	리더스	박민주	석선생 영어학원 중관	유현승	심슨어학원
김영철	전문과외	김현지	이헌 영수 학원 초량분원	구민모	키움학원	박병석	주영학원	윤나예	미래영재
김재원	중촌브레인학원	나유진	채움영어교습소	구지윤	전문과외	박선경	씨투엠학원	윤명원	이지수능교육원
김하나	김하나영어연구소	남경화	전문과외	권보현	대치 다원교육	박소영	JOY	윤상혁	전문과외
나규섭	비전21입시학원	남재호	제니스학원	권영진	경동고등학교	박소하	전문과외	윤성	대치동 새움학원
남영종	엠베스트SE	류미향	류미향입시영어	권원주	권쌤영어	박소현	전문과외	윤은미	CnT영어학원
민지원	민쌤영어교습소	박문기	시너지학원	권재현	icu학원	박숭규	SK 영어연구소	윤정아	윤정아영어
박난정	제일학원	박미진	MJ영어학원	권혜령	전문과외	박예나	강북예일학원	이강희	시은영어학원
박성희	청담프라임학원	박수진	제이앤씨 영어전문학원	길수련	전문과외	박윤주	에이원 아카데미 보습학원	이계훈	이지영어학원
박신지	청명대입학원	박아름	빡스잉글리쉬	김경수	목동탑킴입시연구소	박은경	오늘영어 교습소	이광희	가온에듀 2관
박주형	전문과외	박아림	티움영어교습소	김나결	레이쌤영어교습소	박인선	신촌 나교수어학원	이국재	이은재영어학원
박진선	전문과외	박정희	학림학원	김다온	진인영어학원	박정호	전문과외	이남규	신정송현학원
박진주	아이린인스티튜트	박지우	영어를 ON하다	김라영	목동퀸즈영어학원	박정효	메가스터디학원	이동근	이지스아카데미학원
박현진	전문과외	박지은	박지은영어전문과외방	김명열	대치명인학원	박준영	은평 G1230	이명순	Top Class English
박효진	박효진 영어 교습소	배거용	배거용영어전문학원	김미경	정이조 영어학원	박지연	영어공부연구소	이미영	티엔하버드영어학원
백지수	플랫폼학원	배찬희	에이플러스영어	김미선	낸시영어교습소	박지영	전문과외	이석원	숭실중학교
서윤주	전문과외	서대광	서진단과학원	김미은	오늘도맑은 영어교습소	박진경	JAYz ENGLISH	이석호	교원더퍼스트캠퍼스 학원
송신근	일취월장학원	성장우	전문과외	김미정	아발론랭콘신내캠퍼스	박진아	사과나무학원	이성택	엔아이씨영어학원
심효령	삼부가람	손복건	내신종로학원	김민지	클라라영어교습소	박찬경	펜타곤영어학원	이소민	임팩트영어
안수정	궁극의 사고	손소희	안창모 특목수능영어	김보영	대치 다원교육	박효원	링크영어교습소	이소윤	늘품영수전문학원
양지현	청출어람	손지안	정관 아슬란학원	김상희	스카이플러스	박희삼	대치쿰인학원	이승미	금천정상어학원
오봉희	새미래영수학원	안영실	개금국제어학원	김새온	온클래스영어교습소	방요한	대치에스학원	이시현	YBM학원
오지현	영어의 꿈 & 영재의 꿈	안정희	GnB영어전문학원양성캠퍼스	김석주	올림포스학원	배수경	강일연세학원	이아진	에이제이 인스티튜트
우희진	전문과외	오세창	범천반석단과학원	김선경	마크영어	배수현	남다른 이해 학원	이영건	감탄교육
유정인	제니영어	오정안	장산역 우영어학원	김선영	압구정 플래티넘 아카데미	백주희	레인메이커학원	이운정	전문과외
윤영숙	스칼렛영어	유수진	전문과외	김세현	필오름학원	변지예	북두칠성학원	이유빈	채움학원
이고은	고은영어	윤지영	잉글리쉬 무무	김수진	리더스영어보습학원	서승희	대치동 함영원학원	이유영	지앤비우이캠퍼스
이길형	빌드업영어	윤혜은	링구아어학원 동래본원	김승환	Arnold English Class	서은조	용강중학교	이은정	전문과외
이대희	청명대입학원	이상석	상석영어	김아름	ABC학습방향연구소	선지혜	최선메이트 본사	이재연	대원여자고등학교
이성구	나린학원	이선영	매리쌤잉글리쉬	김여진	전문과외	성수빈	전문과외	이정경	더스터디 영수학원
이수미	둔산0505	이순실	CDK국제어학당	김연희	전문과외				

이정혜 서초고려학원
이종현 대원고등학교
이지연 석률학원
이지연 중계케이트영어학원
이지향 전문과외
이철웅 비상하는 또또학원
이태희 진학학원 고등관
이헌승 스탠다드학원
이현민 대원고등학교
이혜숙 사당대성보습학원
이혜정 이루리학원
이희진 씨앤씨학원
임서은 H&J 형설학원
임지효 전문과외
장근아 씨티에이정도학원
장민정 전문과외
장서영 전문과외
장서희 전문과외
장재원 전문과외
장혜민 에스클래스 영어전문학원
전다은 동화세상에듀코_ 와와센터
전보람 상명대학교사범대학부속여자고등학교
전성연 대성학원고척캠퍼스주식회사
전여진 진중고등영어
정가람 촘촘영어
정경록 미즈원어학원
정경아 정쌤영어교습소
정민혜 정민혜밀착영어학원
정성준 팁탑영어
정원경 대원고등학교
정유진 탑잉글리쉬매쓰학원
정윤하 전문과외
정은미 류헌규영어학원
정은아 헨리영어학원
정재욱 씨알학원
정해림 전문과외
조미영 튼튼영어마스터클럽구로학원
조민석 더원영수학원
조민재 정성학원
조봉현 조셉영어국어학원
조봉희 자이온엘연구소
조아라 강북청솔학원
조연아 전문과외
조용현 바른스터디학원
조윤나 오세용어학원
조윤신 조이스 영어 교습소
조정현 동원중학교
조현미 조현미 영어 클래스
주정연 DYB최선학원 마포캠퍼스
지현진 목동JSB영어학원
진수범 이상숙학원
진영민 브로든영어학원
진주현 EMC
차주훈 트라인 영어 수학 학원
채민지 전문과외
채상우 클레어영어
채에스더 문래중학교
최민주 전문과외
최유리 아이디어스 아카데미
최윤정 잉글리쉬앤 매쓰매니저 학원
최정문 한성학원
최진 금천정상학원
최혜선 수재학원
최형미 전문과외

최혜선 디와이비최선어학원 마포캠퍼스
최희재 이주화어학원
하슬기 세종학원
한문진 이룸영어
한안미 한스잉글리시영어교습소
한인혜 레나잉글리쉬
함규민 클레어영어
허동녕 학림학원
허유정 YJ최강영어
홍대균 선덕고등학교 특강강사
홍영민 성북상상학원
홍제기 정상어학원
황규진 잉글리쉬잇업
황상희 어나더레벨 영어전문학원
황혜정 석선생영어학원
황혜진 이루다 영어

세종
강봉식 맥스터디학원
곽영우 연세국제영어
권은경 전문과외
김지원 도램14영어
박혜진 전문과외
방종영 세움학원
백승희 백승희 영어
손대령 강한영어학원
송지원 베이 영어 & 입시컨설팅
안성주 더타임학원
안초롱 21세기학원
윤성근 만점영어학원
이다솜 세종장영실고등학교
이민지 공부방 마스터잉글리쉬
이지영 세종중학교
장소영 상위권학원
지영주 제나쌤의 영어교실

울산
강상배 1%단과전문학원
김경수 핀포인트영어학원
김내경 박정민영어
김성희 1%단과전문학원
김윤정 전문과외
김한중 스마트영어전문학원
김해섭 에임하이학원
양혜정 양혜정영어
이서경 오선생학원
이수현 제이엘영어교습소
정은선 한국ESL어학원
조충일 YBM 울산언양제1학원
최나비 더오름 high-and 학원
한건수 한스영어
한아련 블루미영어교습소
허부배 비즈단과학원

인천
강미현 로렌영어
곽소희 인명여자고등학교
구하라 동인천 종로 엠
김남주 전문과외
김미경 김선생 영어/수학교실
김서애 제이+영어
김선나 태풍영어학원
김성률 좋은나무학원
김영재 강화펜타스학원
김영태 에듀터학원
김영호 조주석 수학&영어 클리닉학원

김윤경 엠베스트SE학원
김재혁 토피아 어학원
김정형 연평고등학교
김정훈 TNL 영어 교습소
김종만 문일여자고등학교
김지연 인천 송도탑영어학원
김지우 청담 에이프릴 어학원
김진용 학산학원
김태무 전문과외
김택수 부개제일학원
나일지 두드림 HIGH학원
문지현 전문과외
박나혜 TOP과외
박세웅 서인천고등학교
박소희 북인천SLP
박재형 들결영어교습소
박종근 유빅학원
박주현 Ashley's English Corner
박진영 인천외국어고등학교
신영진 엉끌쌤과외
신은주 명문학원
신한경 청라 미라클 어학원
안진용 Tiptop학원
안현정 진심을교육하는학원
양현진 지니어스영어
양희진 지니어스영어
오성택 소수정예 중고등영어
오희정 교습소
원준 전문과외
윤희영 세실영어
이가회 S&U영어
이금선 전문과외
이미선 고품격EM EDU
이슬 청라외써영어학원
이윤주 Triple One
이은정 인천논현고등학교
이용제 숭덕여자고등학교
임현주 원소수과외
장승혁 지엘학원
전혜원 제일고등학교
정도영 대신학원
정수진 11월의 비상
정은혜 즐거운 정쌤 영어학원
정지웅 정지웅 영어교실
정춘기 올어바웃잉글리쉬
조윤정 원당중학교
최민지 빅뱅영어
최윤정 BK영어전문학원
최지유 J(제이)영수전문학원
최지혜 유베스타 어학원
최창영 학산학원
한보륜 더뉴에버
한승완 청라하이츠영수학원
허대성 방과후1교시
홍덕창 송현학원 계양분원
홍승표 보스턴영어학원
홍정희 지성의 숲
황성현 인천외국어고등학교

전남
강용문 JK영어입시전문
강유미 목포남악정상어학원
고경희 에이블잉글리쉬
김미선 여수영어교습
김수희 Irin영어

김아름 지앤비 어학원
김은정 BestnBest 영어전문
김지현 이써밋수학원
김채연 전문과외
라희선 재스민영어 전문과외
류성준 타임영어학원
박동규 정상학원
박온유 함평월광기독학교
박팔주 하이탑학원
손성호 아름다운 11월 학원
심명희 SP에듀학원
양명승 엠에스 어학원
오은주 순천금당고
이상호 스카이입시학원
이영주 재키리 영어학원
조소수 수잉글리쉬
차형진 상아탑학원
황상윤 K&H 영어 전문학원

전북
강지훈 고려학원
길지만 비상잉글리시아이영어학원
김나은 애플영어학원
김나해 전문과외
김대환 엠베스트se
김설아 에듀캠프학원
김수정 베이스탑스터디
김숙 매딘원영어
김영해 피렌체 어학원
김종찬 부안최강학원
김태연 전문과외
김현영 하이어잉글리쉬 영어교습소
나종훈 와이엠에스입시전문학원
박욱현 군산외대학원
박준근 이투스247
박차희 연세바움
배영섭 YMS 입시학원
서명원 군산 한림학원
신원섭 리종영어학원
심미연 호남고등학교
안지은 안지은영어학원
유영목 유영목영어전문
이경훈 리더스영수전문학원
이예진 고려대EIE 어학원
이윤경 코드영수전문학원
이지원 탄탄영어수학전문학원
이한결 DNA영어학원
이현준 전문과외
이효상 에임하이영수학원
장동욱 의치약한수학원
정병헌 익산투탑영수학원
조형진 대니아빠앤디영어교습소
최석원 전주에듀캠프학원
최유화 순창 탑학원
허욱 YMS입시전문학원
홍진영 지니영어교습소

제주
강수빈 전문과외
고보경 제주여자고등학교
고승웅 RNK 알앤케이 영어수학학원
김민정 제주낭만고등학교
김태형 Top Class Academy
김희 전문과외
박시연 에임하이학원

배동환 뿌리와샘
송미현 세렌디피티 영어과외 공부방
이지은 제주낭만고등학교
임정열 엑셀영어 전문과외
정승현 J's English
한동수 위드유 학원

충남
고유미 고유미영어
권선교 합덕토킹스타학원
김선영 어플라이드 영어학원
김인영 더오름영어
김일환 김일환어학원
김창식 서산 꿈의학교
김창현 타임영어학원
김현구 프렌잉글리시로엘입시전문학원
남궁선 공부의맵 학원
박아영 닥터윤 영어학원
박재영 로제타스톤 영어교실
박제희 대안학교 레드스쿨
박태혁 인디고학원
박희진 박쌤 과외
백일선 명사특강
설재윤 마스터입시학원
송수아 송수아 영어 교습소
심현정 홀리영어
오근혜 셀렌쌤영어
유정선 메가수학메가영어학원
이규현 글로벌학원
이사랑 오성GnB영어학원
이정찬 두빛나래영수학원
이종화 오름에듀
이지숙 마이티영어학원
이호영 이플러스학원
이황 천안강대학교
임한수 탑클래스학원
임혜지 전문과외
장성은 상승기류
장완기 장완기학원
장진아 종로엠스쿨
주희 천안 탑씨크리트영어학원
채은주 위너스학원
최용원 서일고등학교
허길 에듀플러스학원
허지수 전문과외

충북
강홍구 청주오창비상아이비츠학원
김도현 에스라이팅학원
마종수 새움다움학원
박광수 필립영어전문
박상하 상하영어
박수열 팍스잉글리쉬학원
신유정 비타민 영어클리닉 학원
연수지 탑클랜영어수학학원
우선규 우선규영어교습소
윤홍석 대학가는길학원
이경수 더에스에이티영수단과학원
이재욱 대학가는 길 학원
이재은 파머스영어와이즈톡학원
임원용 KGI의대학원
최철우 최쌤영어
최하나 라이트에듀영어교습소
최하나 전문과외
하선빈 어썸영어전문학원

GRAMMAR MASTER

Beginner
Level

WRITERS

사태숙 이윤정 김진아 홍석현 조은영 홍미정 구미순 이천우 홍인혁 복나희

STAFF

발행인 정선욱

퍼블리싱 총괄 남형주

개발 김태원 김한길 박하영 송경미

기획 · 디자인 · 마케팅 조비호 김정인 강윤정

유통 · 제작 서준성 신성철

Grammar Master Beginner 202205 제3판 1쇄 202407 제3판 4쇄

펴낸곳 이투스에듀(주) 서울시 서초구 남부순환로 2547

고객센터 1599-3225

등록번호 제2007-000035호

ISBN 979-11-389-0846-7 [53740]

• 이 책은 저작권법에 따라 보호받는 저작물이므로 무단전재와 무단복제를 금합니다.

• 잘못 만들어진 책은 구입처에서 교환해 드립니다.

문법을 공부하는 이유

Why do you study English grammar?

처음 영어를 배우던 때를 기억하세요?

알파벳을 배우고 원어민 발음을 따라 말하면서 재미있는 놀이로 영어를 배웠습니다.
낯선 단어의 철자를 하나하나 알게 되고 제법 긴 문장도 말할 수 있구요.
영어로 읽고 말하는 내가 정말 자랑스럽죠?
그런데 가끔 궁금할 때가 있지 않아요?
우리말로는 같은 뜻인데 영어로는 왜 각각 다르게 쓸까요?

I was a little boy. 나는 작은 소년이었다.

You were a little boy. 너는 작은 소년이었다.

많은 학생이 초등학교부터 영어를 배워 오면서 우리말의 규칙과 영어의 규칙이 다르다는
것을 어렴풋이 알고 있지만 그 규칙이 무엇인지는 정확하게 알고 있지 않습니다.
그런데 규칙을 알게 되면 처음 보는 문장도 규칙을 적용하여 쉽게 이해할 수 있게 됩니다.
그래서 규칙을 따로 배우게 되는데, 그게 바로 「문법」인 것이죠.
문법을 공부하면 단어만으로는 알 수 없었던 문장의 뜻을 명쾌하게 알게 되고
영어로 문장을 쓸 때도 아주 유용합니다.

영어 문장의 규칙을 발견하는 기쁨을 여러분 스스로 느껴 보시기 바랍니다. 준비되었나요?
이투스 Grammar Master가 여러분이 문법을 통달하는 데 든든한 동행이 되겠습니다.

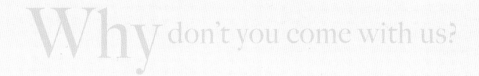

Why don't you come with us?

Structures

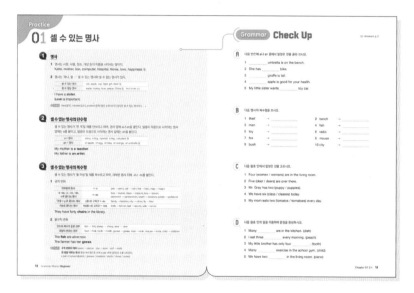

Grammar Practice

꼭 알아 두어야 할 문법 내용을 쉽게 핵심만 정리하였습니다. 학습에 가장 적절한 예문을 통해 문법 내용을 바로 확인해 볼 수 있습니다. 반드시 암기해야 하고, 짚고 넘어가야 할 내용 ⊕ PLUS 로 제시했습니다.

Grammar Check Up

학습한 문법 내용을 적용해 볼 수 있는 다양한 형태의 문제를 제공합니다. 반복적으로 연습함으로써 문법 내용을 외우지 않아도 자연스럽게 학습이 되는 구조입니다.

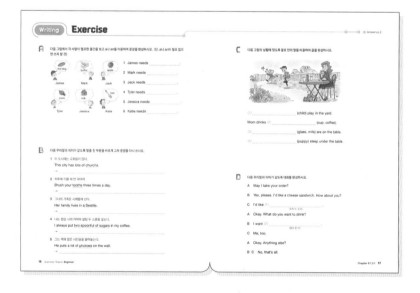

Writing Exercise

다양한 유형의 쓰기 문제를 통해 학습한 문법 내용을 문장이나 글에서 자연스럽게 익힐 수 있으며, 더 나아가 스스로 영어로 글을 써 볼 수 있는 기본기를 다질 수 있습니다.

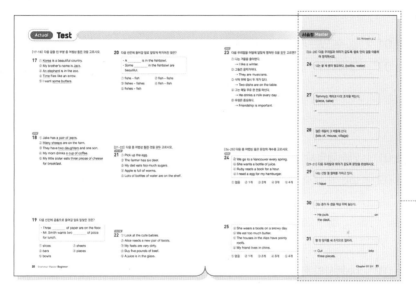

Actual Test

내신형 문제를 Chapter당 총 35문항으로 구성하여 충분한 연습이 되도록 하였습니다. 특히 최근 내신 빈출 유형과 서술형 문제의 비중을 높여 완벽한 내신 대비가 가능합니다. 내신 빈출 과 고난도 를 표시하여 문제를 풀며 주요 객관식 문제를 확인할 수 있습니다.

서술형 Master

학교 내신 서술형 문제에 대비할 수 있는 문항들을 회별 10문항 수록하여 서술형 대비 학습을 마스터할 수 있습니다

Workbook

본책보다 난이도가 조금 높은 문제들로 영작/ 서술형 대비 충분한 분량의 문제를 반복 학습함으로써 본책의 내용을 완벽히 체득하도록 하였습니다. 또한 Chapter Test로 내신형 문제를 한 번 더 풀며 단원을 마무리하도록 구성하였습니다.

Contents

Pre-study

01 문장의 구성

영어 문장은 **주어, 동사, 목적어, 보어, 수식어**의 다섯 가지 요소로 이루어진다.
이 중 필수적인 요소는 주어와 동사이고 동사에 따라 뒤에 보어나 목적어가 오며,
수식어를 사용하여 문장을 좀 더 자세하고 명확하게 만들 수 있다.

주어

'누가' 또는 '무엇이'에 해당하는 부분으로 주로 문장 맨 앞에 온다. 명사와 대명사가 주로 주어로 쓰인다.

> Steve is handsome.
> 주어(명사)
>
> The mountain is high.
>   주어(명사)
>
> They are hungry.
> 주어(대명사)

동사

'~이다' 또는 '~하다'에 해당하는 부분으로 주로 주어 다음에 오며 주어의 상태나 동작을 나타낸다.

> Mom is angry.
>   주어 동사(상태)
>
> The dog runs.
>   주어   동사(동작)
>
> He studies.
> 주어 동사(동작)

목적어

'~을' 또는 '~를'에 해당하는 부분으로 주로 동사 다음에 오며 동사의 대상이 된다. 주로 명사나 대명사, 명사나 대명사의 목적격이 목적어로 쓰인다.

> Inha drinks milk.
> 주어   동사   목적어(명사)
>
> The cat likes fish.
>   주어   동사 목적어(명사)
>
> My mom loves me.
>   주어   동사 목적어(대명사의 목적격)

| 보어 | '주어는 ～이다' 또는 '주어는 ～하다'에서 '～'에 해당하는 부분으로 주로 동사 다음에 오며 주어를 자세히 설명해 준다. 보어로는 보통 명사나 형용사가 쓰인다. |

> Robert is a doctor.
>   주어   동사 보어(명사)
> The teacher is kind.
>   주어   동사 보어(형용사)
> She is pretty.
> 주어 동사 보어(형용사)

| 수식어 | 문장을 구성하는 데 꼭 필요하진 않지만 명사, 동사 등 다른 요소들을 꾸며 주어 문장의 의미를 명확하고 자세하게 해 주는 역할을 한다. 수식어로는 형용사와 부사가 있으며, 형용사는 명사를 꾸며 주고 부사는 동사, 형용사, 다른 부사, 문장 전체를 꾸며 준다. |

> Anne is a nice nurse.
>   형용사 └──┘명사 nurse 수식
> The girl sings well.
>   동사 sings 수식 └──┘ 부사
> It is very hot.
>   부사 └──┘형용사 hot 수식

(02) 문장의 종류

영어의 문장에는 **평서문, 의문문, 명령문, 감탄문** 등이 있다.

| 평서문 | ❶ 사실이나 상태, 상황들을 설명하는 문장으로 「주어 + 동사 ～.」의 형태이다. |

> I am from Canada.
> My favorite food is spaghetti.

❷ 사물의 위치나 존재를 나타내는 표현으로 「There is[are]」 구문이 있으며 '～이 있다'라는 의미이다.

> There is a dog in the garden.
> There are two bathrooms in the house.

의문문   사실이나 상태, 상황 등에 대해 질문하는 문장으로 의문사가 없는 의문문과 의문사가 있는 의문문이 있다.

❶ 의문사가 없는 의문문: 「동사 + 주어 ~?」의 형태이다.

Are you sure?	– Yes, I am sure.
Do you want some more?	– Yes, please.

❷ 의문사가 있는 의문문: 「의문사 + 동사 + 주어 ~?」의 형태이다.

Where is the bank?	– It is next to the library.
When do you get up?	– I get up at 7:00.

cf. 1. 동사가 be동사일 경우는 그대로 be동사를 이용하고, 일반동사일 경우는 do동사를 이용한다.
  2. 의문사에는 who(누가), when(언제), where(어디서), what(무엇을), how(어떻게), why(왜)가 있다.

명령문   상대방에게 '~해라', 또는 '~하세요'라고 명령, 지시하는 문장으로 「동사원형 ~.」의 형태이다.

Go straight and turn right at the corner.
Slow down, please.

감탄문   '정말 ~하구나!'라고 놀람의 감정을 나타내는 문장으로 「What + a[an] + 명사!」 또는 「How + 형용사 /부사!」의 형태이다.

What a surprise!
What a smart boy!
How fast!

Chapter

01

명사

01 셀 수 있는 명사

1 명사

1 명사는 사람, 사물, 장소, 개념 등의 이름을 나타내는 말이다.
Kate, mother, lion, computer, hospital, Korea, love, happiness 등

2 명사는 '하나, 둘 …' 셀 수 있는 명사와 셀 수 없는 명사가 있다.

셀 수 있는 명사	cat, apple, cup, tiger, girl, desk 등
셀 수 없는 명사	water, money, love, peace, China 등 two loves (×)

I have **a sister**.
Love is important.

⊕ **PLUS** idea(생각), mistake(실수), problem(문제) 등은 눈에 보이지 않지만 셀 수 있는 명사이다.

2 셀 수 있는 명사의 단수형

셀 수 있는 명사가 '한 개'일 때를 단수라고 하며, 명사 앞에 a나 an을 붙인다. 발음이 자음으로 시작하는 명사 앞에는 a를 붙이고, 발음이 모음으로 시작하는 명사 앞에는 an을 붙인다.

a + 명사	a boy, a dog, a pencil, a ring, a student 등
an + 명사	an apple, an egg, an idea, an orange, an umbrella 등

My mother is **a teacher**.
My father is **an artist**.

3 셀 수 있는 명사의 복수형

셀 수 있는 명사가 '둘 이상'일 때를 복수라고 하며, 대부분 명사 뒤에 -s나 -es를 붙인다.

1 규칙 변화

대부분의 명사	+ -s	pen → pens, cat → cats, hat → hats, map → maps
-s -ss, -x, -ch, -sh, -o로 끝나는 명사	+ -es	bus → buses, class → classes, box → boxes, sandwich → sandwiches, brush → brushes, potato → potatoes
「자음 + y」로 끝나는 명사	y를 i로 고치고 + -es	family → families, city → cities, fly → flies
-f(e)로 끝나는 명사	f(e)를 v로 고치고 + -ves	knife → knives, leaf → leaves, wife → wives

They have forty **chairs** in the library.

2 불규칙 변화

단수와 복수가 같은 경우	fish → fish, sheep → sheep, deer → deer
모양이 변하는 경우	foot → feet, tooth → teeth, goose → geese, man → men, mouse → mice, child → children

The fish are alive now.
The farmer has ten **geese**.

⊕ **PLUS** 규칙 변화의 예외: piano → pianos   zoo → zoos   roof → roofs
한 쌍을 이루는 명사: 항상 복수형으로 쓰며 a pair of(한 쌍의)로 수를 나타낸다.
a pair of scissors[pants / glasses / sneakers / shorts / shoes / socks]

Grammar Check Up

📖 Answers p.2

A 다음 빈칸에 a나 an 중에서 알맞은 것을 골라 쓰시오.

1 _____ umbrella is on the bench.

2 She has _____ bike.

3 _____ giraffe is tall.

4 _____ apple is good for your health.

5 My little sister wants _____ toy car.

B 다음 명사의 복수형을 쓰시오.

1 thief	→ _____	2 bench	→ _____

1 thief → _____   2 bench → _____

3 man → _____   4 fish → _____

5 toy → _____   6 radio → _____

7 fox → _____   8 mouse → _____

9 bush → _____   10 city → _____

C 다음 괄호 안에서 알맞은 것을 고르시오.

1 Four (women / womans) are in the living room.

2 Five (deer / deers) are over there.

3 Mr. Gray has two (puppy / puppies).

4 We have six (class / classes) today.

5 My mom eats two (tomatos / tomatoes) every day.

D 다음 괄호 안의 말을 이용하여 문장을 완성하시오.

1 Many _____ are in the kitchen. (dish)

2 I eat three _____ every morning. (peach)

3 My little brother has only four _____. (tooth)

4 Many _____ exercise in the school gym. (child)

5 We have two _____ in the living room. (piano)

02 셀 수 없는 명사

1 셀 수 없는 명사의 종류

1 사람, 사물, 장소 등의 고유한 이름을 나타내는 명사 (고유명사)
Thomas, London, Korea, Eiffel Tower 등   **cf.** 고유명사는 첫 글자를 대문자로 쓴다.

2 일정한 형태가 없는 물질을 나타내는 명사 (물질명사)
gas, water, money, butter, air, cheese, salt, sugar, paper, bread 등

3 생각, 감정 등 추상적인 개념을 나타내는 명사 (추상명사)
love, peace, happiness, success, truth, health, hope, time 등

2 셀 수 없는 명사의 특징

1 '하나, 둘 …' 셀 수 없으므로 복수형으로 쓸 수 없다.
I want some **bread**. (○)   I want some **breads**. (×)

2 앞에 '하나'를 의미하는 a/an이나 수를 나타내는 one, two 등을 쓸 수 없다.
I need **salt**. (○)   I need **a salt**. (×)

3 some/any(약간), much/lots of/a lot of(많은) 등으로 양을 나타낸다.
I want **some orange juice**.   He spends **a lot of money**.

4 단위 표현을 이용하여 수량을 나타낸다.
Give me **a bottle of** water.

> **PLUS** **some과 any:** some은 긍정문과 권유문에 쓰이고, any는 부정문과 의문문에 쓰인다.
> I want **some** coffee. 〈긍정문〉 I don't have **any** money now. 〈부정문〉 Do you have **any** questions? 〈의문문〉

3 셀 수 없는 명사의 수량 표현

셀 수 없는 명사의 수량을 나타낼 때는 다음과 같은 단위 표현을 이용한다.

a cup of coffee[tea] 커피[차] 한 잔	a glass of water[milk] 물[우유] 한 잔
a loaf[slice] of bread 빵 한 덩이[조각]	a sheet[piece] of paper 종이 한 장
a bottle of juice 주스 한 병	a bowl of soup 수프 한 그릇
a spoonful[spoon] of sugar 설탕 한 스푼[숟가락]	a piece[slice] of cheese[pizza] 치즈[피자] 한 조각

I need **a piece of** paper.
Can you bring me **two bottles of** juice?
Put **three spoonfuls of** oil into the pot.
My mom drinks **a cup of** coffee every morning.

> **PLUS** **수량 표현의 복수형:** 셀 수 없는 명사의 수량을 나타낼 때는 단위 표현을 복수형으로 만든다. 셀 수 없는 명사는 복수형으로 만들 수 없음에 유의한다.
> two **pounds** of **meat** (○)   two **pound** of **meats** (×)   two **pounds** of **meats** (×)

A 다음 [보기]에서 셀 수 없는 명사를 모두 골라 쓰시오.

> 보기
>
> | church | New York | coin | luck | money |
> | art | London | singer | happiness | |

_____

B 다음 괄호 안에서 알맞은 것을 고르시오.

1 We want (peace / a peace).

2 (Time / Times) goes fast.

3 Gabriel is from (America / an America).

4 My dad drinks some (tea / teas) every day.

C 다음 우리말과 의미가 같도록 [보기]에서 알맞은 말을 골라 문장을 완성하시오. (단, 필요하면 형태를 바꿀 것)

> 보기
>
> a loaf of   a spoonful of   a bowl of   a slice of

1 그 샌드위치에 치즈 한 장이 들어 있다.

→ The sandwich has _____ _____ _____ cheese in it.

2 샐러드 위에 올리브 오일 세 스푼을 넣어라.

→ Put _____ _____ _____ olive oil on the salad.

3 나는 매일 빵 두 덩이를 산다.

→ I buy _____ _____ _____ bread every day.

4 수프 세 그릇이 식탁 위에 있다.

→ _____ _____ _____ soup are on the table.

D 다음 문장에서 어법상 틀린 부분을 찾아 바르게 고쳐 쓰시오.

1 He puts too much salts into the soup. _____ → _____

2 Mr. Smith teaches an English. _____ → _____

3 My brother wants three pieces of pizzas. _____ → _____

A 다음 그림에서 각 사람이 필요한 물건을 보고 a나 an을 이용하여 문장을 완성하시오. (단, a나 an이 필요 없으면 쓰지 말 것)

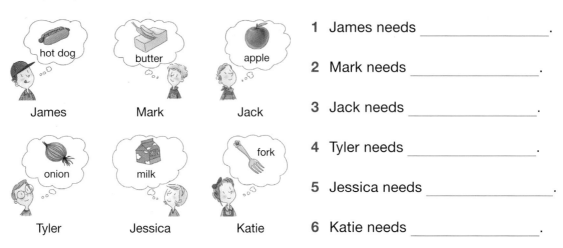

1 James needs _____ .

2 Mark needs _____ .

3 Jack needs _____ .

4 Tyler needs _____ .

5 Jessica needs _____ .

6 Katie needs _____ .

B 다음 우리말과 의미가 같도록 밑줄 친 부분을 바르게 고쳐 문장을 다시 쓰시오.

1 이 도시에는 교회들이 많다.

This city has lots of churchs.

→ _____

2 하루에 이를 세 번 닦아라.

Brush your tooths three times a day.

→ _____

3 그녀의 가족은 시애틀에 산다.

Her family lives in a Seattle.

→ _____

4 나는 항상 나의 커피에 설탕 두 스푼을 넣는다.

I always put two spoonful of sugars in my coffee.

→ _____

5 그는 벽에 많은 사진들을 붙여놓는다.

He puts a lot of photoes on the wall.

→ _____

C 다음 그림의 상황에 맞도록 괄호 안의 말을 이용하여 글을 완성하시오.

(1) _____ (child) play in the yard.

Mom drinks (2) _____ (cup, coffee).

(3) _____ (glass, milk) are on the table.

(4) _____ (puppy) sleep under the table.

D 다음 우리말과 의미가 같도록 대화를 완성하시오.

A May I take your order?

B Yes, please. I'd like a cheese sandwich. How about you?

C I'd like (1) _____ .
　　　　　　　　　　　　　　　(피자 두 조각)

A Okay. What do you want to drink?

B I want (2) _____ .
　　　　　　　　　　　　　　(콜라 한 잔)

C Me, too.

A Okay. Anything else?

B C No, that's all.

Actual Test

01 다음 중 빈칸에 a나 an을 넣을 때 들어갈 말이 나머지와 <u>다른</u> 것은?

① _____ rose   ② _____ ant
③ _____ onion   ④ _____ umbrella
⑤ _____ eraser

02 다음 중 셀 수 있는 명사와 셀 수 없는 명사로 구분할 때 성격이 나머지와 <u>다른</u> 것은?

① story   ② artist
③ park   ④ sand
⑤ idea

[03-04] 다음 중 명사의 단수형과 복수형이 잘못 짝지어진 것을 고르시오.

03 ① lily – lilies   ② foot – feet
③ leaf – leaves ④ beach – beaches
⑤ mouse – mouses

04 ① city – cities   ② deer – deers
③ piano – pianos ④ class – classes
⑤ baby – babies

[05-06] 다음 밑줄 친 부분을 바르게 고칠 때, 알맞지 <u>않은</u> 것을 고르시오.

05 ① I need some <u>papers</u>. (→ paper)
② We have three <u>chair</u>. (→ chairs)
③ I like <u>a sugar</u>. (→ sugar)
④ I cut <u>tomatos</u>. (→ tomatoes)
⑤ He has two <u>watch</u>. (→ watchs)

내신 빈출

06 ① Give me <u>cup of a coffee</u>.
      (→ a cup of coffee)
② She drinks six <u>glasses of waters</u> every day.
      (→ glasses of water)
③ We need ten <u>cans of sodas</u>.
      (→ cans of soda)
④ I make three <u>bowl of salad</u> every day.
      (→ bowls of salads)
⑤ Bring him a <u>pieces of cake</u>.
      (→ piece of cake)

[07-08] 다음 빈칸에 들어갈 말로 알맞지 <u>않은</u> 것을 고르시오.

07
> There is a _____ on the dish.

① strawberry   ② potato
③ banana   ④ melon
⑤ orange

08
> A pair of _____ is in the box.

① pants   ② shoes
③ jeans   ④ socks
⑤ glass

09 다음 우리말을 어법에 알맞게 영작한 것은?

> Julia는 치즈 두 조각을 먹는다.

① Julia eats two cheese.
② Julia eats two cheeses.
③ Julia eats two slice of cheeses.
④ Julia eats two slices of cheese.
⑤ Julia eats two slices of cheeses.

[12-13] 다음 밑줄 친 부분 중 어법상 틀린 것을 고르시오.

12 ①Children ②need ③loves ④from ⑤their parents.

13 ①I ②need four ③spoonful of ④sugar and ⑤pepper.

[10-11] 다음 빈칸에 들어갈 말로 알맞은 것을 고르시오.

10 Three _____ are in the garden.

① girl   ② goose
③ man   ④ women
⑤ childrens

[14-16] 다음 문장에서 어법상 틀린 부분을 찾아 바르게 고쳐 쓰시오.

14 Ten foxes and five wolfs are in the zoo.

_____ → _____

15 She wants a piece of sneakers.

_____ → _____

11 My sister drinks two bottles of _____ every day.

① waters   ② juice
③ bread   ④ milks
⑤ cheese

16 He uses his new scissor.

_____ → _____

[17-18] 다음 밑줄 친 부분 중 어법상 틀린 것을 고르시오.

17 ① <u>Korea</u> is a beautiful country.
② My brother's name is <u>Jack</u>.
③ <u>An elephant</u> is in the zoo.
④ Time flies like <u>an arrow</u>.
⑤ I want <u>some butters</u>.

고난도
18 ① Jake has <u>a pair of jeans</u>.
② <u>Many sheeps</u> are on the farm.
③ They have <u>two daughters</u> and a son.
④ My mom drinks <u>a cup of coffee</u>.
⑤ My little sister eats <u>three pieces of cheese</u> for breakfast.

19 다음 빈칸에 공통으로 들어갈 말로 알맞은 것은?

> • Three _____ of paper are on the floor.
> • Mr. Smith wants two _____ of pizza for lunch.

① slices ② sheets
③ bars ④ pieces
⑤ bowls

20 다음 빈칸에 들어갈 말로 알맞게 짝지어진 것은?

> • A _____ is in the fishbowl.
> • Some _____ in the fishbowl are beautiful.

① fishs – fish ② fish – fishs
③ fishes – fishes ④ fish – fish
⑤ fishes – fish

[21-22] 다음 중 어법상 틀린 것을 모두 고르시오.
내신 빈출
21 ① Pick up the egg.
② The farmer has six deer.
③ My dad eats too much sugars.
④ Apple is full of worms.
⑤ Lots of bottles of water are on the shelf.

내신 빈출
22 ① Look at the cute babies.
② Alice needs a new pair of boots.
③ My feets are very dirty.
④ Buy five pounds of beef.
⑤ A juice is in the glass.

고난도
23 다음 우리말을 어법에 알맞게 영작한 것을 <u>모두</u> 고르면?

① 나는 겨울을 좋아한다.
→ I like a winter.
② 그들은 음악가이다.
→ They are musicians.
③ 식탁 위에 접시 두 개가 있다.
→ Two dishs are on the table.
④ 그는 매일 우유 한 잔을 마신다.
→ He drinks a milk every day.
⑤ 우정은 중요하다.
→ Friendship is important.

[24-25] 다음 중 어법상 옳은 문장의 개수를 고르시오.

고난도
24

ⓐ We go to a Vancouver every spring.
ⓑ She wants a bottle of juice.
ⓒ Ruby reads a book for a hour.
ⓓ I need a egg for my hamburger.

① 없음　② 1개　③ 2개　④ 3개　⑤ 4개

25

ⓐ She wears a boots on a snowy day.
ⓑ We eat too much butter.
ⓒ The houses in the Alps have pointy roofs.
ⓓ My friend lives in china.

① 없음　② 1개　③ 2개　④ 3개　⑤ 4개

[26-28] 다음 우리말과 의미가 같도록 괄호 안의 말을 이용하여 영작하시오.

26

나는 물 세 병이 필요하다. (bottle, water)

→ _____

27

Tommy는 케이크 다섯 조각을 먹는다.
(piece, cake)

→ _____

28

많은 쥐들이 그 마을에 산다.
(lots of, mouse, village)

→ _____

[29-31] 다음 우리말과 의미가 같도록 문장을 완성하시오.

29

나는 신발 열 켤레를 가지고 있다.

→ I have _____ .

30

그는 종이 두 장을 책상 위에 놓는다.

→ He puts _____ on
the desk.

31

빵 한 덩이를 세 조각으로 잘라라.

→ Cut _____ into
three pieces.

32 다음 그림을 보고, 괄호 안의 말을 이용하여 글을 완성하시오.

This bird looks funny. It has three
_____ (eye), two _____ (tooth),
four _____ (wing), and two _____
(leg).

33 다음 밑줄 친 ①~⑤ 중 명사의 복수형이 틀린 것을 2개 골라 기호를 쓰고, 바르게 고쳐 쓰시오.

> A lot of ①tigers, rabbits, and donkeys
> are in the zoo. In the zoo's Africa area, we
> can see ②giraffes and zebras. There are
> also many ③sheeps and deers. Lots of
> ④childs like ⑤dolphins. They can see a
> dolphin show at the zoo!

(1) _____ → _____
(2) _____ → _____

34 다음 그림을 보고, 두 번째 문장의 알맞은 위치에 a나 an을 넣어 문장을 다시 쓰시오.

This is my lunch. I have sandwich, egg,
mango, and apple. They are all good for my
health.

→ _____

35 다음 표를 보고, [조건]에 맞게 질문에 대한 대답을 완성하시오.

Q: What do they want for breakfast?

Mina	chicken soup (one)
Jinsu	pizza (two)
Melissa	bread (three)

┤ 조건 ├
- 단위 표현 slice, bowl, loaf를 한 번씩 사용할 것
- 괄호 안에 주어진 수량을 반영할 것

(1) Mina wants _____.
(2) Jinsu _____.
(3) Melissa _____.

Chapter

02

대명사

01 인칭대명사

1 인칭대명사의 종류

인칭대명사는 사람, 사물, 동물을 대신해서 쓰는 대명사이며, 1인칭, 2인칭, 3인칭이 있다.

	1인칭	2인칭	3인칭		
단수	I (나)	you (너)	he (그)	she (그녀)	it (그것)
복수	we (우리)	you (너희들)	they (그들)		they (그것들)

1 1인칭: 나 또는 나를 포함한 여러 사람을 말한다.

I am a student.　　**We** are students.

2 2인칭: 나의 말을 듣고 있는 한 사람 또는 여러 사람을 말한다.

You are a smart girl.　　**You** are smart girls.

3 3인칭: 나와 너를 제외한 제3자를 말하며, 단수일 때 남자는 he, 여자는 she, 사물·동물은 it으로 쓰고, 복수일 때는 they로 쓴다.

My uncle is a teacher. **He** is kind.　　**My aunt** is a pilot. **She** is kind, too.

The hospital is big. **It** is near my house.

Susie and Mark work together. **They** are so happy.

2 인칭대명사의 격

문장에서의 역할에 따라 주격, 소유격, 목적격으로 나뉜다.

	인칭	주격	소유격	목적격
단수	1인칭	I	my	me
	2인칭	you	your	you
	3인칭	he / she / it	his / her / its	him / her / it
복수	1인칭	we	our	us
	2인칭	you	your	you
	3인칭	they	their	them

1 주격: 문장에서 주어 역할을 하며, '~가', '~는'으로 해석한다.

I have long hair.　　**She** has short hair.

2 소유격: 명사 앞에 쓰여 소유 관계를 나타내며, '~의'라고 해석한다.

My bike is old.　　I like **her** new bike.

3 목적격: 문장에서 동사 또는 전치사의 목적어 역할을 하며, '~을', '~를'로 해석한다.

Mom smiles at **me**.　　I love **her**.

Paul meets **us** every day.

⊕ **PLUS**　**명사의 소유격:** 명사 뒤에 's를 붙여서 만든다.

It is **Mike's** cat.

Answers p.3

A 다음 그림의 상황에 맞도록 [보기]에서 알맞은 말을 골라 문장을 완성하시오.

보기
| I | she | you | they |

1
_____ is a cook.

2
_____ am a pilot.

3
_____ are firefighters.

4
_____ are a doctor.

B 다음 우리말과 의미가 같도록 빈칸에 알맞은 인칭대명사를 쓰시오.

1 나의　　→ _____

2 우리를　　→ _____

3 너희들은　　→ _____

4 그들을　　→ _____

5 그것의　　→ _____

6 그들의　　→ _____

7 우리는　　→ _____

8 그것을　　→ _____

C 다음 밑줄 친 부분을 알맞은 대명사로 바꿔 쓰시오.

1 Mrs. Lee drives carefully.　　→ _____

2 James and I are classmates.　　→ _____

3 Her children play tennis after school.　　→ _____

4 My favorite subject is math.　　→ _____

D 다음 괄호 안에서 알맞은 것을 고르시오.

1 (They / Them) are good neighbors.

2 I wash (its / it) every week.

3 Philip sometimes helps (our / us).

4 I miss (me / my) friends.

5 This is (you / your) new teacher.

6 (Him / His) sneakers are very old.

7 (Them / Their) house is clean.

8 We visit (she / her) every weekend.

02 this, that, it

1 this

1 가까이 있는 사람이나 사물을 가리키며, 대명사와 형용사로 쓰인다.

대명사	이것, 이분, 이 사람	**This** is her computer. **This** is my homeroom teacher.
형용사	이 ~	**This** room is big.

2 복수형은 these로 쓴다.
These are her pants.
These kittens are cute.

2 that

1 멀리 있는 사람이나 사물을 가리키며, 대명사와 형용사로 쓰인다.

대명사	저것, 저분, 저 사람	**That** is his old camera. **That** is Tom's cousin.
형용사	저 ~	I remember **that** man.

2 복수형은 those로 쓴다.
Those are his glasses.
Those baseball players are handsome.

3 비인칭 주어 it

시간, 요일, 날짜; 계절, 날씨, 명암, 거리 등을 나타내는 문장은 주어로 대명사 it이 쓰인다. 이것을 비인칭 주어 it이라고 하며 it은 따로 해석하지 않는다.
It is 4 o'clock. (시간)
It is Sunday today. (요일)
It is October 5. (날짜)
It is spring. (계절)
It is hot and humid. (날씨)
It is dark in the room. (명암)
It is 1 kilometer to my school. (거리)

⊕ **PLUS** **인칭대명사 it:** it이 사물이나 동물을 대신하는 경우는 '그것'이라고 해석한다는 점에 주의한다.
I like this book. **It** is very interesting.

A 다음 그림의 상황에 맞도록 [보기]에서 알맞은 말을 골라 문장을 완성하시오.

| 보기 |
| this   that   these   those |

1

_____ is my ball.

2

_____ are ducks.

3

_____ is a brown dog.

4

_____ are funny books.

B 다음 괄호 안에서 알맞은 것을 고르시오.

1 (That / These) is Alice's daughter.

2 (That / Those) rings are beautiful.

3 She needs (that / these) candles.

4 (This / It) is sunny and cool.

C 다음 우리말과 의미가 같도록 빈칸에 알맞은 대명사를 쓰시오.

1 이 치즈 피자는 맛있다.   → _____ cheese pizza is delicious.

2 저 사진들을 주워라.   → Pick up _____ pictures.

3 여기는 매우 어둡다.   → _____ is very dark here.

4 지금 몇 시니?   → What time is _____ now?

D 다음 문장에서 어법상 **틀린** 부분을 찾아 바르게 고쳐 쓰시오. (단, 한 단어만 고칠 것)

1 I like this sneakers.   _____ → _____

2 This is winter in Sydney.   _____ → _____

3 That are my shoes.   _____ → _____

4 These is a very popular model.   _____ → _____

A 다음 빈칸에 알맞은 대명사를 쓰시오.

1 Ms. Kim teaches English. _____ is an English teacher.

2 Thomas drives a taxi. _____ is a taxi driver.

3 I have a camera. _____ is very tiny.

4 Jenny and I like movies. _____ go to the movies every week.

5 Julie is kind. Lots of friends like _____ .

6 This boy is my son. _____ name is William.

7 Cathy and Sue are sisters. _____ house is near the school.

8 You and Harry are from Canada. _____ are Canadians.

B 다음 우리말과 의미가 같도록 괄호 안의 말을 바르게 배열하시오.

1 뉴욕은 여름이다. (summer, it, is)

→ _____ in New York.

2 저 피아노들은 굉장히 비싸다. (are, those, pianos)

→ _____ very expensive.

3 이분은 나의 할머니이시다. (my, grandmother, is, this)

→ _____ .

4 이것들은 너에게 주는 나의 선물들이다. (are, gifts, these, my)

→ _____ for you.

5 눈이 오고 바람이 분다. (snowy, it, windy, is, and)

→ _____ .

C 다음 그림의 상황에 맞도록 [보기]에서 알맞은 말을 골라 글을 완성하시오. (단, 중복 사용 가능)

| 보기 |
| this   that   these   those   he   they   our |

Dad and I have many pets. (1) _____ is a cat. His name is Prince. He is very

cute. (2) _____ are puppies. (3) _____ are always cheerful. (4) _____

are turtles. (5) _____ are green and slow. Oh, (6) _____ is my father.

(7) _____ is an animal doctor. He and I love (8) _____ pets.

D 다음 그림을 보고, 대화를 완성하시오.

1 A: What time is _____ now?
   B: _____ _____ _____ a.m.

2 A: What date _____ _____ today?
   B: _____ _____ _____ 5.

3 A: What day _____ _____ today?
   B: _____ _____ .

4 A: How is the weather today?
   B: _____ _____ _____ .

01 다음 명사를 대명사로 바꿀 때 알맞지 <u>않은</u> 것은?

① an ant → it
② James → he
③ Ms. Lee → she
④ you and I → you
⑤ a dog and a sheep → they

02 다음 그림에 맞는 대명사로 알맞지 <u>않은</u> 것은?

① this
② those
③ these
④ they
⑤ that

04 |_____ books are exciting.|

① This
② Those
③ It
④ That
⑤ You

05 |_____ is 4 miles to our school.|

① This
② I
③ That
④ Its
⑤ It

06 |_____ is my sister.|

① He
② We
③ She
④ They
⑤ You

[03-06] 다음 빈칸에 들어갈 말로 알맞은 것을 고르시오.

03 | This is your new bike. Do you like _____ ? |

① them
② it
③ its
④ me
⑤ you

[07-09] 다음 밑줄 친 부분을 대명사로 바꿀 때 알맞은 것을 고르시오.

07 | Jennifer loves <u>John</u>. |

① he
② him
③ her
④ his
⑤ you

08

> Look at Sue's new car.

① she　　　　　② your
③ her　　　　　④ its
⑤ my

09

> What is the cell phone's color?

① it　　　　　② it's
③ that's　　　　④ its
⑤ your

10 다음 우리말을 어법에 알맞게 영작하지 <u>않은</u> 것은?

① 이것은 나의 비옷이다.
　→ This is my raincoat.
② 이것들은 그녀의 강아지들이다.
　→ This is her puppies.
③ 저분은 Smith 선생님이시다.
　→ That is Mr. Smith.
④ 이분은 나의 사장님이시다.
　→ This is my boss.
⑤ 저것들은 로봇들이다.
　→ Those are robots.

고난도
11 다음 질문에 대한 대답으로 알맞은 것은?

> A: Do you know the men over there?
> B: Yes, _____.

① he is my neighbor
② he knows every student well
③ she teaches Korean history
④ they are very famous singers
⑤ it calls her on Saturdays

[12-13] 다음 빈칸에 들어갈 말로 알맞지 <u>않은</u> 것을 고르시오.

12

> I know _____ well.

① you　　　　　② them
③ her　　　　　④ we
⑤ him

13

> This is _____ computer.

① my　　　　　② your
③ him　　　　　④ her
⑤ our

고난도
14 다음 빈칸에 공통으로 들어갈 말로 알맞은 것은?

> · Look at the butterfly. _____ is yellow.
> · _____ is windy and cold today.
> · _____ is far from here to my house.

① This　　　　② That
③ She　　　　④ It
⑤ I

내신 빈출
15 다음 밑줄 친 부분을 바르게 고친 것끼리 짝지어진 것은?

> · I have three sisters. <u>She</u> love Korean culture.
> · <u>These</u> is Jin's house. It has a beautiful garden.

① They – This　　② Their – This
③ They – Those　④ It – This
⑤ Its – Those

[16-17] 다음 우리말과 의미가 같도록 빈칸에 들어갈 말이 알맞게 짝지어진 것을 고르시오.

16

이 병은 거의 가득 찼지만, 저 병은 단지 반만 찼다.
→ _____ bottle is nearly full, but
_____ bottle is only half full.

① This – that　　② That – this
③ These – those　④ Those – these
⑤ This – those

17

이것들은 나의 운동화야.
→ _____ are _____ sneakers.

① This – my　　② That – your
③ These – me　④ Those – our
⑤ These – my

[18-19] 다음 밑줄 친 부분 중 어법상 틀린 것을 고르시오.

18 ① This is a beautiful flower.
② My parents love I.
③ I need your cell phone.
④ Those are his fish.
⑤ It is warm and sunny.

고난도
19 ① They are lions.
② I help them.
③ She is a lovely girl.
④ He needs our help.
⑤ These letter is for you.

[20-21] 다음 중 어법상 틀린 것을 고르시오.

20 ① Look at them.
② Those pants are nice.
③ These are my notebooks.
④ This is cold and cloudy.
⑤ Our teacher is kind to us.

21 ① Those cages are big.
② They clean their classroom.
③ This pianist plays the piano well.
④ Listen to me.
⑤ Is it you camera?

내신 빈출
22 다음 중 밑줄 친 It의 쓰임이 나머지와 다른 것은?
① A: What time is it now?
　 B: It is three o'clock.
② A: It is hot in here.
　 B: Right. Let's turn off the heater.
③ A: This is my new cap.
　 B: Oh. It looks good on you.
④ A: How far is it to your school?
　 B: It is not far from my house.
⑤ A: How is the weather in Boston?
　 B: It is snowy.

23 다음 대화의 빈칸에 들어갈 말로 알맞은 것은?

A: Wow! Your cat is very cute.
B: Thank you. _____ name is White.

① He
② It
③ It's
④ She
⑤ Its

[26-28] 다음 우리말과 의미가 같도록 괄호 안의 말을 바르게 배열하시오.

26
이분은 나의 삼촌이시다. (my, is, this)

→ _____ uncle.

27
나는 매주 그를 만난다. (meet, I, him)

→ _____ every week.

내신 빈출
24 다음 중 어법상 옳은 것으로 알맞게 짝지어진 것은?

ⓐ That are their crayons.
ⓑ I love she voice a lot.
ⓒ Those are my friends, Brian and Nancy.
ⓓ Its a luxury hotel.
ⓔ He brushes his teeth after meals.

① ⓐ, ⓑ
② ⓑ, ⓔ
③ ⓒ, ⓔ
④ ⓑ, ⓓ, ⓔ
⑤ ⓒ, ⓓ, ⓔ

28
저것들은 그들의 자전거들이다. (those, their, are)

→ _____ bikes.

[29-31] 다음 우리말과 의미가 같도록 괄호 안의 말을 이용하여 문장을 완성하시오.

29
저 쌍둥이는 똑같이 생겼다. (twins)

→ _____ look exactly the same.

30
그들은 우리를 매우 그리워한다. (miss)

→ They _____ a lot.

25 다음 밑줄 친 ⓐ~ⓔ 중 어법상 틀린 것을 모두 고르면?

ⓐThis is my brother. ⓑHim name is Oliver. ⓒHe is 17 years old. He collects old games. He often shows ⓓit to us. ⓔThey look wonderful. I envy him.

① ⓐ
② ⓑ
③ ⓒ
④ ⓓ
⑤ ⓔ

31
오늘은 바람이 분다. (windy)

→ _____ today.

32 다음 밑줄 친 ①~④를 대명사로 바꿔 쓰시오.

> I have two close friends, Ann and James. ①Ann, James, and I go to the same school. Ann and James are very different. Ann loves games. ②Ann plays computer games every night. James loves books. ③James reads a book every night. But ④Ann and James have a lot in common, too.

① _____ ② _____
③ _____ ④ _____

34 다음 우리말과 의미가 같도록 [조건]에 맞게 글을 완성하시오.

┌ 조건 ┐
• 비인칭 주어 It을 사용할 것 (단, 중복 사용 가능)
• [보기]에 주어진 단어 중 알맞은 것을 사용할 것

┌ 보기 ┐
sunny   humid   cool   hot   weather

이곳 태국은 7시야. 여기는 습하고 더워. 서울의 날씨는 어떠니?

→ (1) _____ o'clock here in Thailand. (2) _____ here. How is the (3) _____ in Seoul?

33 다음 각 대화에서 어법상 틀린 대명사를 찾아 바르게 고쳐 쓰시오.

> (1) A: I like this pants.
>   B: Me too. They are not expensive.
>
> (2) A: Joe, that is already dark outside. Come home early.
>   B: OK, Mom. I'm on my way home.

(1) _____ → _____
(2) _____ → _____

35 다음 그림의 상황에 맞도록 빈칸에 알맞은 말을 넣어 글을 완성하시오.

(1) _____ _____ _____ today. It is going to rain soon. (2) _____ _____ _____ a.m. now. Do you see two dogs on the floor? (3) _____ have long hair. I brush (4) _____ hair every two days. (5) _____ feels soft.

Chapter

03

be동사

01 be동사의 현재형

① be동사의 의미

be동사는 주어 뒤에서 '~이다', '~에 있다'라는 의미로 쓰이며, 주어의 상태, 성격, 신분, 존재 등을 나타낸다.

You **are** a great cook.

She **is** happy now.

They **are** in the living room.

② be동사의 현재형

1 be동사는 주어의 인칭과 수에 따라 형태가 변한다.

	단수		복수	
1인칭	I	am	We	are
2인칭	You	are	You	are
3인칭	He / She / It	is	They	are

I **am** a middle school student.

He **is** at home.

It **is** my cap.

You **are** smart students.

You **are** late again.

She **is** a fashion model.

We **are** thirsty now.

They **are** in the yard.

2 「주어 + be동사」는 줄여 쓸 수 있다.

주어 + be동사	줄임말	주어 + be동사	줄임말
I am	I'm	We are	We're
You are	You're	You are	You're
He is / She is / It is	He's / She's / It's	They are	They're

I'm in the hospital.

He's from New Zealand.

It's a small box.

They're ballerinas.

You're a writer.

She's a dentist.

We're in the library.

⊕ **PLUS** **주어가 명사일 때 be동사 형태:** 단수 명사는 is를 사용하고, 복수 명사는 are를 사용한다.
The dog **is** angry.   The bags **are** very expensive.

it's와 its: it's는 it is의 줄임말이고, its는 it의 소유격이다.
It's[It is] a dictionary.   **Its** tail is round and short.

Grammar Check Up

A 다음 빈칸에 am, are, is 중 알맞은 것을 골라 쓰시오.

1 I _____ from Seoul, Korea.

2 Jack _____ always kind to me.

3 It _____ an easy question.

4 You _____ good at swimming.

5 They _____ our club members.

B 다음 「주어 + be동사」를 줄여 쓰시오.

1 It is   → _____   2 I am   → _____

3 He is   → _____   4 You are → _____

5 She is → _____   6 We are → _____

7 They are → _____

C 다음 괄호 안에서 알맞은 것을 고르시오.

1 (He / I) am sleepy now.

2 (You / He) are very funny.

3 (You / She) is healthy.

4 (It / We) are the same age.

5 (You / She) is at the airport.

6 (We / He) are from Australia.

D 다음 빈칸에 알맞은 형태의 be동사를 쓰시오.

1 Jessica _____ a famous web designer.

2 Many white rabbits _____ in the cage.

3 The weather _____ nice.

4 He and his sister _____ scientists.

5 That dictionary _____ very old and thick.

02 be동사의 부정문과 의문문

❶ be동사의 부정문

1 형태: be동사 뒤에 not을 써서 「주어 + be동사 + not ~.」의 형태로 쓴다.
2 의미: '~이 아니다', '~에 있지 않다'라는 의미이다.

	주어	be동사 + not	「주어 + be동사」의 줄임말 + not
1인칭	I	am not	I'm not
	We	are not	We're not
2인칭	You	are not	You're not
3인칭	He / She / It	is not	He's not / She's not / It's not
	They	are not	They're not

I'm not weak.　　　　　　　　　　**You're not** short.
He's not an animal doctor.　　　　**They're not** cheetahs.

3 「be동사 + not」의 줄임말: is not은 isn't로, are not은 aren't로 줄여 쓸 수 있다.
She **is not** a liar. = She**'s not** a liar. = She **isn't** a liar.
You **are not** dancers. = You**'re not** dancers. = You **aren't** dancers.

➕ **PLUS**　**am not**의 줄임말: am not은 줄여 쓸 수 없으므로 amn't로 쓰지 않도록 주의한다.
I **amn't** a swimmer. (×)

❷ be동사의 의문문

1 형태: be동사를 주어 앞에 써서 「Be동사 + 주어 ~?」의 형태로 쓴다.
2 의미: '~이니?', '~에 있니?'라는 의미이다.
3 대답: 「Yes, 주어 + be동사.」 / 「No, 주어 + be동사 + not.」으로 한다.

	의문문	긍정의 대답		부정의 대답	
1인칭	Am I ~?	Yes, you are.		No, you aren't.	
	Are we ~?	Yes, we[you] are.		No, we[you] aren't.	
2인칭	Are you ~?	단수	Yes, I am.	단수	No, I'm not.
		복수	Yes, we are.	복수	No, we aren't.
3인칭	Is he[she / it] ~?	Yes, he[she / it] is.		No, he[she / it] isn't.	
	Are they ~?	Yes, they are.		No, they aren't.	

Are you nervous? - Yes, I am. / No, I'm not.
Is she American? - Yes, she is. / No, she isn't.
Are you upstairs? - Yes, we are. / No, we aren't.
Are they baseball players? - Yes, they are. / No, they aren't.

A 다음 빈칸 중 알맞은 곳에 not을 쓰시오.

1 He _____ is _____ a _____ violinist.

2 I _____ am _____ very _____ busy.

3 They _____ are _____ in _____ the library.

4 It _____ is _____ my _____ house.

B 다음 괄호 안에서 알맞은 것을 고르시오.

1 (Is / Are) it your bag? - Yes, it (is / isn't).

2 (Is / Are) you free this afternoon? - Yes, (I am / you are).

3 (Is / Are) your mother in Seoul? - No, she (aren't / isn't).

4 (Is / Are) we late? - No, (they aren't / we aren't).

C 다음 [보기]와 같이 빈칸에 알맞은 말을 쓰시오.

┌─ 보기 ┌───┐
He is not an actor. = He's not an actor. = He isn't an actor.
└──┘

1 You _____ brave. = _____ brave. = _____ brave.

2 We _____ rich. = _____ rich. = _____ rich.

3 It _____ heavy. = _____ heavy. = _____ heavy.

4 They _____ kind. = _____ kind. = _____ kind.

5 He _____ at home. = _____ at home. = _____ at home.

D 다음 [보기]와 같이 주어진 문장을 의문문으로 바꿔 쓰고, 그에 대한 대답을 완성하시오.

┌─ 보기 ┌───┐
It is light. → Is it light?   Yes, it is. / No, it isn't.
└──┘

1 He is a police officer.   → _____ a police officer? Yes, _____ .

2 It is a scary story.   → _____ a scary story?   No, _____ .

3 They are diligent.   → _____ diligent?   Yes, _____ .

4 The plate is dirty.   → _____ dirty?   No, _____ .

5 We are in the same class. → _____ in the same class?

                              No, _____ .

03 be동사의 과거형

1 be동사의 과거형

1 형태: 주어에 따라 형태가 다르다.

주어	be동사의 과거형
I / He / She / It	was
We / You / They	were

2 의미: '~였다', '~에 있었다'라는 의미로 과거의 상황이나 상태를 나타낸다.

I **am** at the zoo **now**.　　　I **was** at the zoo **yesterday**.
└→ 지금 있다 ←┘　　　　　　└→ 어제 있었다 ←┘

They **were** very excited last night.

⊕ **PLUS** **과거란?**: 이미 지나간 일이나 때, 즉 '조금 전', '어제', '작년' 등에 일어난 일을 말한다.

2 be동사 과거형의 부정문

1 형태: 「주어 + was[were] + not ~.」의 형태로 쓴다.

주어	be동사 과거형 + not
I / He / She / It	was not
We / You / They	were not

2 의미: '~이 아니었다', '~에 있지 않았다'라는 의미이다.

3 줄임말: was not은 wasn't로, were not은 weren't로 줄여 쓸 수 있다.

I **was not** in the school.　　　　　　Jim and his brother **were not** teenagers.

My daughter **wasn't** fat.　　　　　　We **weren't** sleepy.

3 be동사 과거형의 의문문

1 형태: 「Was[Were] + 주어 ~?」의 형태로 쓴다.

2 의미: '~이었니?', '~에 있었니?'라는 의미이다.

3 대답: 「Yes, 주어 + was[were].」 / 「No, 주어 + wasn't[weren't].」로 한다.

주어	의문문	긍정의 대답	부정의 대답
I / He / She / It	Was I[he / she / it] ~?	Yes, 주어 + was.	No, 주어 + wasn't.
We / You / They	Were we[you / they] ~?	Yes, 주어 + were.	No, 주어 + weren't.

Was it cold yesterday? - Yes, it was. / No, it wasn't.

Was Sally sick yesterday? - Yes, she was. / No, she wasn't.

Were they famous before? - Yes, they were. / No, they weren't.

📖 Answers p.5

A 다음 밑줄 친 부분을 과거형으로 고쳐 쓰시오.

1 A stranger <u>is</u> near my house. → A stranger _____ near my house.
2 I <u>am</u> 13 years old. → I _____ 13 years old.
3 The puppies <u>are</u> in the cage. → The puppies _____ in the cage.
4 She <u>is</u> a bus driver. → She _____ a bus driver.
5 The students <u>are</u> bored. → The students _____ bored.

B 다음 [보기]와 같이 그림의 상황에 맞도록 빈칸에 알맞은 말을 쓰시오.

> 보기
>
> Sam <u>wasn't</u> sad. He <u>was</u> happy.

1　The puppies _____ on the table. They _____ on the sofa.
2　The children _____ in the library. They _____ in the playground.
3　Kelly _____ hungry. She _____ full.

C 다음 [보기]와 같이 주어진 문장을 의문문으로 바꿔 쓰고, 그에 대한 대답을 완성하시오.

> 보기
>
> It was snowy. → <u>Was it</u> snowy?　Yes, <u>it was</u>. / No, <u>it wasn't</u>.

1 He was a movie director.　→ _____ a movie director?
　Yes, _____.
2 It was an exciting game.　→ _____ an exciting game?
　No, _____.
3 We were in the car.　→ _____ in the car?
　No, _____.
4 The vegetables were fresh.　→ _____ fresh?
　Yes, _____.
5 You were surprised.　→ _____ surprised?
　Yes, _____.

04 There is[are]

1 There is[are]의 의미

1 There is[are]는 '~이 있다'라는 의미로 there는 따로 해석하지 않는다.

There is a cushion on the sofa.

2 「There is + a[an] + 단수 명사」, 「There are + 복수 명사」로 쓰이며, 이때 be동사 뒤에 오는 명사가 문장의 주어이다.

There is *a big market* near here.

There are *many people* on the subway.

> ⊕ **PLUS** 부사 **there**: 부사로 쓰인 there는 '거기에'라는 의미이다. Who is **there**? (거기에 누구니?)
> **주어가 셀 수 없는 명사일 때**: 셀 수 없는 명사는 단수로만 쓰이므로 There is와 함께 쓰인다.
> **There is** *some juice* in the glass.

2 There is[are]의 부정문과 의문문

1 부정문: be동사 뒤에 not을 붙여 There is[are] not ~의 형태로 쓰이며, '~이 없다'라는 의미이다.

There is not[isn't] a window in this room.

There is not[isn't] any milk in the refrigerator.

There are not[aren't] many trees in the park.

2 의문문: be동사를 there 앞에 써서 Is[Are] there ~?의 형태로 쓴다. '~이 있니?'라는 의미이며 대답도 there를 이용한다.

의문문	긍정의 대답	부정의 대답
Is there + 주어 ~?	Yes, there is.	No, there isn't.
Are there + 주어 ~?	Yes, there are.	No, there aren't.

Is there a cat in the house? - Yes, there is. / No, there isn't.

Are there many comic books in the library? - Yes, there are. / No, there aren't.

Are there toys in the box? - Yes, there are. / No, there aren't.

3 There is[are]의 과거형

be동사의 과거형 was, were를 사용하며 '~이 있었다'라는 의미이다.

긍정문	부정문	의문문	의문문에 대한 대답
There was ~.	There was not[wasn't] ~.	Was there ~?	Yes, there was. / No, there wasn't.
There were ~.	There were not[weren't] ~.	Were there ~?	Yes, there were. / No, there weren't.

There was a rainbow in the sky.

There were two dice on the table.

Was there a pen on the desk? - Yes, there was. / No, there wasn't.

Were there any pigs on the farm? - Yes, there were. / No, there weren't.

A 다음 괄호 안에서 알맞은 것을 고르시오.

1 There (is / are) three bottles of water in the refrigerator.

2 There (is / are) an alarm clock on the table.

3 There (is / are) some cheese on the shelf.

4 There (was / were) a big tree on the hill.

5 There (was / were) three birds on the branch.

B 다음 그림의 상황에 맞도록 [보기]에서 알맞은 말을 골라 문장을 완성하시오.

┌─ 보기 ┐

| There was | There were | There isn't | There aren't |

1　2　3　4

1 _____ any bread on the dish.

2 _____ a cat in the yard last night.

3 _____ any eggs in the refrigerator.

4 _____ some kids at my house yesterday.

C 다음 문장을 괄호 안의 지시대로 바꿔 쓸 때, 빈칸에 알맞은 말을 쓰시오. (단, 줄임말로 쓸 것)

1 There was a picture on the wall.

→ _____ a picture on the wall. (부정문)

→ _____ a picture on the wall? (의문문)

2 There is a bank in this town.

→ _____ a bank in this town. (부정문)

→ _____ a bank in this town? (의문문)

3 There were many cars on the street last night.

→ _____ many cars on the street last night. (부정문)

→ _____ many cars on the street last night? (의문문)

A 다음 우리말과 의미가 같도록 be동사를 이용하여 문장을 완성하시오.

1 그는 늘 쾌활하다. → _____ always cheerful.

2 우리는 소방관들이 아니다. → _____ firefighters.

3 내 방에 야구방망이가 두 개가 있다. → _____ two bats in my room.

4 Jake는 아프니? → _____ sick?

  아니, 그렇지 않아.   No, _____.

5 연못에는 많은 물고기들이 있니? → _____ many fish in the pond?

  응, 있어.   Yes, _____.

B 다음 빈칸에 알맞은 be동사의 과거형을 쓰고, 괄호 안의 지시대로 문장을 바꿔 쓰시오. (단, 줄임말로 쓸 것)

1 You _____ alone in your house.

  → You _____ in your house. (부정문)

  → _____ in your house? (의문문)

2 He _____ 6 years old in 2015.

  → He _____ in 2015. (부정문)

  → _____ in 2015? (의문문)

3 The chairs _____ comfortable.

  → The chairs _____. (부정문)

  → _____? (의문문)

4 There _____ a lot of snow on the ground.

  → There _____ on the ground. (부정문)

  → _____ on the ground? (의문문)

5 There _____ many stars in the sky.

  → There _____ in the sky. (부정문)

  → _____ in the sky? (의문문)

C 다음 그림의 상황에 맞도록 Robin의 일기를 완성하시오.

It (1) _____ rainy yesterday, but it (2) _____ sunny today. I (3) _____ in

the library after school. Some friends (4) _____ in the library, too. Suddenly,

I (5) _____ sick. Now I (6) _____ in the hospital. I am sad.

D 다음 그림의 상황에 맞도록 There is[are] 구문을 이용하여 대화를 완성하시오.

10 years ago

now

A (1) _____ a pond in the yard 10 years ago?

B Yes, there (2) _____ . But now there _____ a pond.
_____ a table.

A (3) _____ swings in the yard 10 years ago?

B Yes, (4) _____ . But now _____ swings.
_____ a dog house.

A (5) _____ flowers in the yard 10 years ago?

B No, (6) _____ . But now _____ flowers in the yard.

01 다음 중 주어와 be동사가 잘못 짝지어진 것은?

① An egg – is

② Katie – was

③ Ms. White – is

④ She and I – was

⑤ The students – were

02 다음 중 줄임말로 알맞지 <u>않은</u> 것은?

① is not → isn't

② am not → amn't

③ was not → wasn't

④ are not → aren't

⑤ were not → weren't

내신 빈출

03 다음 밑줄 친 부분을 바르게 고칠 때, 알맞지 <u>않은</u> 것은?

① She <u>are</u> my art teacher. (→ is)

② You <u>is</u> a little girl. (→ are)

③ We <u>is</u> happy now. (→ were)

④ There <u>are</u> some juice. (→ is)

⑤ There <u>was</u> many apple trees. (→ were)

04 다음 중 not이 들어갈 위치로 알맞은 곳은?

Bob (①) was (②) my (③) English (④)
teacher (⑤).

[05-07] 다음 빈칸에 들어갈 말로 알맞은 것을 고르시오.

05

Its hair _____ brown.

① is ② are

③ were ④ am not

⑤ are not

06

The dictionaries _____ very thick.

① am ② is

③ was ④ are not

⑤ is not

07

They _____ late for school yesterday.

① is ② was

③ were ④ are not

⑤ was not

[08-09] 다음 빈칸에 들어갈 말로 알맞지 <u>않은</u> 것을 고르시오.

08

The _____ are on the floor.

① potatoes ② shoes

③ books ④ glass

⑤ boxes

고난도
09

> There isn't any _____ in the refrigerator.

① water   ② butter
③ onions   ④ juice
⑤ cheese

[10-11] 다음 우리말과 의미가 같도록 빈칸에 들어갈 알맞은 말을 고르시오.

10

> 풀밭에 많은 개미들이 있다.
> → _____ are many ants in the grass.

① Here   ② There
③ They   ④ These
⑤ Those

11

> 그 농장에는 닭들이 없다.
> → There _____ any chickens on the farm.

① is   ② isn't
③ were   ④ aren't
⑤ weren't

내신 빈출
12 다음 빈칸에 들어갈 말로 알맞게 짝지어진 것은?

> • _____ there a post office around here?
> • Lisa and Nancy _____ in the same class in 2021.

① Is – is   ② Is – are   ③ Is – were
④ Are – are   ⑤ Are – were

13 다음 대화 중 가장 자연스럽지 <u>않은</u> 것은?

① A: Is he a famous chef?
   B: Yes, he is.
② A: Are those women kind?
   B: No, they aren't.
③ A: Are these bananas fresh?
   B: Yes, they are.
④ A: Are you a good student?
   B: Yes, I am.
⑤ A: Are Joan and Jim from Mexico?
   B: No, she isn't.

고난도
14 다음 중 빈칸에 들어갈 말이 나머지와 <u>다른</u> 것은?

① We _____ young.
② My grandparents _____ doctors.
③ Daniel and I _____ in the living room.
④ There _____ some water in the bottle.
⑤ These games _____ very exciting.

15 다음 밑줄 친 부분의 줄임말로 알맞지 <u>않은</u> 것은?

① <u>You are</u> a very nice kid. → You're
② <u>They are</u> in the igloo. → They're
③ <u>It is not</u> foggy. → It isn't
④ <u>It is</u> a penguin. → Its
⑤ <u>I am not</u> strong. → I'm not

[16-17] 다음 질문에 대한 대답으로 알맞은 것을 고르시오.

16

> Was the test difficult?

① Yes, it is.　　　② No, it isn't.
③ Yes, it was.　　④ No, it was.
⑤ No, there wasn't.

17

> Are there three lanterns in the tent?

① Yes, they are.
② No, they aren't.
③ Yes, there are.
④ No, there wasn't.
⑤ Yes, there were.

[18-19] 다음 우리말을 어법에 알맞게 영작한 것을 고르시오.

18

> 어젯밤에 너구리 한 마리가 마당에 있었다.

① There is a raccoon in the yard last night.
② There was a raccoon in the yard last night.
③ It is a raccoon in the yard last night.
④ It isn't a raccoon in the yard last night.
⑤ They're a raccoon in the yard last night.

19

> 이 접시들은 깨끗하지 않다.

① These plates is clean.
② There are not clean plates.
③ There plates is not clean.
④ These plates aren't clean.
⑤ They are not clean plates.

20 다음 대화의 빈칸에 들어갈 말로 알맞게 짝지어진 것은?

> A: _____ you at the beach?
> B: No, we _____.

① Am – am not　　② Is – aren't
③ Are – is not　　④ Were – were
⑤ Are – aren't

고난도
21 다음 중 밑줄 친 There[there]의 의미가 나머지와 다른 것은?

① There is a blue bird in the cage.
② There are many desks in the classroom.
③ Are there many rivers in Seoul?
④ Were there spiders on the web?
⑤ Look at the boy over there.

[22-23] 다음 중 어법상 틀린 것을 고르시오.

22 ① Its color is yellow.
② There was a rainbow.
③ The twins are very cute.
④ Is she in Paris last year?
⑤ I'm not hungry now.

23 ① Your brother are brave.

② Is your computer new?

③ Is there a subway station near here?

④ I was short last year but I am tall now.

⑤ There is some butter on the plate.

[26-28] 다음 밑줄 친 부분을 바르게 고쳐 쓰시오.

26

It <u>is</u> stormy last Sunday.

→ _____

내신 빈출
24 다음 중 어법상 옳은 문장의 개수는?

ⓐ There is a girl and a cat.

ⓑ Were there a bat and a ball in the yard?

ⓒ Is she 5 years old at that time?

ⓓ Was Cindy and you at home last night?

ⓔ There isn't a bus stop around here.

① 1개   ② 2개   ③ 3개   ④ 4개   ⑤ 5개

27

Is there many fish in the aquarium?

→ _____

28

Your sister <u>are not</u> lazy.

→ _____

[29-31] 다음 우리말과 의미가 같도록 괄호 안의 말을 이용하여 문장을 완성하시오.

29

어제는 비가 오지 않았다. (rainy)

→ _____ yesterday.

25 다음 문장의 틀린 부분을 바르게 고칠 때, 알맞지 <u>않은</u> 것은?

① We are not in the office that day.

(→ We were not in the office that day.)

② There were four benches in the park now.

(→ There are four benches in the park now.)

③ I am late for the meeting yesterday.

(→ I was late for the meeting yesterday.)

④ Was Mary and Alice born in England?

(→ Are Mary and Alice born in England?)

⑤ Is Sumi and Jenny at the shopping mall?

(→ Are Sumi and Jenny at the shopping mall?)

30

나의 아빠는 작년에는 편찮으셨는데, 지금은 건강하시다. (sick, healthy)

→ My dad _____ last year, but he _____ now.

31

서랍에 돈이 조금 있다. (some money)

→ _____ in the drawer.

32 다음 우리말과 의미가 같도록 대화를 완성하시오.

A: (1) _____ there houses here
before?
(전에 이곳에 집들이 있었니?)
B: No, there (2) _____ . (3) _____
_____ a parking lot.
(아니, 없었어. 주차장이 하나 있었어.)

34 다음 글을 읽고, 어법상 <u>틀린</u> 것을 <u>2개</u> 찾아 바르게 고쳐 문장을 다시 쓰시오.

Wong and I work together. She is from
China. Last month, she is with her family
in her hometown. Now, she was alone in
Korea. She is happy with her life here.

(1) _____
(2) _____

33 다음 그림을 보고, 빈칸에 알맞은 말을 넣어 문장을 완성하시오.

Yesterday	Today

(1) It _____ rainy yesterday.
(2) Today, _____ _____
_____ .
(3) _____ _____ three ducks in
the pond yesterday.
(4) Today, _____ _____ a duck in
the pond.

35 다음 그림을 보고, 빈칸에 알맞은 말을 넣어 대화를 완성하시오.

Last Night		
Jina	Nick	Brian and Susan

(1) A: _____ sad last night?
B: Yes, _____ .
(2) A: _____ at the party
last night?
B: _____
(3) A: _____ at the
movie theater last night?
B: _____

Chapter

04

일반동사 1

01. 일반동사의 현재형

1 일반동사

주어의 동작이나 상태를 나타내는 말을 일반동사라고 한다.
go(가다), run(뛰다), study(공부하다), become(~이 되다), want(원하다), eat(먹다) 등
They **go** to school by subway.
I **eat** breakfast at 8 o'clock every morning.

2 일반동사 현재형의 쓰임

1 현재의 사실이나 반복적인 습관을 나타낸다.
My father **wants** a new car.
I **play** badminton every day.

2 변하지 않는 사실이나 진리를 나타낸다.
The earth **moves** around the Sun.

3 일반동사 현재형의 형태

1 주어가 1, 2인칭 단수 또는 복수일 때는 일반동사를 그대로 쓰고, 3인칭 단수일 때는 동사에 -(e)s를 붙인다.

I / You / We / They / 복수 명사	동사원형
He / She / It / 단수 명사	동사원형 + -(e)s

You **use** your smartphone too much.
She **uses** her smartphone too much.

2 3인칭 단수형 만드는 방법

대부분의 동사	동사원형 + -s	love → loves, come → comes, eat → eats, run → runs, play → plays
-o, -s, -ss, -ch, -sh, -x로 끝나는 동사	동사원형 + -es	do → does, go → goes, pass → passes, watch → watches, brush → brushes, fix → fixes
「자음 + y」로 끝나는 동사	y를 i로 고치고 + -es	study → studies, try → tries, fry → fries, cry → cries
예외	have → has	

She **comes** from the US.
Michael **watches** cartoons on Sundays.
Cindy **studies** Korean every evening.
Eric **has** a good voice.

⊕ PLUS **have**의 두 가지 의미: '가지고 있다'라는 의미와 '먹다'라는 의미가 있다.
She **has** a car. (가지고 있다) / She **has** lunch at noon. (먹다)

Grammar Check Up

A 다음 동사의 3인칭 단수형을 쓰시오.

1 go → _____   2 carry → _____

3 have → _____   4 wash → _____

5 keep → _____   6 buy → _____

7 mix → _____   8 cross → _____

B 다음 괄호 안에서 알맞은 것을 고르시오.

1 Jane (clean / cleans) the living room every day.

2 I (teach / teaches) music at school.

3 Jim (drys / dries) his hair in the bathroom.

4 Henry (plaies / plays) computer games every night.

5 The children (smile / smiles) brightly.

C 다음 괄호 안의 말을 이용하여 현재형 문장을 완성하시오.

1 He _____ a bike every Sunday. (ride)

2 My brother _____ very hard. (study)

3 They _____ books every night. (read)

4 Water _____ at 0℃. (freeze)

5 She _____ work at 6 p.m. (finish)

D 다음 문장에서 어법상 틀린 부분을 찾아 바르게 고쳐 쓰시오. (단, 주어는 고치지 말 것)

1 The babies cries a lot. _____ → _____

2 We has too much homework every Tuesday. _____ → _____

3 Alice feel tired every night. _____ → _____

4 He buies new clothes every month. _____ → _____

5 My sister want some cake after dinner. _____ → _____

02 일반동사 현재형의 부정문과 의문문

1 일반동사 현재형의 부정문

「do[does] not + 동사원형」의 형태로 쓰며 '~하지 않는다'라는 의미이다.

I / You / We / They / 복수 명사	do not[don't] + 동사원형
He / She / It / 단수 명사	does not[doesn't] + 동사원형

I **keep** a diary.

→ I **don't keep** a diary.

He **drinks** coffee at night.

→ He **doesn't drink** coffee at night.

The dolphins **help** fishermen.

→ The dolphins **don't help** fishermen.

The soup **tastes** good.

→ The soup **doesn't taste** good.

2 일반동사 현재형의 의문문

• 「Do[Does] + 주어 + 동사원형 ~?」의 형태로 쓰며 '~하니?'라는 의미이다.

• 대답은 「Yes, 주어 + do[does].」 / 「No, 주어 + don't[doesn't].」로 한다.

주어	의문문	긍정의 대답	부정의 대답
I / you / we / they / 복수 명사	Do + 주어 + 동사원형 ~?	Yes, 주어 + do.	No, 주어 + don't.
he / she / it / 단수 명사	Does + 주어 + 동사원형 ~?	Yes, 주어 + does.	No, 주어 + doesn't.

You **go** to school by bike.

→ **Do you go** to school by bike? - Yes, I do. / No, I don't.

He **remembers** her name.

→ **Does he remember** her name? - Yes, he does. / No, he doesn't.

They **eat** cereal for breakfast.

→ **Do they eat** cereal for breakfast? - Yes, they do. / No, they don't.

It **flies** high in the sky.

→ **Does it fly** high in the sky? - Yes, it does. / No, it doesn't.

⊕ PLUS   do 동사의 다양한 쓰임

일반동사	'~하다'의 의미	I **do** yoga. 나는 요가를 한다.
조동사	일반동사의 부정문과 의문문을 만들 때 쓰임	I **don't** do yoga. 나는 요가를 하지 않는다. **Do** you do yoga? 너는 요가를 하니?

* 조동사: 일반동사나 be동사 앞에 쓰여 의미를 보충해 주는 동사로 can, will, must 등이 있다.

A 다음 괄호 안에서 알맞은 것을 고르시오.

1 Cathy (don't / doesn't) call her parents every day.

2 (Do / Does) the girls live next door?

3 Does he (brush / brushes) his teeth after meals?

4 Sam and you don't (get / gets) up early in the morning.

B 다음 그림의 상황에 맞도록 주어진 단어를 이용하여 문장을 완성하시오. (단, 줄임말로 쓸 것)

1
play

The kids _____ baseball.

They _____ basketball.

2
eat

Carl _____ an apple.

He _____ an orange.

3
do

Sally _____ her homework.

She _____ yoga.

C 다음 괄호 안의 말을 이용하여 일반동사 현재형 대화를 완성하시오.

1 A: _____ your sister _____ her best? (try)

B: Yes, she _____ .

2 A: _____ you _____ your mom often? (help)

B: No, I _____ .

3 A: _____ James _____ exercise? (do)

B: No, he _____ .

4 A: _____ you _____ any questions? (have)

B: Yes, I _____ .

Writing Exercise

A 다음 문장의 주어를 바꿔 쓸 때, 빈칸에 알맞은 말을 쓰시오.

1 We go to work at 7. → My father _____ to work at 7.

2 I learn Chinese at school. → Minsu _____ Chinese at school.

3 They have a large house. → Ms. Green _____ a large house.

4 Lucas and I don't like milk. → Jake _____ milk.

5 My sons don't go to church. → Charlie _____ to church.

B 다음 문장을 괄호 안의 지시대로 바꿔 쓸 때, 빈칸에 알맞은 말을 쓰시오. (단, 줄임말로 쓸 것)

1 David listens to music in the morning.

→ David _____ to music in the morning. (부정문)

→ _____ to music in the morning? (의문문)

- Yes, _____. (긍정의 대답)

2 The children clean up the desk.

→ The children _____ the desk. (부정문)

→ _____ the desk? (의문문)

- No, _____. (부정의 대답)

3 The dog barks loudly.

→ The dog _____ loudly. (부정문)

→ _____ loudly? (의문문)

- No, _____. (부정의 대답)

4 Your brother wears a school uniform.

→ Your brother _____ a school uniform. (부정문)

→ _____ a school uniform? (의문문)

- Yes, _____. (긍정의 대답)

C 다음 그림의 상황에 맞도록 괄호 안의 말을 이용하여 글을 완성하시오.

I (1) _____ (like) rabbits. I (2) _____ (have) a rabbit. It (3) _____ (live)

in the cage. It (4) _____ (have) red eyes and a short tail. It (5) _____ (eat)

vegetables. It (6) _____ (drink) water. Sometimes it (7) _____ (jump).

It (8) _____ (look) cute. I really (9) _____ (love) my rabbit.

D 다음 우리말과 의미가 같도록 [보기]에서 알맞은 말을 골라 문장을 완성하시오.

┌─ 보기 ┐
| live   work   like   watch   teach |
└──────────────────────────────────┘

1 너는 영화를 좋아하니? – 응, 그래. 나는 주말마다 영화를 봐.

→ _____ movies?

– Yes, _____ . I _____ movies on weekends.

2 그는 도시에 사니? – 아니, 그렇지 않아. 그는 시골에 살아.

→ _____ in the city?

– No, _____ . He _____ in the country.

3 Amy는 영어를 가르치니? – 아니, 그렇지 않아. 그녀는 독일어를 가르쳐.

→ _____ English?

– No, _____ . She _____ German.

4 그들은 열심히 일하니? – 응, 그래. 그들은 늦게까지 일해.

→ _____ hard?

– Yes, _____ . They _____ late.

01 다음 중 동사의 원형과 3인칭 단수 현재형이 잘못 짝지어진 것은?

① carry – carries
② fix – fixies
③ go – goes
④ have – has
⑤ take – takes

02 다음 중 주어와 동사가 잘못 짝지어진 것은?

① It – rains
② We – asks
③ You – study
④ Kate – buys
⑤ Eric – hits

[03-04] 다음 빈칸에 들어갈 말로 알맞은 것을 고르시오.

03
The young boy _____ a kite every morning.

① fly
② flys
③ flis
④ flies
⑤ flyes

04
These books _____ exciting.

① look
② looks
③ lookes
④ lookies
⑤ lookied

05
_____ your father eat breakfast?

① Do
② Dos
③ Does
④ Is
⑤ Was

내신 빈출

06 다음 중 빈칸에 들어갈 말이 나머지와 <u>다른</u> 것은?

① _____ Mr. Nam live in Seoul?
② _____ a spider have four legs?
③ _____ Greg work at a restaurant?
④ _____ the movie start at 7 p.m.?
⑤ _____ your parents like Italian food?

07 다음 중 not이 들어갈 위치로 알맞은 곳은?

(①) My brother (②) does (③) do (④) his homework (⑤) before dinner.

[08-09] 다음 밑줄 친 부분 중 어법상 <u>틀린</u> 것을 고르시오.

08 ① My uncle <u>reads</u> the newspaper every day.
② I <u>takes</u> a shower in the morning.
③ She <u>doesn't eat</u> chocolate.
④ We <u>learn</u> history at school.
⑤ <u>Does</u> it walk slowly?

09 ① Do they <u>live</u> in the sea?

② Sally <u>sings</u> in her room.

③ The players <u>practice</u> very hard.

④ Does the turtle <u>swims</u> very well?

⑤ My husband <u>washes</u> the dishes after dinner.

내신 빈출

10 다음 중 어법상 옳은 것을 <u>모두</u> 고르면?

① Do I run fast?

② The horse don't eat carrots.

③ Minhee know many English words.

④ Does Peter study in the library?

⑤ The workers doesn't wear helmets.

11 다음 중 주어를 바꿔 쓴 문장이 어법상 <u>틀린</u> 것은?

① I like oranges.

→ She likes oranges.

② You have a cell phone.

→ He has a cell phone.

③ We take a walk.

→ Yuna takes a walk.

④ They move fast.

→ The animals moves fast.

⑤ John goes hiking.

→ John's parents go hiking.

12 다음 우리말과 의미가 같도록 괄호 안의 말을 배열할 때 <u>세 번째</u> 오는 단어는?

> 그녀는 남동생이 있니?
> (a, does, she, have, brother)?

① a   ② does   ③ she

④ have   ⑤ brother

13 다음 문장을 의문문으로 바르게 바꾼 것은?

> Helen plays the violin very well.

① Is Helen play the violin very well?

② Do Helen play the violin very well?

③ Do Helen plays the violin very well?

④ Does Helen play the violin very well?

⑤ Does Helen plays the violin very well?

14 다음 질문에 대한 대답으로 알맞은 것은?

> Does your mom bathe your dog?

① Yes, she is.   ② No, she isn't.

③ Yes, she do.   ④ No, she don't.

⑤ No, she doesn't.

[15-16] 다음 대화의 빈칸에 들어갈 말로 알맞게 짝지어진 것을 고르시오.

15
> A: _____ you like cooking?
> B: Yes, I _____ .

① Do – do   ② Do – don't

③ Do – does   ④ Does – does

⑤ Does – don't

고난도

16
> A: Does Mrs. Lee _____ a cat as a pet at home?
> B: No, she _____ .

① keep – does   ② keep – doesn't

③ keeps – does   ④ keeps – doesn't

⑤ keep – don't

고난도
17 다음 빈칸에 공통으로 들어갈 말로 알맞은 것은?

> • I _____ exercise every day.
> • They _____ not study together.
> • _____ the kids like candy?

① am[Am]　　　② do[Do]
③ does[Does]　　④ have[Have]
⑤ go[Go]

[20-21] 다음 밑줄 친 부분 중 어법상 틀린 것을 고르시오.

20
> ①Does ②he ③has lunch ④with ⑤you?

21
> ①Many ②students ③don't ④likes tests ⑤a lot.

[18-19] 다음 우리말을 어법에 알맞게 영작한 것을 고르시오.

18
> 우리는 오늘 영어 수업이 없다.

① We have English class today.
② We don't have English class today.
③ We doesn't have English class today.
④ We not have English class today.
⑤ We not do have English class today.

고난도
22 다음 중 밑줄 친 부분의 쓰임이 나머지와 다른 것은?

① I do not wear a cap.
② Does it have long tails?
③ He does his homework.
④ We do not eat meat.
⑤ Do you know her name?

19
> 너의 아버지는 토요일마다 하이킹을 가시니?

① Is your father go hiking every Saturday?
② Do your father go hiking every Saturday?
③ Do your father goes hiking every Saturday?
④ Does your father go hiking every Saturday?
⑤ Does your father goes hiking every Saturday?

고난도
23 다음 대화 중 가장 자연스럽지 않은 것은?

① A: Do you like cola?
　 B: Yes, I do.
② A: Does Kelly play soccer well?
　 B: Yes, she does.
③ A: Does your father wash his car?
　 B: Yes, he does.
④ A: Do they help you?
　 B: Yes, they do.
⑤ A: Does your mom drive you to school?
　 B: No, she don't.

내신 빈출
24 다음 우영이의 오답노트 중 우영이가 고친 내용이 <u>틀린</u> 것은?

① Does it rains a lot in Thailand?
→ 주어가 3인칭 단수이니까 Do에만 -es를 붙이고 뒤에는 동사원형 rain을 써야 해.

② The early bird catchs the worm.
→ catch처럼 -ch로 끝나는 동사의 3인칭 단수형은 -es를 붙여서 catches라고 써야 해.

③ He doesn't goes to work by bus.
→ 주어가 3인칭인 일반동사 현재형의 부정문이니까 doesn't 뒤에 동사원형 go를 써야 해.

④ Do the young boy wear glasses?
→ 이 문장은 주어가 3인칭 단수임을 나타내지 않았어. wear를 wears로 고쳐야 해.

⑤ We aren't like the new comic books.
→ 일반동사 현재형의 부정문이고 주어가 복수이니까 aren't를 don't로 고쳐야 해.

25 다음 (A)~(C)의 각 네모 안에서 알맞은 것끼리 짝지어진 것은?

· Your voice (A) sound / sounds odd.
· We don't (B) listen / listens to loud music.
· Does the class (C) begin / begins at 8 o'clock?

	(A)	(B)	(C)
①	sound	– listen	– begin
②	sound	– listen	– begins
③	sound	– listens	– begin
④	sounds	– listen	– begin
⑤	sounds	– listens	– begins

[26-27] 다음 우리말과 의미가 같도록 괄호 안의 말을 바르게 배열하시오.

26 그녀가 나의 전화번호를 아니? (know, does, she)

→ _____ my phone number?

27 우리는 학교에서 스페인어를 배우지 않는다. (learn, we, don't)

→ _____ Spanish at school.

[28-31] 다음 우리말과 의미가 같도록 괄호 안의 말을 이용하여 문장을 완성하시오.

28 너는 그 사전을 사용하니? (use)

→ _____ the dictionary?

29 나는 열이 없다. (have)

→ _____ a fever.

30 Julie는 아침에 머리에 빗질을 하니? (brush)

→ _____ her hair in the morning?

31 Jake는 패스트푸드를 먹지 않는다. (eat)

→ _____ fast food.

Answers p.8

32 다음 주말 일과표를 보고, 대화를 완성하시오.

	Saturday	Sunday
I	clean the bathroom	walk our dog
My brother	walk our dog	wash the dishes

(1) _____ the
bathroom on Saturdays?
- Yes, I _____ .

(2) _____ the dishes
on Sundays?
- No, I _____ . My brother
_____ on
Sundays.

(3) _____ your dog
on Saturdays?
- Yes, _____ .

33 다음 글을 읽고, 어법상 틀린 부분을 3개 찾아 바르게 고쳐 쓰시오.

> Annie has some rules for her health.
> First, she don't drink soda. Second, she
> doesn't eats anything at night. Last, she
> does yoga before bed. Do she go to bed
> early? Of course she does.

(1) _____ → _____
(2) _____ → _____
(3) _____ → _____

34 다음 미나의 방학 생활계획표를 보고, 빈칸에 알맞은 말을 넣어 글을 완성하시오.

Mina (1) _____ at 7:30. She jogs from
9:30 to 11:00. She (2) _____ books for an
hour before lunch. She (3) _____ the piano
at 1:00. After dinner, she (4) _____ TV
and (5) _____ English. She goes to bed at
10:30.

35 다음 밑줄 친 우리말과 의미가 같도록 [조건]에 맞게 문장을 완성하시오.

Yuna: What do you do on weekends?
Tony: (1) 아빠와 나는 주말마다 자원봉사를 해.
We help the old people at a nursing
home.
Yuna: What do you do there?
Tony: (2) 나는 이불을 빨아. (3) 그리고 아빠는 고장
난 기계를 고치셔.

/ 조건 /
• 다음 표현을 한 번씩 사용할 것
(volunteer work, repair, do, the blankets, wash)

(1) My dad and I _____
on weekends.
(2) I _____ .
(3) And my dad _____ a broken
machine.

Chapter

05

일반동사 2

01 일반동사의 과거형

1 일반동사의 과거형

1 일반동사의 과거형은 과거의 상태나 과거에 일어난 일을 나타낸다.

I **finish** my work at 6 on weekdays. (현재)
I **finished** my work at 9 last Thursday. (과거)

2 주로 yesterday, last week[night / year], a year[month] ago 등 과거를 나타내는 표현과 함께 쓰인다.

I **visited** my uncle **last year**.
I **cleaned** my room **yesterday**.

2 일반동사 과거형의 형태

1 주어의 인칭과 단수·복수에 상관없이 대부분의 동사에 -(e)d를 붙인다.

He **watched** the movie on TV.
My parents **looked** surprised at my news.

2 일반동사 과거형 만드는 방법

대부분의 동사	동사원형 + -ed	call → called, visit → visited, wash → washed, clean → cleaned
-e로 끝나는 동사	동사원형 + -d	love → loved, move → moved, live → lived, hate → hated
「자음 + y」로 끝나는 동사	y를 i로 고치고 + -ed	cry → cried, dry → dried, try → tried, study → studied, fry → fried
「단모음 + 단자음」으로 끝나는 동사	자음 한 번 더 쓰고 + -ed	stop → stopped, drop → dropped, chat → chatted, plan → planned

Bill **called** me this morning.
I **moved** to a new house.
I **dried** my sister's hair.
They **stopped** the game.

3 불규칙 변화

현재형과 과거형이 같은 동사	put → put, cut → cut, hit → hit, read → read
현재형과 과거형이 다른 동사	go → went, come → came, do → did, have → had, give → gave, know → knew, buy → bought, teach → taught, eat → ate, make → made, meet → met, run → ran, take → took, drink → drank, see → saw, write → wrote, get → got

She **put** her bag on the chair.
I **met** an old friend this morning.
Sean **wrote** an email.
The strange boy **ran** away.

⊕ **PLUS** **3인칭 단수 주어일 때:** 과거형 동사는 주어에 의해 형태가 변하지 않으므로 -(e)s를 붙이지 않는다.
She **drinks** milk. (○)   She **drank** milk. (○)   She **dranks** milk. (×)

Grammar Check Up

A 다음 동사의 과거형을 쓰시오.

1 arrive → _____   2 cry → _____

3 have → _____   4 break → _____

5 know → _____   6 play → _____

7 run → _____   8 teach → _____

B 다음 괄호 안에서 알맞은 것을 고르시오.

1 My father (washes / washed) his car last week.

2 The singers (sing / sang) two songs last night.

3 Julia (bought / boughts) the armchair last year.

4 My mom (cuted / cut) her finger on a knife yesterday.

5 Jack (wears / wore) a red tie yesterday.

C 다음 괄호 안의 말을 이용하여 과거형 문장을 완성하시오.

1 He _____ his camera on the ground yesterday. (drop)

2 My daughter _____ to the emergency room last night. (go)

3 Sujin _____ for only four hours last night. (sleep)

4 I _____ some bread for breakfast this morning. (eat)

5 They _____ Cathy in a restaurant 30 minutes ago. (see)

D 다음 문장의 밑줄 친 부분을 바르게 고쳐 쓰시오.

1 Mr. Thomson drives for an hour yesterday.   → _____

2 John Pemberton invents Coca-Cola in 1885.   → _____

3 My sister meet her husband first last year.   → _____

4 My dad and I make a time capsule last Saturday.   → _____

5 I do too much exercise yesterday.   → _____

02 일반동사 과거형의 부정문과 의문문

1 일반동사 과거형의 부정문

「did not[didn't] + 동사원형」의 형태로 쓰며 '~하지 않았다'라는 의미이다.

I / You / We / They / 복수 명사	did not[didn't] + 동사원형
He / She / It / 단수 명사	

I **bought** vegetables.
→ I **didn't buy** vegetables.

Kevin **visited** his uncle.
→ Kevin **didn't visit** his uncle.

She **knew** your name.
→ She **didn't know** your name.

We **heard** the news.
→ We **didn't hear** the news.

He **drove** his car yesterday.
→ He **didn't drive** his car yesterday.

⊕ **PLUS** 주어의 인칭과 수에 상관없이 「**did not[didn't]** + 동사원형」으로 쓴다.
It **didn't bark** last night. (○) It **dids not** bark last night. (×)
She **didn't do** her homework. (○) She **didn't does** her homework. (×)

2 일반동사 과거형의 의문문

• 「Did + 주어 + 동사원형 ~?」의 형태로 쓰며 '~했니?'라는 의미이다.
• 대답은 「Yes, 주어 + did.」 / 「No, 주어 + didn't.」로 한다.

의문문	긍정의 대답	부정의 대답
Did + 주어 + 동사원형 ~?	Yes, 주어 + did.	No, 주어 + didn't.

You **went** to bed early last night.
→ **Did you go** to bed early last night? - Yes, I did. / No, I didn't.

They **stayed** at the hotel.
→ **Did they stay** at the hotel? - Yes, they did. / No, they didn't.

He **got** her text message.
→ **Did he get** her text message? - Yes, he did. / No, he didn't.

It **rained** yesterday.
→ **Did it rain** yesterday? - Yes, it did. / No, it didn't.

Jiho **found** your smartphone.
→ **Did Jiho find** your smartphone? - Yes, he did. / No, he didn't.

⊕ **PLUS** 주어의 인칭과 수에 상관없이 「**Did** + 주어 + 동사원형 ~?」으로 쓴다.
Did she meet you? (○) **Dids she meet** you? (×)
Did he sleep well last night? (○) **Did he sleeps** well last night? (×)

Grammar Check Up

A 다음 괄호 안에서 알맞은 것을 고르시오.

1 He (doesn't / didn't) study with us yesterday.

2 (Does / Did) Mark water the plants yesterday morning?

3 I (don't / didn't) have any pancakes this morning.

4 (Do / Did) the children play basketball here last Sunday?

5 It didn't (snow / snowed) a lot here in Seoul.

6 Did she (take / takes) a math test last Monday?

B 다음 어제 했던 일을 나타낸 그림의 상황에 맞도록 주어진 단어를 이용하여 문장을 완성하시오. (단, 줄임말로 쓸 것)

1 **go**

Luna _____ to the Eiffel Tower yesterday.

She _____ to Tower Bridge yesterday.

2 **eat**

Michael _____ pizza last night.

He _____ a hamburger last night.

3 **wash**

Sally and her sister _____ their cat.

They _____ their puppy.

C 다음 괄호 안의 말을 이용하여 대화를 완성하시오.

1 A: _____ you _____ Julie last week? (help)

   B: No, I _____ .

2 A: _____ Billy _____ you home last night? (drive)

   B: No, he _____ .

3 A: _____ they _____ their best in the last game? (do)

   B: Yes, they _____ .

A 다음 괄호 안의 말을 이용하여 문장을 완성하시오. (단, 줄임말로 쓸 것)

1 I _____ my homework an hour ago. (finish)

2 Tony _____ a shower last night. (not, take)

3 _____ your dad _____ the newspaper yesterday? (read)

4 Sue _____ a teddy bear last week. (buy)

5 They _____ the chair yesterday. (not, make)

6 _____ the baby _____ last night? (cry)

B 다음 문장을 괄호 안의 지시대로 바꿔 쓸 때, 빈칸에 알맞은 말을 쓰시오. (단, 줄임말로 쓸 것)

1 Judy listened to music until late last night.

→ _____ to music until late last night. (부정문)

→ _____ to music until late last night? (의문문)

- Yes, _____. (긍정의 대답)

2 He studied science yesterday.

→ _____ science yesterday. (부정문)

→ _____ science yesterday? (의문문)

- No, _____. (부정의 대답)

3 They sent a gift to my cousin last week.

→ _____ a gift to my cousin last week. (부정문)

→ _____ a gift to my cousin last week? (의문문)

- No, _____. (부정의 대답)

4 Ms. Green wore sunglasses yesterday.

→ _____ sunglasses yesterday. (부정문)

→ _____ sunglasses yesterday? (의문문)

- Yes, _____. (긍정의 대답)

C 다음은 Mark가 여름 캠프에서 있었던 일을 설명한 글이다. 그림의 상황에 맞도록 괄호 안의 말을 이용하여 글을 완성하시오.

I (1) _____ (go) to a summer camp. It was very exciting. First, I (2) _____ (set)

up a tent with my friend. The teacher (3) _____ (help) us. Then, we (4) _____

(climb) a mountain. It was fun. After that, we (5) _____ (eat) dinner. Then, our

teacher (6) _____ (tell) funny stories. Finally, we (7) _____ (sleep) in the tent.

We (8) _____ (have) a great time.

D 다음 우리말과 의미가 같도록 괄호 안의 말을 이용하여 대화를 완성하시오.

A You look tired today. What's wrong?

B I (1) _____ (have) a stomachache last night. (나는 어젯밤에 배가 아팠어.)
So, I (2) _____ (sleep) well. (그래서 나는 잠을 잘 못 잤어.)

A (3) _____ (see) a doctor? (너는 병원에 갔었니?)

B No, (4) _____ . (아니, 그러지 않았어.)
I (5) _____ (take) medicine and rested. (나는 약을 먹고 쉬었어.)

[01-02] 다음 중 동사의 현재형과 과거형이 잘못 짝지어진 것을 고르시오.

01
① carry – carried
② do – doed
③ learn – learned
④ dance – danced
⑤ chat – chatted

02
① know – knew
② hit – hitted
③ teach – taught
④ buy – bought
⑤ tell – told

03 다음 중 동사의 현재형과 과거형이 다른 것을 2개 고르면?
① cut   ② come   ③ sit
④ read   ⑤ hurt

[04-07] 다음 빈칸에 들어갈 말로 알맞은 것을 고르시오.

04
The dog _____ loudly last night.

① bark   ② barks
③ barked   ④ barkeds
⑤ barkied

05
My daughter _____ some flowers to me yesterday.

① give   ② gives
③ gived   ④ gave
⑤ gaved

06
I _____ the museum last Monday.

① not visited   ② don't visit
③ doesn't visit   ④ didn't visit
⑤ didn't visited

07
_____ you change your hairstyle last week?

① Is   ② Are
③ Do   ④ Does
⑤ Did

[08-09] 다음 빈칸에 들어갈 말로 알맞지 않은 것을 고르시오.

08
I lost my wallet _____.

① yesterday   ② tomorrow
③ last year   ④ last month
⑤ a moment ago

09

> I didn't _____ the book.

① read   ② buy
③ lose   ④ wrote
⑤ like

13

> Henry Ford는 그의 첫 번째 차를 1896년에 만들었니?

① Do Henry Ford built his first car in 1896?
② Built Henry Ford his first car in 1896?
③ Did Henry Ford built his first car in 1896?
④ Did Henry Ford build his first car in 1896?
⑤ Did Henry Ford builds his first car in 1896?

[10-11] 다음 밑줄 친 부분 중 어법상 틀린 것을 고르시오.

10
① He gots up early this morning.
② Did they live in Singapore last year?
③ Jim sang songs alone last night.
④ Did your father fix your bike?
⑤ She looked lovely that night.

14 다음 밑줄 친 부분을 바르게 고친 것으로 알맞게 짝지어 진 것은?

> · Paul keeps a diary last year.
> · King Sejong invents Hangeul in 1443.

① keep – invent
② keeped – invent
③ keeped – invented
④ kept – invent
⑤ kept – invented

고난도
11
① The soup tasted delicious.
② I didn't do my homework.
③ My mom took a walk this morning.
④ He didn't go shopping last evening.
⑤ Did you saw any dolphins in the sea last summer?

[15-16] 다음 대화의 빈칸에 들어갈 말로 알맞게 짝지어진 것을 고르시오.

내신 빈출
15

> A: _____ you use your cell phone in class yesterday?
> B: No, I _____.

① Do – do   ② Does – doesn't
③ Do – did   ④ Did – does
⑤ Did – didn't

[12-13] 다음 우리말을 어법에 알맞게 영작한 것을 고르시오.

12

> 그는 접시를 바닥에 떨어뜨렸다.

① He drops the dish on the floor.
② He droped the dish on the floor.
③ He dropped the dish on the floor.
④ He droppd the dish on the floor.
⑤ He dropeds the dish on the floor.

16

> A: Did she _____ a novel?
> B: Yes, she _____.

① write – does   ② write – doesn't
③ write – did   ④ wrote – didn't
⑤ wrote – did

내신 빈출

17 다음 문장을 부정문으로 바르게 바꾼 것은?

> Charlie drank milk today.

① Charlie not drank milk today.
② Charlie doesn't drank milk today.
③ Charlie doesn't drink milk today.
④ Charlie didn't drink milk today.
⑤ Charlie didn't drank milk today.

18 다음 대화 중 가장 자연스러운 것은?

① A: Did the frog eats the insects?
　B: Yes, it did.
② A: Did you enjoy the movie last night?
　B: No, we weren't.
③ A: Do Michael save much money last year?
　B: Yes, he did.
④ A: Did Brian knowed your secret?
　B: No, he didn't.
⑤ A: Did you help your sister with her homework?
　B: Yes, I did.

고난도

19 다음 빈칸에 공통으로 들어갈 말로 알맞은 것은?

> • I _____ yoga 10 minutes ago.
> • They _____ not stay up late last night.
> • _____ it snow heavily yesterday?

① am[Am]　　　　② do[Do]
③ does[Does]　　④ did[Did]
⑤ have[Have]

20 다음 질문에 대한 대답으로 알맞은 것은?

> Did Jessica close the windows?

① Yes, she is.
② No, she did.
③ Yes, she was.
④ No, she doesn't.
⑤ Yes, she did.

[21-22] 다음 빈칸에 들어갈 말로 알맞게 짝지어진 것을 고르시오.

고난도

21

> Steve _____ a muffin and milk for breakfast every morning. But he _____ bacon and eggs yesterday morning.

① have – have
② has – have
③ had – has
④ has – had
⑤ had – had

22

> Martin _____ up at 7:00 every morning. But he _____ up at 7:30 yesterday.

① get – got
② gets – getted
③ gets – gets
④ gots – getted
⑤ gets – got

23 다음 중 어법상 **틀린** 것은?

① I didn't like tomatoes.

② Did you wash your hands?

③ He gave a gift to me yesterday.

④ My father went to work by bus.

⑤ Sujin didn't bought the scarf.

24 다음은 어제 했던 일에 관한 표이다. 표의 내용과 일치하는 것은?

Who Did What?

	go to the zoo	meet friends	play soccer
I	○	×	×
my mother	×	○	×
my brothers	×	×	○

① I didn't go to the zoo yesterday.

② My mother went to the zoo yesterday.

③ My brothers met their friends yesterday.

④ My mother didn't meet her friends yesterday.

⑤ My brothers played soccer yesterday.

내신 빈출
25 다음 중 어법상 옳은 문장의 개수는?

ⓐ I heared the new album last night.

ⓑ Did you passed the test last week?

ⓒ I don't play the violin an hour ago.

ⓓ Did you call your boss this morning?

ⓔ Nick and I fight yesterday.

① 1개   ② 2개   ③ 3개   ④ 4개   ⑤ 5개

[26-27] 다음 문장을 괄호 안의 지시대로 바꿔 쓰시오.

26 The thief runs away.

→ The thief _____ away. (과거)

27 Bill wore a nice cap.

→ _____ a nice cap? (의문문)

[28-29] 다음 우리말과 의미가 같도록 괄호 안의 말을 바르게 배열하시오.

28 그들은 지난달에 그 농장을 방문했니?
(visit, they, did, the farm)

→ _____ last month?

29 나는 오늘 아침에 조깅을 하러 가지 않았다.
(didn't, I, go jogging)

→ _____ this morning.

[30-31] 다음 우리말과 의미가 같도록 괄호 안의 말을 이용하여 문장을 완성하시오.

30 그는 어젯밤에 우리에게 그 소식을 전했다. (tell)

→ _____ the news to us last night.

31 Harry는 어제 다리를 다쳤니? (hurt)

→ _____ his leg yesterday?

32 다음 문장을 [보기]와 같이 바꿔 쓰시오.

> ┤ 보기 ├
> I swim in this pool.
> → I <u>swam in this pool</u> yesterday.

(1) They take a picture of the wedding.

→ _____

yesterday.

(2) He spends time with his family.

→ _____

yesterday.

34 다음 중 어법상 <u>틀린</u> 문장을 3개 골라 기호를 쓰고, 바르게 고쳐 문장을 다시 쓰시오.

> ① He drove the car carefully that day.
> ② Tom breaked his arm yesterday.
> ③ Sumin and I went to the park last night.
> ④ Sue hitted the ball and I caught it.
> ⑤ I didn't saw her angry face at that time.

(1) _____ → _____

(2) _____ → _____

(3) _____ → _____

33 다음은 지우가 지난 주말에 했던 일을 적은 메모이다. 메모를 보고, 대답을 완성하시오.

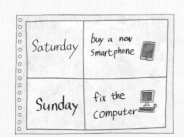

(1) Did Jiwoo fix the computer on Saturday?

- _____, he _____.

He _____ on Sunday.

(2) Did Jiwoo buy a new smartphone on Sunday?

- _____, he _____.

He _____ on Saturday.

35 다음 그림의 상황에 맞도록 [조건]에 맞게 문장을 완성하시오.

> ┤ 조건 ├
> • 동사는 과거형으로 쓸 것
> • [보기]에서 알맞은 표현을 사용할 것

> ┤ 보기 ├
> read a newspaper   ride a bike
> walk the dog   draw a picture

(1) The boy _____ .

(2) The old man _____ .

(3) The girl _____ .

(4) The woman _____ .

06

현재진행형과 미래형

01 현재진행형

1 현재진행형

1 · 현재 진행 중인 일을 표현할 때 사용하며 '~하는 중이다', '~하고 있다'라는 의미이다.
· 「be동사 + 동사원형-ing」의 형태이며, be동사는 주어의 인칭과 수에 따라 바뀐다.

I	am	
You / We / They / 복수 명사	are	동사원형-ing
He / She / It / 단수 명사	is	

I **am brushing** my teeth.
We **are moving** the table.
My father **is taking** a shower.

2 동사의 -ing형 만드는 방법

대부분의 동사	동사원형 + -ing	do → doing, eat → eating, go → going, play → playing, work → working
「자음 + e」로 끝나는 동사	e 빼고 + -ing	come → coming, write → writing, bake → baking, drive → driving, live → living
-ie로 끝나는 동사	ie를 y로 고치고 + -ing	die → dying, lie → lying
「단모음 + 단자음」으로 끝나는 동사	자음 한 번 더 쓰고 + -ing	stop → stopping, drop → dropping, run → running, swim → swimming

2 현재진행형의 부정문

「be동사 + not + 동사원형-ing」의 형태이며, '~하는 중이 아니다', '~하고 있지 않다'라는 의미이다.

I'm **not baking** cookies
They **aren't fighting** each other.
He **isn't watching** TV.

3 현재진행형의 의문문

· 「Be동사 + 주어 + 동사원형-ing ~?」의 형태이며, '~하는 중이니?', '~하고 있니?'라는 의미이다.
· 대답은 「Yes, 주어 + be동사.」 / 「No, 주어 + be동사 + not.」으로 한다.

Are you carrying an umbrella? - Yes, I am. / No, I'm not.
Are they staying at the hotel? - Yes, they are. / No, they aren't.
Is Julie walking in the park? - Yes, she is. / No, she isn't.

⊕ PLUS 진행형으로 쓸 수 없는 동사
· love, like, want, know, have 등 감정, 존재, 소유를 나타내는 동사는 진행형으로 쓸 수 없다.
She **knows** it. (O)　She **is knowing** it. (×)
· have의 경우 '가지고 있다'라는 소유의 의미일 때는 진행형으로 쓸 수 없지만, '먹다'라는 동작의 의미일 때는 진행형으로 쓸 수 있다.
He **is having** a bike. (×)　He **is having** lunch. (O)

Grammar Check Up

A   다음 동사의 -ing형을 쓰시오.

1 go → _____   2 fly → _____

3 have → _____   4 come → _____

5 sit → _____   6 die → _____

7 begin → _____   8 catch → _____

B   다음 괄호 안의 말을 이용하여 현재진행형 문장을 완성하시오.

1 It _____ now. (snow)

2 We _____ our homework. (do)

3 The little boy _____ on the stage. (sing)

4 My mom _____ the tomatoes in half. (cut)

5 Eric and Ron _____ baseball in the playground. (practice)

C   다음 문장을 괄호 안의 지시대로 바꿔 쓸 때, 빈칸에 알맞은 말을 쓰시오.

1 My father is writing a letter.

→ _____ a letter. (부정문)

2 The student is wearing a school uniform.

→ _____ a school uniform? (의문문)

3 He is jumping rope.

→ _____ rope. (부정문)

4 The kids are putting the puzzle together.

→ _____ the puzzle together? (의문문)

D   다음 대화의 빈칸에 알맞은 말을 쓰시오.

1 A: Are you drinking milk?   B: Yes, _____.

2 A: Is she fixing the computer?   B: No, _____.

3 A: Is your dad taking a taxi?   B: No, _____.

4 A: Are those people waiting for the bus?   B: Yes, _____.

02 미래형

1 미래형

1 • 미래에 대한 계획이나 예측 또는 의지를 나타내며 '~할 것이다'라는 의미이다.
   • 「will + 동사원형」 또는 「be동사 + going to + 동사원형」의 형태이다.

I **will take** many pictures tomorrow.
He **is going to visit** us this weekend.

2 주로 tomorrow, next week[month/year], soon 등 미래를 나타내는 표현과 함께 쓰인다.

My father **will be** in Japan **next month**.
They **are going to arrive** soon.

2 will + 동사원형

부정문	주어 + will not[won't] + 동사원형 ~. (~하지 않을 것이다)
의문문	Will + 주어 + 동사원형 ~? (~할 거니?) - Yes, 주어 + will. (응, 할 거야.) / No, 주어 + will not[won't]. (아니, 안 할 거야.)

He **will not attend** the meeting next Monday.
We **won't go** camping tomorrow.
Will they help us? - Yes, they will. / No, they won't.

➕ **PLUS** 「대명사 주어 + will」의 줄임말
I will → I'll / You will → You'll / He will → He'll / She will → She'll / It will → It'll / We will → We'll / They will → They'll

3 be동사 + going to + 동사원형

1 「be동사 + going to + 동사원형」의 형태이며, be동사는 주어의 인칭과 수에 따라 바뀐다.

I	am	
You / We / They / 복수 명사	are	going to + 동사원형 (~할 것이다)
He / She / It / 단수 명사	is	

I **am going to paint** the front gate.
We **are going to watch** the play after school.
He **is going to get** a haircut.

2 부정문과 의문문

부정문	주어 + be동사 + not + going to + 동사원형 ~. (~하지 않을 것이다)
의문문	Be동사 + 주어 + going to + 동사원형 ~? (~할 거니?) - Yes, 주어 + be동사. (응, 할 거야.) / No, 주어 + be동사 + not. (아니, 안 할 거야.)

I'**m not going to go** to school tomorrow.
Is it going to rain soon? - Yes, it is. / No, it isn't.
Are you going to marry Tim? - Yes, I am. / No, I am not.

Grammar Check Up

A 다음 괄호 안에서 알맞은 것을 고르시오.

1 Minsu will (meet / meets) his friends at 7 p.m.

2 It will not (be / is) windy and cold.

3 Will you (bring / brought) your laptop today?

4 I (will / am) going to dye my hair.

5 She is not going to (buy / buys) a new cell phone.

B 다음 문장을 괄호 안의 지시대로 바꿔 쓸 때, 빈칸에 알맞은 말을 쓰시오.

1 I will hide the gift under the bed.

→ _____ the gift under the bed. (부정문)

2 Billy will travel abroad next year.

→ _____ abroad next year? (의문문)

3 The weather is going to be nice.

→ The weather _____ nice. (부정문)

4 They are going to plant apple trees.

→ _____ apple trees? (의문문)

C 다음 대화의 빈칸에 알맞은 말을 쓰시오.

1 A: Julia, will you call me later? B: Yes, _____.

2 A: Tim and Joe, are you going to fight again? B: No, _____.

3 A: Will she be with you tomorrow? B: No, _____.

4 A: Is your brother going to lose weight? B: Yes, _____.

D 다음 문장에서 어법상 틀린 부분을 찾아 바르게 고쳐 쓰시오.

1 Jennifer is going dance in the festival. _____ → _____

2 She will is 13 years old next year. _____ → _____

3 We are going not to join the soccer club. _____ → _____

4 Are they going see a dolphin show? _____ → _____

5 Mr. White won't eats out tonight. _____ → _____

A 다음 우리말과 의미가 같도록 괄호 안의 말을 이용하여 문장을 완성하시오.

1 Judy는 그녀의 방에서 공부를 하는 중이다. (study)

→ Judy ＿＿＿＿＿＿＿＿＿＿＿＿＿＿＿ in her room.

2 나의 아들은 사자를 그리고 있다. (draw)

→ My son ＿＿＿＿＿＿＿＿＿＿＿＿＿＿＿ a lion.

3 나는 영어로 일기를 쓰고 있다. (write)

→ I ＿＿＿＿＿＿＿＿＿＿＿＿＿＿＿ my diary in English.

4 너는 개를 산책시키는 중이니? (walk)

→ ＿＿＿＿＿＿＿＿＿＿＿＿＿＿＿ your dog?

5 그녀는 TV를 보고 있지 않다. (watch)

→ She ＿＿＿＿＿＿＿＿＿＿＿＿＿＿＿ TV.

B 다음 대화를 will 또는 be going to와 괄호 안의 말을 이용하여 완성하시오.

1 ＿＿＿＿＿＿＿＿＿＿＿＿＿＿＿ a large party? (it, be)

- Yes, it will. Bring your friends.

2 ＿＿＿＿＿＿＿＿＿＿＿＿＿＿＿ the poor boy? (they, help)

- Yes, they are. They're so nice people.

3 ＿＿＿＿＿＿＿＿＿＿＿＿＿＿＿ this weekend? (your dad, work)

- No, he isn't. He is going to go fishing with us.

4 ＿＿＿＿＿＿＿＿＿＿＿＿＿＿＿ to Busan? (you, move)

- No, we aren't. We are going to move to Gwangju.

5 ＿＿＿＿＿＿＿＿＿＿＿＿＿＿＿ us for lunch? (you, join)

- No, I won't. I am very busy today.

C 다음은 Sally를 위한 생일 파티 계획을 쓴 글이다. 그림의 상황에 맞도록 be going to와 괄호 안의 말을 이용하여 글을 완성하시오.

| I | Mark | Sue and Jake | My mom |

We (1) _____ (have) a birthday party for Sally.

I (2) _____ (make) a card. Mark (3) _____

(bake) some cookies. Sue and Jake (4) _____ (buy) a gift.

My mom (5) _____ (make) a cake for Sally.

It (6) _____ (be) a great party.

D 다음 괄호 안의 말을 이용하여 대화를 완성하시오.

A (1) _____ your car, Dad? (will, wash)

B Yes, I will. (2) _____ me? (be going to, help)

A Of course.

B (3) _____ some water for me? (will, get)

A Yes, I will. I'll be back soon.

B Thank you.

[01-02] 다음 중 동사의 원형과 -ing형이 잘못 짝지어진 것을 고르시오.

01
① do – doing
② carry – carrying
③ have – haveing
④ work – working
⑤ stop – stopping

02
① die – dieing
② tell – telling
③ set – setting
④ run – running
⑤ leave – leaving

[03-06] 다음 빈칸에 들어갈 말로 알맞은 것을 고르시오.

03
Kelly is _____ on the bench now.

① sit   ② sits
③ siting   ④ sat
⑤ sitting

04
We _____ return the books soon.

① will   ② didn't
③ are   ④ don't
⑤ going to

05
내신 빈출
Mrs. Brown _____ going to have a baby next week.

① be   ② is
③ are   ④ does
⑤ will

06
_____ they travel to New York next winter?

① Do   ② Did
③ Are   ④ Will
⑤ Be

[07-08] 다음 중 not이 들어갈 위치로 알맞은 곳을 고르시오.

07
My friends (①) and I (②) will (③) have dinner (④) together (⑤).

08
내신 빈출
I (①) am (②) going (③) to (④) see (⑤) the doctor.

[09-10] 다음 밑줄 친 부분 중 어법상 틀린 것을 고르시오.

09 ① It will be very hot tomorrow.
② We don't going to work tomorrow.
③ Our team will win the game tomorrow.
④ Are you going to go camping this Sunday?
⑤ They are going to be great singers in the future.

10 ① Is she swimming now?
② Will you come to my house?
③ He isn't playing the guitar.
④ The man parking the car now.
⑤ The girl is patting the dog.

[11-12] 다음 우리말을 어법에 알맞게 영작한 것을 고르시오.

11 | 그는 텐트 안에서 자고 있다. |

① He sleeps in the tent.
② He is sleep in the tent.
③ He is sleeping in the tent.
④ He be sleeping in the tent.
⑤ He sleeping in the tent.

12 | 지금 팽이가 돌고 있지 않다. |

① The top spins now.
② The top not is spinning now.
③ The top will not spinning now.
④ The top is not spinning now.
⑤ The top does not spinning now.

[고난도]
13 다음 중 빈칸에 들어갈 말이 나머지와 다른 것은?

① _____ your sisters baking a cake?
② We _____ going to pick up the laundry.
③ They _____ not going to invite him.
④ My brother and I _____ not go shopping next Sunday.
⑤ _____ you going to stay in Korea?

[고난도]
14 다음 중 밑줄 친 부분의 쓰임이 나머지와 다른 것은?

① You're going to be okay.
② She's going to the library now.
③ He's going to pass the audition.
④ We're going to build a new house.
⑤ They're going to arrive at the airport soon.

15 다음 밑줄 친 부분을 바르게 고칠 때, 알맞지 않은 것은?

① She will turns on the radio. (→ turn on)
② My flight won't left in an hour. (→ leave)
③ Bora spend next winter in Canada.
　　　(→ spends)
④ I will am back in 10 minutes. (→ be)
⑤ We are going not to give up.
　　　(→ are not going)

[16-17] 다음 대화의 빈칸에 들어갈 말로 알맞게 짝지어진 것을 고르시오.

16

A: _____ you leave Seoul tomorrow?
B: No, I _____ .

① Do – do
② Will – will
③ Are – don't
④ Are – am not
⑤ Will – won't

17

A: _____ we going to clean the room?
B: Yes, we _____ .

① Will – will
② Do – will
③ Are – are
④ Are – aren't
⑤ Will – won't

고난도
18 다음 빈칸에 공통으로 들어갈 말로 알맞은 것은?

· I am _____ to the mall.
· We are _____ to buy a new camera.
· Is it _____ to snow tomorrow?

① do
② doing
③ will
④ go
⑤ going

19 다음 질문에 대한 대답으로 알맞은 것은?

Are they swimming across the river?

① Yes, they will.
② Yes, they do.
③ Yes, they are.
④ No, they don't.
⑤ No, they won't.

[20-21] 다음 빈칸에 들어갈 말로 알맞게 짝지어진 것을 고르시오.

20

· Jenny _____ her hair every morning.
· She _____ her hair now.

① washes – washing
② wash – is washing
③ wash – will wash
④ washes – is washing
⑤ wash – is going to wash

고난도
21

· The farmer _____ the peaches now.
· He _____ the peaches tomorrow.

① picks – will pick
② picked – is going to pick
③ is picking – is going to pick
④ picks – is going to pick
⑤ is picking – picked

22 다음 대화 중 가장 자연스럽지 <u>않은</u> 것은?

① A: Are you listening to music?
  B: No, I am not. I'm reading a novel.
② A: Is Mike going to visit San Francisco?
  B: Yes, he is. His parents are there.
③ A: Are you having a good time?
  B: Yes, we are. We are happy now.
④ A: Does Jennifer sing at the school festival next week?
  B: No, she won't. She will dance.
⑤ A: Will the concert start soon?
  B: Yes, it will. Let's hurry.

내신 빈출

23 다음 우리말과 의미가 같도록 빈칸에 들어갈 말이 알맞게
짝지어진 것은?

> ⓐ 그들은 안전벨트를 착용하고 있다.
> They _____ seat belts.
> ⓑ 그녀는 가구를 살 것이다.
> She _____ going to buy furniture.
> ⓒ 몇 분 걸릴 것이다.
> It _____ a few minutes.

① wear   – be   – takes
② wear   – is   – will take
③ will wear   – was – takes
④ are wearing – be   – takes
⑤ are wearing – is   – will take

24 다음 중 어법상 틀린 것은?

① The sun rises in the east.
② We enjoyed the birthday party yesterday.
③ It is going to be sunny tomorrow.
④ My mom is designing my clothes now.
⑤ I will not have dinner with my family
　yesterday.

내신 빈출

25 다음 중 어법상 틀린 것으로 알맞게 짝지어진 것은?

> ⓐ John is talking about his plan now.
> ⓑ The women not are feeding the cats.
> ⓒ We are not going to sleeping late.
> ⓓ Will Julian rent a car next week?
> ⓔ I am go to learn Spanish next year.

① ⓐ, ⓑ   ② ⓐ, ⓒ, ⓓ
③ ⓑ, ⓒ, ⓔ   ④ ⓑ, ⓓ, ⓔ
⑤ ⓓ, ⓔ

[26-28] 다음 우리말과 의미가 같도록 괄호 안의 말을 바르게
배열하시오.

26
> 우리는 다음 주에 새로운 집으로 이사할 것이다.
> (are, move, going, to)

→ We _____ to a
　new house next week.

27
> 그는 지금 그의 자전거를 타고 있지 않다.
> (riding, is, not, his bike)

→ He _____ now.

28
> 네 남동생은 내년에 11살이 되니?
> (be, will, 11 years old, your brother)

→ _____ next year?

[29-31] 다음 우리말과 의미가 같도록 괄호 안의 말을 이용하
여 문장을 완성하시오.

29
> 지금 물이 끓고 있다. (boil)

→ The water _____
　now.

30
> 나의 아빠는 그의 오래된 차를 고치지 않으실 것이다.
> (dad, be going to, fix)

→ _____ his old car.

31
> 너는 이번 겨울에 스키를 타러 갈 거니?
> (be going to, go)

→ _____ skiing this
　winter?

Answers p.11

32 다음 문장을 괄호 안의 말을 이용하여 어법에 알맞게 다시 쓰시오.

> He wears sunglasses.

(1) (right now)

→ _____

(2) (tomorrow)

→ _____

34 다음 글을 읽고, 어법상 틀린 부분을 3개 찾아 바르게 고쳐 쓰시오.

> My family is busy now. My grandfather is watering the garden. My mom and dad is painting the fence. My brother is doing his homework. My sister is rideing her bike in the yard. But I'm not busy. I'm lieing on the sofa!

(1) _____ → _____
(2) _____ → _____
(3) _____ → _____

33 다음 일기예보를 보고, 대화를 완성하시오.

Friday	Saturday	Sunday
snowy	sunny	rainy

A: Will it be sunny on Friday?
B: (1) _____, it (2) _____.
 It will be (3) _____.
A: How about Sunday?
B: (4) _____
 But it (5) _____ on Saturday.

35 다음 소라의 일정표를 보고, [조건]에 맞게 문장을 완성하시오.

date	things to do
6/15	go to my uncle's house in Seoul
6/16	visit the national museum
6/17	come back to Busan

┌ 조건 ┐
- 미래형을 사용할 것
- 괄호 안에 주어진 단어 수를 반영할 것

(1) Sora _____ to her uncle's house in Seoul on June 15. (2단어)
(2) The next day, she _____ the national museum. (4단어)
(3) On June 17, she _____ back to Busan. (2단어)

Chapter

07

조동사

01 조동사 can, may

1 조동사의 의미와 특징

1 조동사는 일반동사나 be동사 앞에서 그 동사만으로는 나타내기 어려운 의미, 즉 능력, 허가, 의무 등을 나타내는 말이다.

I read English books.
　　└→ 읽다

I **can read** English books.
　　　　└→ 읽을 수 있다(능력)

2 주어의 인칭이나 수에 관계없이 형태가 같으며 뒤에 동사원형이 온다.

He **can play** the guitar well.

He **cans play** the guitar well. (×)　　　　He **can plays** the guitar well. (×)

> **⊕ PLUS** 조동사의 부정문: 조동사 뒤에 not을 붙인다.　She **cannot** play tennis.
> 조동사의 의문문: 조동사를 주어 앞에 쓴다. 대답 또한 조동사를 이용한다.
> **Can** you **ride** a bike? - Yes, I can. / No, I can't.

2 can

1 가능·능력: ~할 수 있다

평서문	can (~할 수 있다)
부정문	cannot[can't] (~할 수 없다)
의문문	Can + 주어 + 동사원형 ~? (~할 수 있니?) - Yes, 주어 + can. (응, 할 수 있어.) / No, 주어 + can't. (아니, 할 수 없어.)

I **can** make a hamburger.

He **cannot** pass the test.

Can you drive a car? - Yes, I can. / No, I can't.

2 허가: ~해도 된다

You **can** wear the mask.

Can I sit down here? - Yes, you can. / No, you can't.

3 may

1 허가: '~해도 된다'라는 의미이며, can보다 좀 더 격식을 차린 정중한 표현이다.

You **may** use my cell phone.

You **may not** enter this area.

May I drink some water? - Yes, you may. / No, you may not.

2 추측: ~일지도 모른다

He **may** be angry.

They **may** be in her room.

Grammar Check Up

A 다음 괄호 안에서 알맞은 것을 고르시오.

1 Peter Pan (can / cans) fly in the sky.

2 Mina can (write / writes) stories in French.

3 My cat (not can / cannot) climb a tree.

4 (Can / Do) you go shopping with me tomorrow?

5 She may (stay / stays) with us for a few days.

6 (May ask I / May I ask) you a question?

B 다음 우리말과 의미가 같도록 [보기]에서 알맞은 말을 골라 문장을 완성하시오. (단, 중복 사용 가능)

보기
can   may   cannot

1 너는 이 문제를 풀 수 없다.   → You _____ solve this problem.

2 나의 엄마는 치즈를 직접 만들 수 있다.   → My mom _____ make cheese herself.

3 내가 식탁에 있는 빵을 좀 먹어도 될까?   → _____ I have some bread on the table?

4 그들은 배가 고플지도 모른다.   → They _____ be hungry.

C 다음 그림의 상황에 맞도록 can 또는 may를 이용하여 문장을 완성하시오.

1

This book is not difficult.

I _____ read it.

2

There are many dark clouds in the sky.

It _____ rain soon.

3

The rabbit _____ run fast.

The turtle _____ run fast.

4

The elevator is broken.

You _____ use it.

Practice

02 조동사 must, have to

1 must

1 must: ~해야 한다(의무)

I **must** do some exercise.

We **must** save energy.

You **must** put on your helmet.

2 must not: ~해서는 안 된다(강한 금지)

You **must not** enter the grass area.

We **must not** play balls on the streets.

He **must not** waste his money.

> **⊕ PLUS** 강한 추측을 나타내는 must의 부정형
> '~임에 틀림없다'의 의미를 나타내는 must의 부정형은 cannot(~일 리가 없다)이다.
> She **must** be a teacher. 그녀는 교사임에 틀림없다.
> She **cannot** be a teacher. 그녀는 교사일 리가 없다.

2 have to

1 have to: ~해야 한다(의무)(= must)

I **have to** do my homework by 6 p.m.

You **have to** pay the extra charge.

He **has to** cook his own meals.

2 don't have to: ~할 필요가 없다(불필요)

I **don't have to** use your camera.

You **don't have to** go with me.

She **doesn't have to** take a math test.

> **⊕ PLUS** 주어가 3인칭 단수일 경우
> • 「have to + 동사원형」은 「has to + 동사원형」으로 쓴다.
> • 「don't have to + 동사원형」은 「doesn't have to + 동사원형」으로 쓴다.
>
> **must not과 don't have to**
> must의 부정형인 must not은 금지(~해서는 안 된다)를, have to의 부정형인 don't have to는 불필요(~할 필요가 없다)를 나타낸다.

A 다음 괄호 안에서 알맞은 것을 고르시오.

1 Jenny (must / musts) be proud of herself.

2 Tom and Mina (have to / has to) keep their promise.

3 My dad (don't / doesn't) have to take the medicine.

4 Andrew (must / has) to listen to his parents.

5 You must (turn on not / not turn on) your cell phone during class.

B 다음 빈칸에 must 또는 must not을 이용하여 문장을 완성하시오.

1 You _____ keep quiet in the library. You _____ be noisy.

2 Tony _____ finish his report by tonight. He _____ go out now.

3 We _____ cross the street at a red light. We _____ follow the traffic rules.

4 My sister _____ go to bed early. She _____ be late for school.

C 다음 그림의 상황에 맞도록 have to 또는 don't have to를 이용하여 대화를 완성하시오. (단, 필요하면 형태를 바꿀 것)

1   2   3   4

1 A: I have a fever.

   B: You _____ go to see a doctor.

2 A: Sue has a test tomorrow.

   B: She _____ study hard.

3 A: Today is Friday.

   B: I'm happy. We _____ work on Saturday.

4 A: We cleaned our house.

   B: Oh, your mom _____ clean the house.

A 다음 우리말과 의미가 같도록 알맞은 조동사와 괄호 안의 말을 이용하여 문장을 완성하시오.

1 나의 어린 아들은 잘 걷지 못한다. (walk)

→ My little son _____ well.

2 그녀는 중국어를 잘 말할 수 있다. (speak)

→ She _____ Chinese well.

3 그는 체육관에 있을지도 모른다. (be)

→ He _____ in the gym.

4 제가 창문을 닫아도 될까요? (close)

→ _____ the window?

5 너는 내 재킷을 입어도 돼. (wear)

→ You _____ my jacket.

B 다음 두 문장이 자연스럽게 연결되도록 괄호 안의 말을 바르게 배열하시오. (단, 필요하면 형태를 바꿀 것)

1 There are so many people in the restaurant. (we, wait, have to, for a long time)

→ _____

2 Mr. Kim is a famous cook. (he, can, Chinese food, cook, very well)

→ _____

3 The summer vacation starts tomorrow. (she, go, to school, don't have to)

→ _____

4 Aiden will leave for Seoul tomorrow. (must, he, his bag, pack, tonight)

→ _____

5 It is snowy and cold outside. (you, not, must, open, the window)

→ _____

C 다음은 Robin과 반 친구들의 나쁜 습관에 대해 쓴 글이다. 그림의 상황에 맞도록 must 또는 must not과 괄호 안의 말을 이용하여 글을 완성하시오.

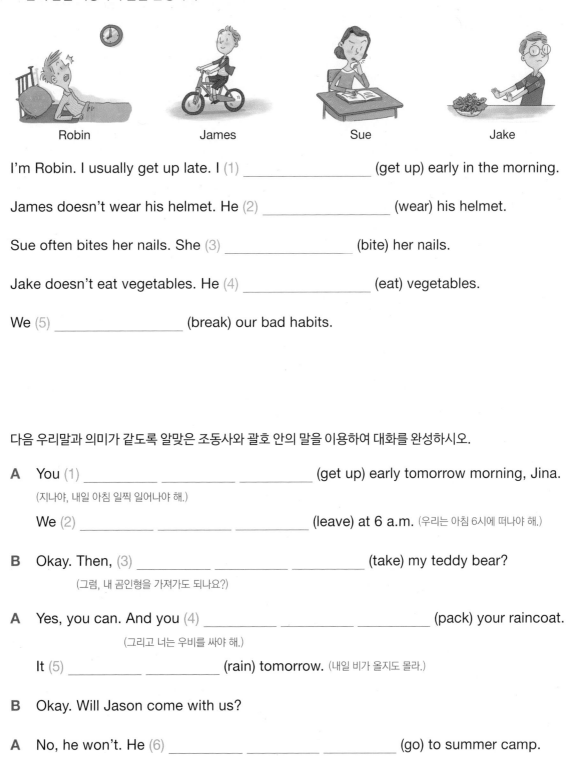

Robin   James   Sue   Jake

I'm Robin. I usually get up late. I (1) _____ (get up) early in the morning.

James doesn't wear his helmet. He (2) _____ (wear) his helmet.

Sue often bites her nails. She (3) _____ (bite) her nails.

Jake doesn't eat vegetables. He (4) _____ (eat) vegetables.

We (5) _____ (break) our bad habits.

D 다음 우리말과 의미가 같도록 알맞은 조동사와 괄호 안의 말을 이용하여 대화를 완성하시오.

A You (1) _____ _____ _____ (get up) early tomorrow morning, Jina.
(지나야, 내일 아침 일찍 일어나야 해.)

We (2) _____ _____ _____ (leave) at 6 a.m. (우리는 아침 6시에 떠나야 해.)

B Okay. Then, (3) _____ _____ _____ (take) my teddy bear?
(그럼, 내 곰인형을 가져가도 되나요?)

A Yes, you can. And you (4) _____ _____ _____ (pack) your raincoat.
(그리고 너는 우비를 싸야 해.)

It (5) _____ _____ (rain) tomorrow. (내일 비가 올지도 몰라.)

B Okay. Will Jason come with us?

A No, he won't. He (6) _____ _____ _____ (go) to summer camp.
(그는 여름 캠프에 가야 해.)

B Oh, I see.

[01-02] 다음 우리말과 의미가 같도록 빈칸에 들어갈 말로 알맞은 것을 고르시오.

01
> Kelly는 3개 국어를 말할 수 있다.
> → Kelly _____ speak three languages.

① can   ② may
③ must   ④ cannot
⑤ has to

02
> 너는 제시간에 회의에 참석해야 한다.
> → You _____ attend the meeting on time.

① can   ② may
③ must   ④ don't have to
⑤ has to

[03-04] 다음 밑줄 친 부분과 의미상 바꿔 쓸 수 있는 것을 고르시오.

03
> You <u>may</u> ride your bike here.

① must   ② can
③ has to   ④ will
⑤ must not

04
> Juliet <u>must</u> eat more vegetables.

① can   ② may
③ has to   ④ will
⑤ have to

[05-07] 다음 빈칸에 들어갈 말로 알맞은 것을 고르시오.

05
> He _____ be hungry. He didn't have lunch.

① won't   ② may
③ must not   ④ has to
⑤ cannot

06
> The crosswalk light is green. We _____ cross the street.

① can   ② must not
③ don't have to   ④ cannot
⑤ may not

07
> You _____ drive fast in school zones.

① must not   ② may
③ don't have to   ④ can
⑤ have to

[08-09] 다음 질문에 대한 대답으로 알맞은 것을 고르시오.

08

A: Can you swim across the Han River?
B: _____

① Yes, I can.
② Yes, I can't.
③ Yes, you can.
④ No, you can't.
⑤ Yes, I do.

09

A: Must I get up early tomorrow?
B: _____

① Yes, you do.
② Yes, I must.
③ Yes, you must not.
④ No, you don't have to.
⑤ No, you doesn't have to.

[10-11] 다음 중 어법상 틀린 것을 고르시오.

10 ① He may be your brother.
② He must take care of animals.
③ The little boy cannot ride a horse.
④ She have to be nice to her friends.
⑤ You must not make noise in the classroom.

고난도
11 ① It may be snowy.
② My mom can help us.
③ Emily must not eat junk food.
④ Nick must to exercise every day.
⑤ You must not throw trash in the park.

[12-13] 다음 빈칸에 공통으로 들어갈 말로 알맞은 것을 고르시오.

고난도
12

· My father _____ be tired.
· You _____ put on my raincoat.

① have to   ② don't have to
③ has to   ④ may
⑤ must not

고난도
13

· We _____ keep our promise.
· He doesn't _____ see a doctor. He is fine now.

① have to   ② must
③ has to   ④ may
⑤ can

[14-15] 다음 중 어법상 옳은 것을 고르시오.

14 ① I has to drink milk.
② He mays be at home.
③ You not must touch the pot.
④ She doesn't have to buy any eggs.
⑤ My mom can makes delicious spaghetti.

15 ① I can't found my yellow cap.
② My dad must fixes the roof.
③ May I to take your order?
④ Can you lend me your pen?
⑤ You doesn't have to worry about me.

[16-18] 다음 밑줄 친 부분의 쓰임이 나머지와 <u>다른</u> 것을 고르시오.

16
① Our team <u>can</u> win the game.
② <u>Can</u> penguins live in the sea?
③ Mr. Park <u>can</u> skate very well.
④ <u>Can</u> your baby speak?
⑤ <u>Can</u> I borrow your cell phone?

17 〔고난도〕
① Mike <u>may</u> know the answer.
② <u>May</u> I introduce myself?
③ You <u>may</u> play soccer after lunch.
④ You <u>may</u> come in now.
⑤ <u>May</u> I turn off the fan?

18
① She <u>must</u> be diligent.
② You <u>must</u> start right now.
③ I <u>must</u> come back home by six.
④ <u>Must</u> we finish it today?
⑤ We <u>must</u> be careful on the street.

[19-20] 다음 중 어법상 <u>틀린</u> 것으로 알맞게 짝지어진 것을 고르시오.

19 〔내신 빈출〕
ⓐ She can't plays tennis well.
ⓑ You may turn on the light.
ⓒ He must eat not salty food.
ⓓ I have to leave work early.

① ⓐ, ⓑ   ② ⓐ, ⓒ
③ ⓑ, ⓒ   ④ ⓐ, ⓒ, ⓓ
⑤ ⓑ, ⓒ, ⓓ

20 〔내신 빈출〕
ⓐ May I go out tonight?
ⓑ You must to do your best.
ⓒ She don't have to worry.
ⓓ Can you come to my house?

① ⓐ, ⓒ   ② ⓑ, ⓒ
③ ⓑ, ⓓ   ④ ⓒ, ⓓ
⑤ ⓐ, ⓑ, ⓓ

21 다음 우리말을 어법에 알맞게 영작한 것을 <u>모두</u> 고르면?
① 네 컴퓨터를 사용해도 될까?
  → Must I use your computer?
② Judy는 유명한 댄서임에 틀림없다.
  → Judy must be a famous dancer.
③ 우리는 도서관에서 조용히 해야 한다.
  → We have be quiet in the library.
④ 나는 이번 여름에 유럽에 갈지도 모른다.
  → I may go to Europe this summer.
⑤ 너는 오늘 서두를 필요가 없다.
  → You must not rush today.

📖 Answers p.13

[22-23] 다음 대화의 빈칸에 들어갈 말로 알맞은 것을 고르시오.

22

> A: I'm very tired now.
> B: You _____ take a break.

① will
② can't
③ have to
④ must not
⑤ don't have to

23

> A: I can ski well. How about you?
> B: I _____ ski well. But I like to ski.

① can
② may
③ must
④ cannot
⑤ must not

[24-25] 다음 중 어법상 옳은 문장의 개수를 고르시오.

내신 빈출
24

> ⓐ It mays snow tonight.
> ⓑ Kangaroos can jump high.
> ⓒ You must not ride a bike at night.
> ⓓ We has to be fair to both players.

① 없음　② 1개　③ 2개　④ 3개　⑤ 4개

내신 빈출
25

> ⓐ She can makes clothes.
> ⓑ You may not run in the room.
> ⓒ He must help his mother.
> ⓓ They don't have to do the work.

① 없음　② 1개　③ 2개　④ 3개　⑤ 4개

[26-28] 다음 우리말과 의미가 같도록 괄호 안의 말을 이용하여 문장을 완성하시오.

26

> 우리는 우리의 지구를 보호해야 한다.
> (save our planet)

→ We _____.

27

> 그녀는 그녀의 점심 도시락을 가지고 올 필요가 없다.
> (bring, lunch)

→ She _____.

28

> 그는 제시간에 여기에 오지 못할지도 모른다.
> (come, in time)

→ He _____.

[29-31] 다음 우리말과 의미가 같도록 괄호 안의 말을 바르게 배열하시오.

29

> 여기서 사진을 찍어서는 안 된다.
> (must, you, take, not, pictures)

→ _____ here.

30

> 제가 여기 잠깐 앉아도 될까요? (I, sit, may, here)

→ _____ for a minute?

31

> 너는 주차할 자리를 예약해야 하니?
> (have to, do, reserve, you)

→ _____ a
parking space?

Answers p.13

32 다음 빈칸에 알맞은 조동사와 괄호 안의 말을 이용하여 글을 완성하시오.

Sora plans to study with her friends today. But she (1) _____ (study) with them. Her parents are going on a business trip. So, she (2) _____ (take care of) her brother for two days.

33 다음은 학생들이 할 수 있는 것과 할 수 없는 것을 나타낸 표이다. 표의 내용과 일치하도록 글을 완성하시오.

	speak English	ride a bike	play the guitar
Mina	○	×	○
Suho	×	○	×
Jina	○	○	×

Mina can speak English well. But she (1) _____. Suho can't play the guitar. But he (2) _____. Jina can speak English. But she (3) _____ _____. They can learn from each other.

34 다음은 은지가 방문할 전시회의 안내문이다. 안내문의 내용과 일치하도록 괄호 안의 조동사를 이용하여 문장을 완성하시오.

Do	Don't
Be quiet	Take pictures

(1) Eunji _____ quiet. (have to)
(2) Eunji _____ pictures. (must)

35 다음 [보기]에서 알맞은 말을 골라 글을 완성하시오.

보기
cannot	be	some mistake
will	must	some news

(at a hotel)
A: Hello. I made a reservation for two nights. My name is Jason Reed.
B: I am sorry. I can't find your name on the list.
A: There _____ _____ _____ _____!

Chapter

08

형용사와 부사

01 형용사

1 형용사의 의미와 쓰임

1 의미: 형용사는 사람, 사물, 동물의 모양, 성질, 상태, 수량 등을 나타내는 말이다.
pretty, cute, kind, white, blue, big, small, one, two, many, much 등

2 쓰임: 명사를 꾸며 주거나 주어를 보충 설명한다.

형용사 + 명사	명사 앞에서 명사를 꾸며 준다.
주어 + 동사 + 형용사	동사 뒤에서 주어를 보충 설명한다.

This is a **new** dress.   This dress is **new**.
⌐ 명사 꾸며 줌   주어를 보충 설명

Look at the **yellow** bird.   The bird is **small** and **cute**.

⊕ PLUS 형용사와 함께 쓰이는 동사
be, become, turn, look, feel, sound, taste, smell 등
The man **became** *popular*. The leaves **turned** *yellow*. She **looks** *happy*.

-thing + 형용사
something, anything과 같이 -thing으로 끝나는 대명사는 형용사가 뒤에서 꾸며 준다.
Is there **anything** *interesting* to watch?

2 수량을 나타내는 형용사 many / much / some / any

1 many / much: '많은'이라는 뜻이다.

many	뒤에 셀 수 있는 명사의 복수형이 온다.
much	뒤에 셀 수 없는 명사가 온다.

We have **many** onions.
There are **many** cars on the road.
I don't have **much** money.
There is too **much** water in the vase.

2 some / any: '조금의', '몇몇의'라는 뜻으로, 셀 수 있는 명사와 셀 수 없는 명사 모두에 쓰인다.

some	긍정문, 권유문에 쓰인다.
any	부정문, 의문문에 쓰인다. 부정문에서는 '조금의 (~도 없다)'라는 의미이다.

I will buy **some** books tomorrow.
Would you have **some** coffee?
I didn't eat **any** meat.
Are there **any** stamps?

Answers p.15

A 다음 문장에서 형용사를 <u>모두</u> 찾아 밑줄을 그으시오.

1 Poor Cinderella must wash dirty clothes.

2 The soccer game was very exciting.

3 The sneakers are old and dirty.

4 There is something special about it.

B 다음 그림의 상황에 맞도록 [보기]에서 알맞은 말을 골라 문장을 완성하시오.

보기

white   sweet   tall   green   short   sleepy

1   2   3   4

1 My cat has _____ hair and _____ eyes.

2 Michael was very _____. So, he went to bed.

3 My father likes something _____.

4 The girl is _____. But the boy is _____.

C 다음 괄호 안에서 알맞은 것을 고르시오.

1 There are (many / much) cities in the world.

2 The chef uses too (many / much) salt and sugar.

3 There are (some / any) ants on the bench.

4 I don't have (some / any) money in my wallet.

D 다음 우리말과 의미가 같도록 빈칸에 알맞은 말을 쓰시오.

1 우리는 많은 시간이 없다.   → We don't have _____ _____.

2 거리에 사람들이 많니?   → Are there _____ _____ on the street?

3 우리는 빵이 조금도 없다.   → We don't have _____ _____.

4 샐러드 좀 드실래요?   → Would you like _____ _____?

02 부사

1 부사의 의미와 쓰임

1 의미: 부사는 장소, 방법, 시간, 빈도 등을 나타내는 말이다.
here, there, kindly, carefully, quietly, early, tomorrow, always, sometimes 등

2 쓰임: 동사, 형용사, 다른 부사, 문장 전체를 꾸며 준다.
He gets up **early**. (동사 꾸며 줌)

This book is **very** interesting. (형용사 꾸며 줌)

She speaks **very** slowly. (다른 부사 꾸며 줌)

Luckily, he passed the exam. (문장 전체 꾸며 줌)

2 부사의 형태

대부분의 부사	형용사 + -ly	nice → nicely, quiet → quietly, sad → sadly, careful → carefully
-y로 끝나는 형용사	y를 i로 바꾸고 + -ly	happy → happily, lucky → luckily
형용사와 형태가 같은 부사		fast(빠른 - 빨리) late(늦은 - 늦게) high(높은 - 높게) early(이른 - 일찍) hard(딱딱한; 어려운; 열심인 - 열심히) near(가까운 - 가까이)
예외		good → well

He closed the door **quietly**.   Minsu smiles at me **happily**.
The kites fly **high** in the sky.   My son plays the guitar **well**.

⊕ PLUS **-ly로 끝나지만 형용사인 단어**
lovely(사랑스러운), friendly(친근한), lonely(외로운), weekly(매주의), monthly(매달의) 등
부사에 -ly가 붙어서 다른 뜻이 되는 부사
lately(최근에), highly(매우), hardly(거의 ~ 않다), nearly(거의)

3 빈도부사

1 의미: 빈도부사는 어떤 일이 얼마나 자주 일어나는지 그 빈도를 나타내는 부사이다.

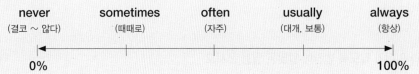

never	sometimes	often	usually	always
(결코 ~ 않다)	(때때로)	(자주)	(대개, 보통)	(항상)

0% ←—————————————————→ 100%

2 위치: 일반적으로 be동사와 조동사 뒤에, 일반동사 앞에 위치한다. sometimes는 문장의 맨 앞이나 맨 끝에도 올 수 있다.
My mom *is* **always** diligent.
Sometimes it can be dangerous.
He **usually** *runs* for exercise.

A 다음 형용사의 부사형을 쓰시오.

1 nice → _____

2 kind → _____

3 easy → _____

4 quick → _____

5 safe → _____

6 fast → _____

7 careful → _____

8 happy → _____

B 다음 괄호 안에서 알맞은 것을 고르시오.

1 (Unlucky / Unluckily), I failed the exam.

2 My brother plays soccer very (well / good).

3 That is a (very tall / tall very) building.

4 He came home (late / lately) yesterday.

C 다음 괄호 안의 말을 이용하여 문장을 완성하시오.

1 She is very busy on weekends. (often)

→ She _____.

2 He jogs in the park. (always)

→ He _____.

3 I will fix the broken computer. (never)

→ I _____.

4 My father skips breakfast. (usually)

→ My father _____.

D 다음 밑줄 친 부분의 우리말 뜻을 쓰시오.

1 He can't sleep on a <u>hard</u> bed. → _____

2 The gardener is <u>hard</u> at work. → _____

3 This problem is <u>hard</u> to me. → _____

4 The swimmer practices <u>hard</u>. → _____

5 I can <u>hardly</u> believe the news. → _____

A 다음 주어진 단어를 알맞은 형태로 써서 문장을 완성하시오.

1 careful

· You must be _____.

· Listen to me _____.

2 early

· The _____ bird catches the worm.

· I go to bed _____ in the evening.

3 good

· The steak tastes _____.

· Jinhee plays the violin very _____.

4 late

· I am often _____ for class.

· The letter arrived two days _____.

B 다음 우리말과 의미가 같도록 괄호 안의 말을 바르게 배열하시오.

1 그는 돈이 많지 않다. (he, much, have, money, doesn't)

→ _____

2 식탁 위에 감자가 몇 개 있다. (there, potatoes, some, on, are, the table)

→ _____

3 나는 무언가 시원한 것을 원한다. (want, cold, I, something)

→ _____

4 나는 종종 줄넘기를 한다. (often, rope, I, jump)

→ _____

5 냉장고에 계란이 좀 있니? (there, any, in the refrigerator, are, eggs)

→ _____

6 많은 학생들이 걸어서 학교에 간다. (many, go, to school, students, on foot)

→ _____

C 다음 그래프를 보고, 운동을 얼마나 자주 하는지에 대해 동사 exercise를 이용하여 글을 완성하시오.

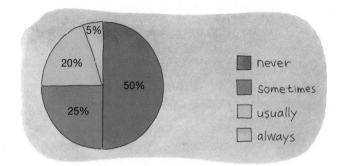

How often do you exercise? We asked a hundred students. Fifty students

(1) _____ . Twenty-five students (2) _____ . And twenty

students (3) _____ . Finally, only five students (4) _____ .

D 다음 대화에서 어법상 틀린 부분을 3개 찾아 바르게 고쳐 쓰시오.

A What is in that?

B Guess! It has a long tail. It climbs trees well very.
It runs fastly. You can ask two questions.

A Is it brown?

B Yes.

A Does it eat much nuts?

B Yes.

A I know the answer. It is a cute squirrel.

B You're right.

(1) _____ → _____

(2) _____ → _____

(3) _____ → _____

01 다음 중 형용사와 부사가 <u>잘못</u> 짝지어진 것은?

① lucky – luckily
② merry – merrily
③ quiet – quietly
④ good – well
⑤ heavy – heavly

[02-04] 다음 빈칸에 들어갈 말로 알맞은 것을 고르시오.

02
> Look at the _____ doll.

① well   ② nicely
③ kindly   ④ lovely
⑤ beautifully

03
> The knight fought _____.

① easy   ② smart
③ bravely   ④ angry
⑤ clever

04
> I have too _____ homework.

① many   ② much
③ easily   ④ any
⑤ importantly

[05-06] 다음 우리말과 의미가 같도록 빈칸에 들어갈 말로 알맞은 것을 고르시오.

05
> 나는 몇 가지 질문이 있다.
> → I have _____ questions.

① any   ② too
③ some   ④ much
⑤ many

06
> 그 마을에는 물이 조금도 없다.
> → There isn't _____ water in the village.

① any   ② too
③ some   ④ much
⑤ many

[07-08] 다음 빈칸에 공통으로 들어갈 말로 알맞은 것을 고르시오.

07
> · This stone is very _____.
> · He worked _____ on his farm.

① soft   ② hard
③ heavy   ④ hardly
⑤ well

08
> · Don't be _____.
> · We arrived _____.

① later   ② sad
③ late   ④ lately
⑤ suddenly

[09-11] 다음 주어진 말이 들어갈 위치로 알맞은 곳을 고르시오.

09 sometimes

My dad (①) and (②) I (③) play (④) chess (⑤) on weekends.

10 always

Mr. Kim (①) is (②) polite (③) to (④) other people (⑤).

11 warm

(①) I (②) need (③) something (④) for sleeping (⑤).

[12-13] 다음 밑줄 친 부분 중 성격이 나머지와 <u>다른</u> 것을 고르시오.

고난도
12 ① I often feel <u>lonely</u>.
② The story is <u>funny</u>.
③ The snake turned <u>ugly</u>.
④ Dogs are always <u>friendly</u>.
⑤ The baby cried <u>loudly</u> last night.

고난도
13 ① The frog jumps <u>high</u>.
② I won't be <u>late</u> again.
③ The movie started a little <u>late</u>.
④ They played golf quite <u>well</u>.
⑤ My friend and I arrived there <u>early</u>.

[14-16] 다음 빈칸에 들어갈 말로 알맞게 짝지어진 것을 고르시오.

14

· It is a _____ day!
· _____, I caught the first train.

① luck – Luckily
② lucky – Luckily
③ luckily – Luck
④ lucky – Luck
⑤ luckily – Lucky

15

· The teacher is _____ to us.
· He showed the way to me _____.

① kind – kind
② kindly – kindly
③ kind – kindly
④ kindly – kind
⑤ kindness – kind

16

· Would you like _____ milk in your tea?
· Are there _____ English speakers here?

① much – much
② many – many
③ some – any
④ any – any
⑤ any – some

17 다음 빈칸에 much가 들어갈 수 <u>없는</u> 것은?

① I don't have _____ land.

② There is too _____ dirt on my car.

③ I saw _____ paintings in the gallery.

④ Tony drank so _____ coffee last night.

⑤ My sister doesn't have _____ interest in music.

[18-19] 다음 중 어법상 <u>틀린</u> 것을 고르시오.

18 ① The plate is hot very.

② My dog never barks.

③ I have some worries.

④ Nick takes pictures well.

⑤ It costs a lot of money.

고난도
19 ① I have some coins in my pocket.

② Look at my lovely baby.

③ Would you have any ice cream?

④ I don't have any plans for today.

⑤ I usually go to a math academy after school.

[20-21] 다음 빈칸에 들어갈 말로 알맞지 <u>않은</u> 것을 고르시오.

고난도
20

My uncle put _____ lemon juice on the salad.

① fresh   ② some

③ sour   ④ many

⑤ a lot of

21

His speech was _____ .

① long   ② boring

③ well   ④ great

⑤ perfect

22 다음 우리말을 어법에 알맞게 영작한 것은?

그는 항상 버스에서 영어를 듣는다.

① He listens to English on the bus.

② He listens always to English on the bus.

③ He always listens to English on the bus.

④ He never listens to English on the bus.

⑤ He listens never to English on the bus.

[23-24] 다음 중 어법상 <u>틀린</u> 것으로 알맞게 짝지어진 것을 고르시오.

내신 빈출
23
ⓐ This soup tastes good.
ⓑ I don't have some problems.
ⓒ There are many salt in the bottle.
ⓓ Sally always is late for class.

① ⓐ, ⓑ   ② ⓐ, ⓒ
③ ⓐ, ⓓ   ④ ⓐ, ⓒ, ⓓ
⑤ ⓑ, ⓒ, ⓓ

내신 빈출
24
ⓐ I stayed up lately last night.
ⓑ He doesn't have any vegetables.
ⓒ He plays often basketball after school.
ⓓ There is something wrong with my computer.

① ⓐ, ⓑ   ② ⓐ, ⓒ
③ ⓑ, ⓒ   ④ ⓐ, ⓒ, ⓓ
⑤ ⓑ, ⓒ, ⓓ

내신 빈출
25 다음 중 어법상 옳은 문장의 개수는?

ⓐ My sister runs fast very.
ⓑ Do you have some friends in Seoul?
ⓒ I want something sweet.
ⓓ Would you like some more?

① 없음   ② 1개   ③ 2개   ④ 3개   ⑤ 4개

[26-28] 다음 문장에서 어법상 <u>틀린</u> 부분을 바르게 고쳐 문장을 다시 쓰시오.

26
My son eats never beans.

→ _____

27
We usually are at home on Sundays.

→ _____

28
I saw strange something last night.

→ _____

[29-31] 다음 우리말과 의미가 같도록 괄호 안의 말을 이용하여 문장을 완성하시오.

29
오늘은 날씨가 꽤 추웠다. (quite, cold, today)

→ It _____ .

30
공기는 우리에게 매우 중요하다.
(air, very, important)

→ _____ to us.

31
사막에는 거의 비가 오지 않는다. (hardly, rain)

→ _____ in the desert.

📖 Answers p.15

32 다음 그림의 상황에 맞도록 빈칸에 알맞은 말을 [보기]에서 골라 글을 완성하시오. (단, 한 번씩만 쓸 것)

┌ 보기 ┐

some   any   many   much

There are _____ cookies and _____ candies on the table. But there isn't _____ apple juice in the bottle. Because I drank too _____ apple juice this morning.

34 다음 글에서 어법상 틀린 부분을 2개 찾아 바르게 고쳐 쓰시오.

> I often visit my grandparents. They live in Busan for a long time. So, they have much friends there. They are very nice. They work hard and help other people. I real love them.

(1) _____ → _____
(2) _____ → _____

33 다음 대화의 밑줄 친 우리말과 의미가 같도록 [조건]에 맞게 영작하시오.

> A: What does your family do on weekends?
> B: <u>우리는 보통 주말에 공원에 가.</u>

┌ 조건 ┐
- 알맞은 빈도부사를 사용할 것
- park, on weekends를 사용할 것
- 8단어로 쓸 것

→ _____

35 다음 인호의 주간 계획표를 보고, 괄호 안의 말을 이용하여 문장을 완성하시오.

> <Inho's Weekly Plan>
> ✗go jogging every morning.
> ✗take piano lessons five times a week
> ✗play soccer with friends once a week

(1) Inho _____ in the morning. (always)
(2) Inho _____. (sometimes)

Chapter

09

전치사

01 장소를 나타내는 전치사

1 전치사의 쓰임

1 전치사는 명사나 대명사 앞에 쓰여 장소, 시간, 방법 등의 의미를 나타낸다.

on the table, **at** nine o'clock, **by** bus 등
   장소   시간   방법

2 전치사 뒤에는 명사(구)가 오며 대명사가 올 경우 목적격으로 써야 한다.

There is a ball **under** *the bench*.

Jason stood **in front of** *me*.

2 at / in

at: ~에	+ 장소의 한 지점	at home, at school, at the airport, at the party, at the store, at the station
in: ~ 안에	+ 공간의 내부, 도시, 국가	in the box, in the room, in the house, in New York, in Korea

I met her **at** the station.

There are some books **in** the box.

There are many cities **in** Korea.

3 on / under

I'll put the candles **on** the cake.

Mary dropped her books **on** the floor.

There is a notebook **under** the book.

➕ **PLUS** **on과 over:** 표면과 접촉한 '위'는 on을 쓰고, 표면과 떨어져 있는 '위'는 over를 쓴다.

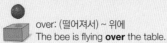

over: (떨어져서) ~ 위에
The bee is flying **over** the table.

4 in front of / behind / next to

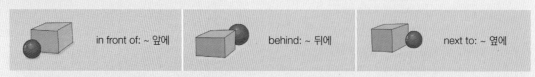

The restaurant is **in front of** my house.

There is a cat **behind** the car.

The puppies are sleeping **next to** their mom.

Grammar Check Up

A 다음 그림의 상황에 맞도록 [보기]에서 알맞은 말을 골라 문장을 완성하시오.

보기

in

on

under

in front of

next to

1 The socks are _____ the desk.

2 There are some books and pencils _____ the desk.

3 The cat is _____ the bed.

4 The box is _____ the cat.

5 A bat and a glove are _____ the box.

B 다음 괄호 안에서 알맞은 것을 고르시오.

1 The library is (at / under) the corner.

2 Some kids are swimming (in / on) the pool.

3 I sat in front of (they / them).

4 There is a taxi (at / next to) the bus.

C 다음 우리말과 의미가 같도록 빈칸에 알맞은 전치사를 쓰시오.

1 나의 친구는 워싱턴에 산다.

 → My friend lives _____ Washington.

2 내 뒤에 한 남자가 서 있다.

 → A man is standing _____ me.

3 그 다리 아래 몇 마리의 오리가 있다.

 → There are some ducks _____ the bridge.

4 그 책 위에 지우개 하나가 있다.

 → There is an eraser _____ the book.

02 시간을 나타내는 전치사

1 at / on / in

at	+ 구체적인 시각, 특정한 시점	at 2 o'clock, at 10 a.m., at noon, at night, at present
on	+ 요일, 날짜, 특정한 날	on Monday, on May 28, on Christmas Eve, on my birthday
in	+ 오전[오후/저녁], 월, 계절, 연도	in the morning[afternoon/evening], in March, in summer, in 2022

I usually get up **at** 7 o'clock.
Most people have dinner **at** night.

We don't have to go to school **on** Sundays.
She always goes to church **on** Christmas Day.

He goes jogging **in** the morning.
My family moved to Seoul **in** 2022.

2 before / after

before	~ 전에	after	~ 후에

You must wash your hands **before** meals.
My father goes to work **before** 9 o'clock.

We often play basketball **after** school.
My sister goes to the library **after** lunch.

3 for / during

for	~ 동안	+ 숫자를 포함한 구체적인 기간	for two days, for a month
during		+ 특정한 때를 나타내는 말	during the summer vacation during the meeting

My dad was in the hospital **for** three days.
I studied English **for** two hours yesterday.

He worked on the farm **during** the winter vacation.
I was very sleepy **during** the math class.

A 다음 괄호 안에서 알맞은 것을 고르시오.

1 (at / on) 9 o'clock
2 (in / on) October 15
3 (in / on) my birthday
4 (in / on) December
5 (at / on) present
6 (in / on) the evening
7 (for / during) the winter
8 (for / during) 30 minutes

B 다음 [보기]에서 빈칸에 들어갈 알맞은 말을 골라 문장을 완성하시오. (단, 중복 사용 가능)

┌ 보기 ┐
| in | at | on | during | for |

1 World War I ended _____ 1918.
2 His cell phone rang _____ the meeting.
3 I lived with my parents _____ a year.
4 We will have a summer festival _____ August 7.
5 There are many stars _____ the sky _____ night.

C 다음 빈칸에 before 또는 after를 써서 문장을 완성하시오.

1 Spring comes _____ winter.
2 October comes _____ November.
3 You must warm up _____ swimming.
4 We clapped _____ his speech.

D 다음 문장에서 어법상 틀린 부분을 찾아 바르게 고쳐 쓰시오.

1 Bake the cookies during 20 minutes. _____ → _____
2 We can tell lies in April 1. _____ → _____
3 Tommy usually jumps rope in 9 p.m. _____ → _____
4 I always take a walk at the evening. _____ → _____

A 다음 그림의 상황에 맞도록 [보기]에서 알맞은 말을 골라 문장을 완성하시오. (단, 중복 사용 가능)

┌ 보기 ┐
at   under   on   in front of   next to   behind

1 A girl is waiting for the bus _____ the bus stop.

A bus driver is _____ the bus.

2 A cat is _____ the bench.

Two puppies are _____ the bench.

There is a basketball _____ the bench.

3 A boy looks at the toys _____ the store.

A backpack is _____ the boy.

B 다음 우리말과 의미가 같도록 [보기]에서 알맞은 전치사와 괄호 안의 말을 골라 문장을 완성하시오.
(단, 필요하면 형태를 바꿀 것)

┌ 보기 ┐
at   on   in   before   after   for   during

1 나의 아버지는 아침 식사 전에 신문을 읽으신다. (read, the newspaper, breakfast)

→ My father _____.

2 우리는 Jenny의 생일 파티를 일요일에 열 것이다. (have, Jenny's birthday party, Sunday)

→ We _____.

3 연주회 동안에는 휴대전화를 끄세요. (turn off, your cell phone, the concert)

→ Please _____.

4 Eric은 자주 밤에 컴퓨터 게임을 한다. (play, computer games, night)

→ Eric often _____.

5 나의 삼촌은 하루에 9시간 동안 일하신다. (work, 9 hours, a day)

→ My uncle _____.

C 다음 Daniel의 계획표에 맞도록 글을 완성하시오.

Monday	3:00 p.m.	go to the library
Tuesday	7:00 a.m. – 8:00 a.m.	go jogging
Wednesday	6:00 p.m. – 7:00 p.m.	have dinner with Mom
	7:00 p.m. – 9:00 p.m.	watch a movie with Mom
Thursday	7:00 a.m.	go swimming
Friday – Sunday		go camping

Daniel will go to the library (1) _____ 3:00 p.m. (2) _____ Monday. He will

jog (3) _____ an hour (4) _____ the morning on Tuesday. On Wednesday,

he will watch a movie with his mom (5) _____ dinner. And he is going to go

swimming (6) _____ 7:00 a.m. on Thursday. Finally, he will go camping

(7) _____ the weekends.

D 다음 지도를 보고, 대화를 완성하시오.

A Excuse me. Where is ABC Department Store?

B It's (1) _____ the hospital.

A Where is the hospital?

B Oh, it's (2) _____ the pet shop.

A I'm sorry. I'm not from this area. Where is the pet shop?

B Look over there. Can you see the flower shop?

A Oh, the pet shop is (3) _____ the flower shop. Thank you.

[01-02] 다음 우리말과 의미가 같도록 빈칸에 들어갈 말로 알맞은 것을 고르시오.

01

나는 아침에 한 시간 동안 운동한다.
→ I exercise _____ an hour in the morning.

① at   ② on   ③ for
④ during   ⑤ after

02

그는 저녁 식사 후에 개를 산책시킨다.
→ He walks his dog _____ dinner.

① at   ② in   ③ for
④ after   ⑤ before

[03-05] 다음 빈칸에 들어갈 말로 알맞은 것을 고르시오.

03

I heard a strange sound _____ night.

① in   ② on   ③ at
④ for   ⑤ next to

04

Australia will host the Summer Olympics _____ 2032.

① in   ② on   ③ at
④ for   ⑤ next to

05

There is an ant _____ your shoulder.

① in   ② on   ③ for
④ after   ⑤ at

[06-08] 다음 빈칸에 공통으로 들어갈 말로 알맞은 것을 고르시오.

06

· I went to school _____ noon yesterday.
· Jacob stayed _____ home.

① in   ② on   ③ at
④ for   ⑤ next

07

· A puppy is sleeping _____ the floor.
· We are happy _____ Christmas Day.

① in   ② on   ③ at
④ for   ⑤ behind

08

· Thanksgiving Day is _____ November.
· The Eiffel Tower is _____ Paris, France.

① in   ② on   ③ at
④ for   ⑤ under

[09-11] 다음 밑줄 친 부분을 어법상 바르게 고친 것을 고르시오.

09

A tall man sat in front of I in the theater.

① my   ② me   ③ mine
④ we   ⑤ our

10

It snowed during five days.

① on   ② at   ③ in
④ for   ⑤ behind

11

Many flowers bloom on spring.

① at   ② in   ③ behind
④ next to   ⑤ for

[12-14] 다음 그림을 보고, 빈칸에 들어갈 말로 알맞은 것을 고르시오.

12

There is a cell phone _____ the bed.

① in   ② on   ③ under
④ next to   ⑤ in front of

13

Jennifer is _____ the post office.

① in   ② on   ③ behind
④ next to   ⑤ in front of

14

The cat is _____ Ms. Green.

① in   ② on   ③ behind
④ next to   ⑤ in front of

[15-16] 다음 빈칸에 들어갈 말이 나머지와 다른 것을 고르시오.

고난도
15 ① I met my friend _____ the station.
② He goes to bed _____ 10 o'clock.
③ We go hiking _____ Sundays.
④ We usually eat lunch _____ noon.
⑤ My mother is_____ the bank now.

고난도

16
① There is an apple _____ the bowl.
② I got many gifts _____ my birthday.
③ My brother studies music _____ Italy.
④ She won two gold medals _____ 2021.
⑤ It often rains _____ summer in Korea.

20
① I cleaned my room for an hour.
② September comes after August.
③ The school is behind the hospital.
④ She arrived at the airport late.
⑤ He lived at Canada for three years.

[17-18] 다음 중 어법상 옳은 것을 고르시오.

17
① Kelly sat next to him.
② A leaf fell down at my head.
③ My father will leave in October 11.
④ Hong Kong is beautiful in night.
⑤ I talked on the phone during two hours.

[21-22] 다음 우리말을 어법에 알맞게 영작한 것을 고르시오.

내신 빈출
21
많은 선물들이 크리스마스트리 아래에 있다.

① A lot of presents are on the Christmas tree.
② A lot of presents are behind the Christmas tree.
③ A lot of presents are under the Christmas tree.
④ A lot of presents are next to the Christmas tree.
⑤ A lot of presents are in front of the Christmas tree.

고난도

18
① Many people go skiing on winter.
② He put the onion next the carrot.
③ I visited the museum in Saturday.
④ There is a dictionary under the chair.
⑤ The swimming pool opens on the summer vacation.

[19-20] 다음 중 어법상 틀린 것을 고르시오.

내신 빈출
19
① I take a shower before dinner.
② The river dried up for the drought.
③ I dropped my glasses on the ground.
④ Would you have dinner with us on Friday?
⑤ Americans have turkey on Thanksgiving Day.

22
나는 수학 시간에 잠이 들었다.

① I fell asleep for the math class.
② I fell asleep on the math class.
③ I fell asleep after the math class.
④ I fell asleep at the math class.
⑤ I fell asleep during the math class.

23 다음 중 어법상 <u>틀린</u> 것으로 알맞게 짝지어진 것은?

ⓐ There is a horse in the barn.
ⓑ Let's have lunch in noon.
ⓒ She stood in front of the mirror.
ⓓ Christmas comes on December.

① ⓐ, ⓑ   ② ⓐ, ⓒ
③ ⓑ, ⓓ   ④ ⓐ, ⓒ, ⓓ
⑤ ⓑ, ⓒ, ⓓ

[24-25] 다음 중 어법상 옳은 문장의 개수를 고르시오.

24
ⓐ My school begins in March 2.
ⓑ There is a picture on the wall.
ⓒ We planted the tree in 2020.
ⓓ I go to the library after breakfast.

① 없음   ② 1개   ③ 2개   ④ 3개   ⑤ 4개

25
ⓐ I usually swim after school.
ⓑ The cat is sleeping in the sofa.
ⓒ He played soccer during two hours.
ⓓ The parking lot is behind the building.

① 없음   ② 1개   ③ 2개   ④ 3개   ⑤ 4개

[26-27] 다음 우리말과 의미가 같도록 알맞은 전치사와 괄호 안의 말을 이용하여 영작하시오.

26
나는 여름 방학 동안 유럽으로 여행을 갈 것이다.
(travel, Europe, the summer vacation)

→ _____

27
나는 시험 전에 항상 머리가 아프다.
(always, have a headache, an exam)

→ _____

[28-29] 다음 두 문장의 의미가 같도록 문장을 완성하시오.

28
The movie theater is in front of the bank.

= The bank _____.

29
Thunder always comes after lightning.

= Lightning _____.

[30-31] 다음 지도를 보고, 괄호 안의 말을 이용하여 문장을 완성하시오.

30
The post office _____.
(the hospital)

31
The bakery _____.
(the park)

[32-33] 다음 그림의 상황에 맞도록 대화를 완성하시오.

32
A: Where is the cat?
B: _____

33
A: I'm looking for my bag. Where is it?
B: _____

34 다음 밑줄 친 문장에서 어법상 틀린 부분을 바르게 고쳐 문장을 다시 쓰시오.

It is coming soon. It is a big holiday at Korea. We'll eat a lot of food and play games together. We'll watch the full moon on the evening. We will have a good time!

(1) _____
(2) _____

35 다음 우리말과 의미가 같도록 [조건]에 맞게 영작하시오.

내 여동생의 생일은 3월 15일이다. It is tomorrow. My family is preparing for her birthday party. On her birthday, we will get up early in the morning and cook. And I will go out to buy her gift today.

┤ 조건 ├
• 알맞은 전치사를 사용할 것
• My sister's birthday, March를 사용할 것
• 7단어로 쓸 것

→ _____

Chapter

10

의문사

01. 의문사 who, what

1 의문사와 의문사 의문문

1 의문사는 '누구', '무엇' 등 구체적인 정보를 물을 때 사용하는 말이다.

who	누구	what	무엇	when	언제	where	어디서	why	왜	how	어떻게

2 의문사는 의문문의 맨 앞에 위치한다.

일반동사 의문문	의문사 + do동사 + 주어 + 동사원형 ~?
조동사 의문문	의문사 + 조동사 + 주어 + 동사원형 ~?
be동사 의문문	의문사 + be동사 + 주어 ~?

He has a robot. → **What** does he have?
└→ 무엇(what)
She can go there by bus. → **How** can she go there?
└→ 어떻게(how)
That girl is Jimin. → **Who** is that girl?
└→ 누구(who)

3 의문사로 물어보는 의문문에는 Yes나 No로 답하지 않고 질문에 대해 구체적으로 답한다.
What is it? - It's my teddy bear.
Who is she? - She is my sister.

2 who

사람에 대해 물을 때 사용하며, 주격, 목적격, 소유격이 있다.
Who opened the window? (누가 – 주격)
- Tony opened it.

Who(m) did you meet? (누구를 – 목적격)
- I met my brother.

Whose car is it? (누구의 – 소유격)
- It's my mother's car.

3 what

1 사물에 대해 묻거나 사람의 이름이나 직업을 물을 때 사용하며, 주어와 목적어로 쓰인다.
What is your name? (무엇이 – 주어)
- My name is Sumi.

What will you eat for lunch? (무엇을 – 목적어)
- I'll eat a hamburger.

2 What + 명사 ~?: 어떤 ~?, 무슨 ~?
What color do you like? - I like green.
What day is it? - It's Tuesday.

Grammar Check Up

Answers p.18

A 다음 괄호 안에서 알맞은 것을 고르시오.

1 (Who / What) is the boy doing?

2 (Who / What) is your best friend?

3 (Who / What) did you buy?

4 (Whom / Whose) did you visit last Sunday?

5 (Whom / Who) drew the picture?

6 (Whom / Whose) keys are these?

B 다음 [보기]에서 빈칸에 들어갈 알맞은 말을 골라 대화를 완성하시오. (단, 중복 사용 가능)

> ─ 보기 ┌
> what   who   whom   whose

1 A: _____ stood in front of your house?   B: My sister stood there.

2 A: _____ is in the basket?   B: A ball is in the basket.

3 A: _____ backpack is on the desk?   B: It's Julia's backpack.

4 A: _____ did you see at the party?   B: I saw my friend, Junho.

5 A: _____ color is your bag?   B: It's blue.

C 다음 밑줄 친 부분을 묻는 의문문이 되도록 빈칸에 알맞은 의문사를 쓰시오.

1 I read comic books last night.

→ _____ did you read last night?

2 Mike ate all of the cake.

→ _____ ate all of the cake?

3 This is Amy's umbrella.

→ _____ umbrella is this?

4 I like action movies the most.

→ _____ kind of movies do you like the most?

5 She talked with her friend, Sue.

→ _____ did she talk with?

02 의문사 when, where, why, how

1 when / where

when	언제	시간, 날짜 등을 물을 때 사용한다.
where	어디에, 어디서	장소, 위치 등을 물을 때 사용한다.

When is your birthday? - My birthday is on June 8.
Where does she live? - She lives in New York.

> **+ PLUS**　**when과 what time**
> when이 '시각'을 묻는 데 사용되면 what time으로 바꿔 쓸 수 있다.
> **When[What time]** do you get up? - I usually get up at seven.

2 why

'왜'라는 의미로 이유나 원인을 물을 때 사용하며, 대답할 때는 보통 because(왜냐하면)를 써서 한다.
Why are you happy? - *Because* I got a good grade.
Why is she absent today? - *Because* she is sick.

3 how

1 '어떻게'라는 의미로 상태나 수단, 방법을 물을 때 사용한다.
How are you today? - I'm not bad.
How do you go there? - I go there by bus.

2 「how + 형용사/부사」: 얼마나 ~한/하게

how old	몇 살의, 얼마나 오래된	how long	얼마나 긴, 얼마나 오래
how tall	얼마나 높은, 얼마나 키 큰	how far	얼마나 멀리
how often	얼마나 자주	how fast	얼마나 빨리
how much	얼마인(가격) / 얼마나 많은(양)	how many	얼마나 많은(수)

How old is your brother? - He is nine years old.
How long is this bridge? - It is 1,050 meters.
How tall is the tower? - It's 80 meters.
How far is your school from here? - It's 2 kilometers to my school.
How often do you take a walk? - I take a walk three times a week.
How fast does he walk? - He walks 3 kilometers an hour.
How much is this blue shirt? - It is 70 dollars.
How much time do you have? - I have about an hour.
How many books did he buy? - He bought five books.

> **+ PLUS**　**how much와 how many**
> how much 뒤에는 셀 수 없는 명사가 오고, how many 뒤에는 셀 수 있는 명사의 복수형이 온다.

Grammar Check Up

📖 Answers p.18

A 다음 [보기]에서 빈칸에 들어갈 알맞은 말을 골라 대화를 완성하시오. (단, 중복 사용 가능)

┌ 보기 ┐
when   where   why   how

1 A: _____ is the weather?　　　　B: It's sunny and warm.

2 A: _____ did she come back from Canada?　　B: She came back yesterday.

3 A: _____ are you going this vacation?　　B: I'm going to Busan.

4 A: _____ do you like Korean people?　　B: Because they are kind.

5 A: _____ old is the house?　　B: It is 100 years old.

B 다음 [보기]에서 빈칸에 들어갈 알맞은 말을 골라 기호를 쓰시오.

┌ 보기 ┐
ⓐ Under the sofa.　　ⓑ Because I had a headache.
ⓒ It's 500 meters away.　　ⓓ An hour ago.

1 A: Where did you find your purse?
　B: _____

2 A: When did you park your car?
　B: _____

3 A: Why did you come home early?
　B: _____

4 A: How far is the library from here?
　B: _____

C 다음 밑줄 친 부분을 묻는 의문문이 되도록 빈칸에 알맞은 의문사를 쓰시오.

1 A: _____ does the post office close?
　B: It closes <u>at 6 p.m.</u>

2 A: _____ is she late?
　B: <u>Because she missed the bus.</u>

3 A: _____ is KTX?
　B: It can run <u>300 kilometers per hour.</u>

4 A: _____ do you talk to your mom or dad?
　B: I talk to my mom or dad <u>every day.</u>

A 다음 빈칸에 알맞은 의문사를 써서 대화를 완성하시오.

1 A: _____ is your favorite actor?
   B: I love Ryan Gosling.

2 A: _____ did you eat lunch with?
   B: I ate lunch with my son.

3 A: _____ was your summer vacation?
   B: It was fantastic!

4 A: _____ will you stay in Seoul?
   B: I'll stay there for three weeks.

5 A: _____ did the train leave?
   B: It just left.

6 A: _____ are you tired?
   B: Because I worked until late last night.

B 다음 괄호 안의 말을 바르게 배열하여 대화를 완성하시오.

1 (you, told, who, the answer)
   A: _____
   B: Martin told me.

2 (did, buy, how much, you, sugar)
   A: _____
   B: One pound.

3 (you, did, your pens, put, where)
   A: _____
   B: I put them on the desk.

4 (why, he, in, is, the hospital)
   A: _____
   B: Because he broke his leg.

5 (did, when, build, you, the house)
   A: _____
   B: I built it last year.

C 다음 빈칸에 알맞은 의문사를 써서 인터뷰를 완성하시오.

Interviewer: Congratulations! You won the gold medal!

Swimmer: Thank you.

Interviewer: (1) _____ do you practice a day?

Swimmer: I practice for six hours every day.

Interviewer: (2) _____ do you do in your free time?

Swimmer: I usually watch movies in my free time.

Interviewer: (3) _____ is your role model?

Swimmer: Michael Phelps is my role model.

Interviewer: Oh, he is a great swimmer. Thank you for your time.

D 다음은 청바지에 대한 대화이다. 알맞은 의문사를 써서 질문을 완성하시오.

1 A: _____ made blue jeans?
  B: Levi Strauss made blue jeans.

2 A: _____ did he come from?
  B: He came from America.

3 A: _____ was he born? And
  _____ did he die?
  B: He was born on February 26, 1829. And he died on September 27, 1902.

4 A: _____ did he make blue jeans?
  B: Because miners needed strong pants. He knew that and made strong blue jeans.

[01-03] 다음 우리말과 의미가 같도록 빈칸에 들어갈 말로 알맞은 것을 고르시오.

01
너는 언제 서울로 이사 왔니?
→ _____ did you move to Seoul?

① Who   ② Whose
③ When   ④ What
⑤ How

02
동굴 안에는 무엇이 있니?
→ _____ is in the cave?

① Who   ② Why
③ When   ④ What
⑤ Where

03
그는 왜 우울하니?
→ _____ is he gloomy?

① Who   ② What
③ When   ④ Where
⑤ Why

[04-07] 다음 대화의 빈칸에 들어갈 말로 알맞은 것을 고르시오.

04
A: _____ did you borrow the book?
B: I borrowed it last Sunday.

① Who   ② What
③ When   ④ Where
⑤ Why

05
A: _____ did you buy at the shopping mall?
B: I bought a shirt.

① Who   ② What
③ When   ④ Where
⑤ Why

06
A: _____ are you crying?
B: Because I lost my puppy!

① Who   ② What
③ When   ④ How
⑤ Why

07
A: _____ is the bus stop from here?
B: It's only 10 meters from here.

① Who   ② What
③ How   ④ Where
⑤ How far

[08-10] 다음 밑줄 친 부분 중 쓰임이 **틀린** 것을 고르시오.

08 ① <u>Where</u> are your pants?
② <u>When</u> do you go to bed?
③ <u>What</u> is your favorite teacher?
④ <u>How often</u> do you practice the piano?
⑤ <u>Why</u> were you absent from school yesterday?

09 ① How old is the palace?
② What color do you need?
③ Why do you wear a suit?
④ How many flour do you need?
⑤ Where did you travel last summer?

13
> How can I get to City Hall?

① You can get there by subway.
② It is very far from here.
③ You can get there in 5 minutes.
④ You will see it soon.
⑤ I go there every day.

10 ① Whose cap is it?
② When will you leave?
③ Why did you buy tomatoes?
④ Where does he come from?
⑤ How does the bank open?

[14-15] 다음 빈칸에 공통으로 들어갈 말로 알맞은 것을 고르시오.

14
> · _____ is your job?
> · _____ will you wear to the party?

① Who ② When
③ Where ④ What
⑤ How much

[11-13] 다음 질문에 대한 대답으로 알맞은 것을 고르시오.

고난도
11
> Whom will you invite to your birthday party?

① I will have my birthday party.
② I will invite Sujin and Mike.
③ I will have the party this Sunday.
④ I will make a big cake for the party.
⑤ I will go to the party with my mom.

12
> Where did you see my bag?

① I saw it yesterday.
② I bought it on the Internet.
③ I saw it on your bed.
④ I bought it last Sunday.
⑤ Because I saw it.

내신 빈출
15
> · _____ was the concert?
> · _____ long will you stay in Korea?

① Who ② How
③ Why ④ What
⑤ When

[16-17] 다음 대화의 밑줄 친 부분 중 어법상 틀린 것을 고르시오.

16

A: ①When ②is the movie ③end?
B: ④It ⑤ends at 6 o'clock.

17

A: ①How long ②do you ③visit your parents?
B: I ④visit ⑤them once a week.

[18-19] 다음 대답에 대한 질문으로 알맞은 것을 고르시오.

18

I take a shower in the evening.

① Do you take a shower?
② When do you take a shower?
③ Where do you take a shower?
④ Why do you take a shower?
⑤ How do you take a shower?

19

Because she had a high fever.

① Who is Sally?
② Where did Sally live?
③ When did Sally go home?
④ Why did Sally go home early?
⑤ What time did Sally go home?

[20-21] 다음 중 어법상 틀린 것을 고르시오.

20 ① Who helped you?
② Why do you like Korea?
③ When did clean the house?
④ Whom did you go camping with?
⑤ How was your trip to Thailand?

내신 빈출
21 ① What fruit do you like?
② How long did he study?
③ Where do you go every morning?
④ How much money do we have?
⑤ Whose showed you the picture?

고난도
22 다음 대화 중 가장 자연스럽지 <u>않은</u> 것은?

① A: Who is your partner?
   B: Billy.
② A: How much is the TV?
   B: It's 500 dollars.
③ A: What are you doing now?
   B: I'm cooking.
④ A: What are you waiting for?
   B: The bus left 5 minutes ago.
⑤ A: How many donuts did you eat?
   B: I ate five donuts.

23 다음 중 어법상 **틀린** 것으로 알맞게 짝지어진 것은?

> ⓐ Why did you lie to me?
> ⓑ How often do you exercise?
> ⓒ Where does Jane lives now?
> ⓓ How many water is there in the bottle?

① ⓐ, ⓑ   ② ⓐ, ⓒ
③ ⓒ, ⓓ   ④ ⓐ, ⓒ, ⓓ
⑤ ⓑ, ⓒ, ⓓ

[24-25] 다음 중 어법상 옳은 문장의 개수를 고르시오.

24
> ⓐ Who idea is it?
> ⓑ Where is the toy store?
> ⓒ What is your favorite season?
> ⓓ How many friends do you have?

① 없음   ② 1개   ③ 2개   ④ 3개   ⑤ 4개

^{고난도}
25
> ⓐ Whom is your teacher?
> ⓑ Why are you so happy?
> ⓒ What floor do you live on?
> ⓓ When did Edison invented the light bulb?

① 없음   ② 1개   ③ 2개   ④ 3개   ⑤ 4개

[26-28] 다음 우리말과 의미가 같도록 알맞은 의문사와 괄호 안의 말을 이용하여 영작하시오.

26
> 누가 그 수학 문제를 풀었니?
> (solve, the math problem)

→ _____

27
> 너는 이 모자를 어디서 샀니? (buy, this hat)

→ _____

28
> 주차장에 얼마나 많은 자동차가 있니?
> (car, there, the parking lot)

→ _____

[29-31] 다음 대화의 밑줄 친 부분을 묻는 질문을 완성하시오.

29
> A: _____ yesterday?
> B: I met Jim yesterday.

30
> A: _____ for lunch?
> B: I will make spaghetti for lunch.

31
> A: _____ the orphanage?
> B: I visit there twice a month.

[32-33] 다음 그림을 보고, 빈칸에 알맞은 말을 써서 대화를 완성하시오.

32

A: _____ _____ Tom doing?

B: He is _____.

34 다음 대화에서 의문사의 쓰임이 틀린 것을 2개 찾아 바르게 고쳐 쓰시오.

> A: Jenny, where are you going?
> B: I'm going to the library.
> A: Oh, really? What are you going to the library?
> B: Because I have to do my homework.
> A: How often will you be there?
> B: For three hours.

(1) _____ → _____

(2) _____ → _____

33

A: _____ _____ days are there in a week?

B: There are _____ _____ in a week.

35 다음 글을 읽고, 밑줄 친 부분을 묻는 질문을 완성하시오.

> Ben likes soccer very much. He (1) usually plays soccer after school. And he goes to the soccer club (2) twice a week. He practices soccer hard there. He wants to be a good soccer player.

(1) _____

(2) _____

Chapter

11

접속사

Practice

01 접속사 and, but, or, so

1 접속사의 쓰임

접속사는 단어와 단어, 구와 구, 문장과 문장을 연결하는 말이다.

My daughter is *smart* **and** *pretty*. (단어와 단어)

You can go there *by bus* **or** *on foot*. (구와 구)

I like carrots, **but** *he doesn't like them*. (문장과 문장)

2 and

'~와', '그리고'의 뜻으로 내용상 비슷하거나 연속적인 것을 연결한다.

Jake **and** *I* are best friends.

I have *a dog* **and** *a cat*.

She *ate a piece of pizza* **and** *drank a glass of milk*.

I played the piano, **and** *my sister danced*.

⊕ **PLUS** 세 개 이상의 단어를 연결할 때

「A, B, and C」의 형태로 쓴다.

I want a cap, a bat, **and** a glove. (O)   I want a cap **and** a bat **and** a glove. (×)

3 but

'그러나'의 뜻으로 내용상 서로 반대인 것을 연결한다.

My brother is *young* **but** *talented*.

This fruit *smells bad* **but** *tastes good*.

I ate all the bread, **but** *I was still hungry*.

It is an old car, **but** *it is very safe*.

4 or

'또는', '혹은'의 뜻으로 둘 이상의 선택 사항을 연결한다.

Judy **or** *you* must cook dinner.

I put my keys *on the table* **or** *on the sofa*.

He *plays soccer* **or** *watches TV* on weekends.

You can make pizza, **or** *I can order it*.

5 so

'그래서'의 뜻으로 내용상 앞 문장에 대한 결과인 것을 연결한다.

The movie was sad, **so** I cried.

She is very kind, **so** I like her.

He has a cold, **so** he goes to the hospital.

A 다음 괄호 안에서 알맞은 것을 고르시오.

1 The poor man needed some money (and / so) food.

2 Jinho (or / but) I will wash the dishes after lunch.

3 Most of my friends love baseball, (but / or) Kelly doesn't like it.

4 My brother jogs every day, (so / but) he is healthy.

5 I'll stay at home (or / and) go to the movies this weekend.

B 다음 그림의 상황에 맞도록 [보기]에서 알맞은 말을 골라 문장을 완성하시오.

┌ 보기 ┐
| so | but | or | and |

1   2   3   4

1 Jessica plays the guitar _____ sings a song.

2 I got up late, _____ I was late for school.

3 Do you want a brown puppy _____ a black one?

4 He did his best, _____ he didn't win.

C 다음 두 문장을 and, but, or, so 중 알맞은 것을 이용하여 한 문장으로 연결하시오. (단, 단어를 생략하지 말 것)

1 I can drive a car. + I can't ride a bike.

→ _____

2 I went to the window. + I looked out.

→ _____

3 It was Jenny's birthday. + We phoned her.

→ _____

4 Will you fix the computer? + Will you buy a new computer?

→ _____

02 접속사 when, because

① when

'~할 때', '~하면'의 뜻으로 시간이나 때를 나타내는 부사절을 이끈다.

You must be careful **when** you cross the street.
└→ 주절　　　　　　　└→ 시간을 나타내는 부사절

Wear a helmet **when** you ride a bicycle.

I listen to music **when** I feel down.

When I met him, he looked happy.
└→ 부사절이 주절 앞에 올 경우 부사절 뒤에 콤마(,)를 찍는다.

⊕ PLUS　**부사절의 위치**
부사절은 주절 앞과 뒤, 어디에나 올 수 있고, 앞에 올 경우 부사절 뒤에 콤마(,)를 찍는다.

시간을 나타내는 부사절의 동사 형태
미래에 일어날 일을 현재형으로 표현한다. 즉 주절은 미래형일지라도 부사절은 현재형으로 써야 한다.
When I **arrive**, I**'ll call** you. (O)　　**When** I **will arrive**, I**'ll call** you. (×)

그 밖의 시간을 나타내는 접속사
I finished my homework **before** I had dinner. (before: ~ 전에)
I had dinner **after** I finished my homework. (after: ~ 후에)

② because

'~ 때문에'의 뜻으로 이유를 나타내는 부사절을 이끈다.

I was very sad **because** my best friend moved to Los Angeles.
└→ 주절　　　　　　└→ 이유를 나타내는 부사절

I like her **because** she sings and dances very well.

I will go to the dentist **because** I have a bad toothache.

Because it was very cold, I didn't go outside.

Because he didn't have lunch, he feels hungry.

⊕ PLUS　**because와 because of**
because는 접속사이기 때문에 뒤에 「주어 + 동사」가 이어지지만, 같은 의미인 because of는 뒤에 명사(구)가 이어진다.
I went home early **because** *I had a headache*.
I went home early **because of** *a headache*.

A 다음 괄호 안에서 알맞은 것을 고르시오.

1 Turn off the lights (because / when) you go out.

2 (Because / Because of) the heavy snow, we can't leave now.

3 Water becomes ice (when / because of) it freezes.

4 Tom didn't enjoy his holiday (because / because of) he had a bad cold.

5 I'll take a shower when I (get / will get) home tonight.

B 다음 우리말과 의미가 같도록 빈칸에 when과 because 중에서 알맞은 것을 골라 쓰시오.

1 그는 말을 할 수 없기 때문에 수화를 한다.

→ He uses sign language _____ he can't speak.

2 나의 도움이 필요하면 나에게 전화해.

→ _____ you need my help, call me.

3 비가 많이 와서 우리는 체험 학습을 가지 않았다.

→ We didn't go on the field trip _____ it rained a lot.

4 나의 아버지는 정원에서 일하실 때 항상 모자를 쓰신다.

→ My father always wears a hat _____ he works in the garden.

5 여름이 오면 많은 사람은 해변으로 간다.

→ Many people go to the beach _____ summer comes.

C 다음 두 문장을 when과 because 중 알맞은 것을 이용하여 한 문장으로 연결하시오. (단, 순서를 그대로 쓸 것)

1 There were many people in the station. + We arrived there.

→ _____

2 I was very tired. + I stayed home all day long.

→ _____

3 I couldn't arrive at the airport on time. + I missed the train.

→ _____

4 She was six years old. + She wrote her first story.

→ _____

A 다음 [보기]에서 빈칸에 들어갈 알맞은 말을 골라 문장을 완성하시오.

보기

so he won first prize in the math contest	but it is difficult
so she didn't say a word all day long	or you can go to a hotel
and they study a lot of things	

1 Exercise is good for us, _____.

2 Karin was angry, _____.

3 They go to school, _____.

4 You can stay at my home, _____.

5 Billy studied math hard, _____.

B 다음 우리말과 의미가 같도록 괄호 안의 말을 이용하여 문장을 완성하시오.

1 나의 엄마는 책을 읽을 때 안경을 쓰신다. (read books)

→ My mom wears glasses _____.

2 그녀는 아팠기 때문에 약을 먹었다. (sick)

→ _____, she took some medicine.

3 나의 컴퓨터는 오래되었기 때문에 너무 느리다. (old)

→ My computer is too slow _____.

4 신호등이 초록색일 때 사람들은 길을 건넌다. (the crosswalk light, green)

→ _____, people cross the street.

5 나는 배탈 때문에 지난밤에 잠을 잘 잘 수 없었다. (of, a stomachache)

→ I couldn't sleep well last night _____.

Answers p.20

C 다음 그림의 상황에 맞도록 [보기]에서 알맞은 말을 골라 글을 완성하시오. (단, 중복 사용 가능)

보기

| and | so | because | when |

Dear Diary,

My brother (1) _____ I did housework (2) _____ Mom was sick.

(3) _____ I came home from school, she was in bed. She had a headache

(4) _____ a fever. I gave some medicine to her (5) _____ she took it.

I washed the dishes (6) _____ my brother cleaned the living room. Dad bought

pizza for dinner, (7) _____ we didn't cook. We hope she gets better soon.

D 다음 우리말과 의미가 같도록 괄호 안의 말을 이용하여 대화를 완성하시오.

A May I help you?

B I want a ring (1) _____ (scarf). (반지와 스카프를 원해요.)

A I'm sorry. We have many scarves, (2) _____ (any rings).
(저희는 스카프는 많이 있지만 반지는 없어요.)

B Then, please show me your scarves.

A OK. These two scarves are the most popular.
Do you prefer the green one (3) _____ (blue one)?
(초록색 스카프 또는 파란색 스카프 중 어떤 게 마음에 드세요?)

B I like the blue one. I'll take it.

[01-03] 다음 우리말과 의미가 같도록 빈칸에 들어갈 말로 알맞은 것을 고르시오.

01
> 그는 수학과 과학을 잘한다.
> → He is good at math _____ science.

① and
② but
③ or
④ when
⑤ so

02
> 내 컴퓨터가 자주 고장 났기 때문에 나는 새것을 샀다.
> → I bought a new computer _____ mine often broke down.

① and
② but
③ so
④ because
⑤ when

03
> 나는 스케이트는 탈 수 있지만 스키는 탈 수 없다.
> → I can skate, _____ I can't ski.

① and
② but
③ or
④ when
⑤ because

[04-06] 다음 빈칸에 들어갈 말로 알맞은 것을 고르시오.

내신 빈출
04
> You should take a rest _____ take some medicine.

① but
② so
③ or
④ because
⑤ when

05
> We went to the zoo _____ we didn't see the zebras.

① and
② so
③ or
④ when
⑤ but

06
> _____ she heard the news, she cried.

① And
② So
③ Or
④ When
⑤ But

[07-08] 다음 밑줄 친 부분 중 쓰임이 틀린 것을 고르시오.

07 ① You can call me or text me.
② I was busy because I didn't eat lunch.
③ He knew the secret but he didn't tell it.
④ I got bad grades so my mom was angry.
⑤ I bought some cheese because I didn't have any.

08 ① Is this your hat or his hat?
② So I am nervous, my legs shake.
③ I don't like her because she always lies.
④ I lost my dictionary, so I have to borrow one.
⑤ I ate an apple and drank a glass of water.

[09-11] 다음 빈칸에 공통으로 들어갈 말로 알맞은 것을 고르시오.

09

> · You must turn off your computer _____ you aren't using it.
> · They use forks _____ they eat food.

① or   ② so
③ and   ④ but
⑤ when

10

> · I need a cup, a plate, _____ a jar.
> · I ordered steak _____ onion soup.

① and   ② but
③ so   ④ when
⑤ because

11

> · Please answer either yes _____ no.
> · I'll leave for Busan tomorrow _____ next Monday.

① and   ② but
③ or   ④ because
⑤ when

고난도
12 다음 밑줄 친 When[when]의 의미가 나머지와 다른 것은?

① When I study, I listen to music.
② When did you water the garden?
③ I feel happy when I help other people.
④ A fly came into my room when I opened the window.
⑤ When I got up in the morning, I saw a fire across the street.

[13-14] 다음 두 문장의 의미가 같도록 빈칸에 알맞은 것을 고르시오.

13

> I sweated a lot because it was too hot.
> = It was too hot, _____ I sweated a lot.

① and   ② but
③ so   ④ when
⑤ because

14

> I take my dog for a walk after I have dinner.
> = I have dinner _____ I take my dog for a walk.

① so   ② but
③ when   ④ before
⑤ because

[15-16] 다음 빈칸에 들어갈 말로 알맞게 짝지어진 것을 고르시오.

15

> · I took the bus _____ my car was broken.
> · We can't see well _____ the fog.

① so – so
② because – because
③ when – because
④ because of – because
⑤ because – because of

16

> · When the class finishes tomorrow, we _____ to the gym.
> · When he _____ here, I'll tell him.

① will go – will come
② will go – came
③ go – will come
④ go – comes
⑤ will go – comes

[17-18] 다음 중 어법상 <u>틀린</u> 것을 고르시오.

17 ① I like Daniel because his confidence.
② He is rich, so he has a large house.
③ When I called back, nobody answered.
④ I don't know him, but my husband knows him.
⑤ I'll call today or tomorrow.

18 ① Because I lost my eraser, I bought one.
② When Sarah will graduate, she will go to Japan.
③ Junk food tastes good, but it is not good for our health.
④ Do you prefer farm life or city life?
⑤ The cake was delicious, so we ate it all.

[19-20] 다음 빈칸에 들어갈 접속사가 나머지와 <u>다른</u> 것을 고르시오.

내신 빈출
19 ① She has a dog _____ two cats.
② Yuna _____ I go to the same school.
③ I got up _____ had breakfast.
④ I met Tom _____ I played tennis with him.
⑤ He worked hard, _____ he failed.

내신 빈출
20 ① He moved here _____ he was thirteen.
② She lived in Canada _____ she was young.
③ He can't go there _____ he's busy today.
④ I was surprised _____ I heard the news.
⑤ I often listen to music _____ I exercise.

[21-22] 다음 우리말을 어법에 알맞게 영작한 것을 고르시오.

21
나는 Green 씨를 알지만 그는 나를 알지 못한다.

① I know Mr. Green and he doesn't know me.
② I know Mr. Green, so he doesn't know me.
③ I know Mr. Green or he doesn't know me.
④ I know Mr. Green, but he doesn't know me.
⑤ I know Mr. Green because he doesn't know me.

22
Jenny가 집에 오면 우리는 함께 저녁을 먹을 것이다.

① When we will have dinner together, Jenny comes home.
② We will have dinner together when Jenny will come home.
③ We will have dinner together when Jenny comes home.
④ We will have dinner together because Jenny comes home.
⑤ Because we will have dinner together, Jenny comes home.

23 다음 밑줄 친 부분 중 쓰임이 **틀린** 것으로 알맞게 짝지어
진 것은?

> ⓐ My car is old but nice.
> ⓑ I came back early so it rained a lot.
> ⓒ I'll call you when dinner is ready.
> ⓓ I was ill for a year, but I lost my job.

① ⓐ, ⓑ
② ⓑ, ⓓ
③ ⓒ, ⓓ
④ ⓐ, ⓒ, ⓓ
⑤ ⓑ, ⓒ, ⓓ

[24-25] 다음 중 어법상 옳은 문장의 개수를 고르시오.

고난도
24

> ⓐ The bus was late because the snow.
> ⓑ I was hungry, so I had some cookies.
> ⓒ She or I has to take care of the child.
> ⓓ I traveled a lot when I was small.

① 없음　② 1개　③ 2개　④ 3개　⑤ 4개

고난도
25

> ⓐ He took a walk and felt relaxed.
> ⓑ I bought the book, but I didn't read it.
> ⓒ We will start when you will be ready.
> ⓓ We went out because of we needed
> 　some fresh air.

① 없음　② 1개　③ 2개　④ 3개　⑤ 4개

[26-28] 다음 우리말과 의미가 같도록 알맞은 접속사와 괄호
안의 말을 이용하여 문장을 완성하시오.

26

> 우리는 저녁 식사로 국수나 밥을 먹을 수 있다.
> (eat, noodles, rice, for dinner)

→ We can _____ .

27

> 나는 한 시간 동안 걸었기 때문에 너무 피곤했다.
> (very tired, for an hour)

→ I was _____ .

28

> 칼을 사용할 때는 조심해야 한다.
> (careful, use, a knife)

→ You must _____ .

[29-31] 다음 두 문장을 알맞은 접속사를 이용하여 한 문장으
로 연결하시오.

29

> · He took a look at the red car.
> · He bought it right away.

→ _____

30

> · The test was very difficult.
> · She passed it.

→ _____

31

> · I drank too much coffee.
> · I'm not sleepy.

→ _____

32 다음 빈칸에 알맞은 접속사를 써서 대화를 완성하시오.

> A: We need to buy a tent, food,
>   (1) _____ sleeping bags for camping.
> B: I know, (2) _____ we don't have
>   enough money. We should ask our
>   parents for money (3) _____ decide
>   not to go camping.

(1) _____
(2) _____
(3) _____

33 다음 우리말과 의미가 같도록 [조건]에 맞게 영작하시오.

> ┌ 조건 ┐
> • 접속사로 시작할 것
> • cook, kitchen, listen to를 사용할 것
> • 10단어로 쓸 것

그녀는 부엌에서 요리할 때 음악을 듣는다.

→ _____
  _____

34 다음 밑줄 친 우리말과 의미가 같도록 5단어로 영작하시오.

> Sally got up late this morning. 그녀는 버스를 놓쳤기 때문에, she had to walk to school. So, she was late for school. She was very tired when she arrived at school.

→ _____

35 다음 글을 읽고, 물음에 답하시오.

> My mother is a teacher. She teaches English to students. I love her. And I respect her, ①but I will become a teacher when I ②will grow up.

(1) 밑줄 친 ①을 문맥에 맞게 고쳐 쓰시오.

   → _____

(2) 밑줄 친 ②를 알맞은 형태로 쓰시오.

   → _____

Chapter

12

명령문, 청유문, 감탄문

01. 명령문, 청유문

❶ 명령문

1 '~해', '~해 줘'라는 의미로 상대방에게 명령하거나 지시하는 문장이며, 주어인 you를 생략하고 동사원형으로 시작한다.

You clean your room. → **Clean** your room.

2 긍정 명령문과 부정 명령문이 있다.

긍정 명령문	동사원형 ~.	~해라.
부정 명령문	Don't + 동사원형 ~.	~하지 마라.

Wash your hands.
Take off your wet clothes.
Wear a helmet.
Don't watch TV too much.
Don't waste your time.
Don't be angry.

➕ **PLUS** be동사의 경우에는 원형인 be를 사용하여 명령문을 만든다.
　　　Be careful.　**Don't be** shy.

❷ 청유문

1 '~하자'라고 상대방에게 권유하는 문장으로 Let's 뒤에 동사원형을 쓴다.
Let's play soccer.

2 긍정 청유문과 부정 청유문이 있다.

긍정 청유문	Let's + 동사원형 ~.	~하자.
부정 청유문	Let's not + 동사원형 ~.	~하지 말자.

Let's be quiet.
Let's start right now.
Let's go on a picnic this Sunday.
Let's not be rude.
Let's not hurry.
Let's not open the window.

Grammar Check Up

📖 Answers p.21

A 다음 괄호 안에서 알맞은 것을 고르시오.

1 (Eat / Eats) more vegetables.

2 (Not / Don't) use your cell phone in the library.

3 (Do / Be) kind to your friends.

4 Tom, (don't is / don't be) afraid.

5 (Let's / Let) plant trees and flowers in the garden.

B 다음 그림의 상황에 맞도록 [보기]에서 알맞은 말을 골라 문장을 완성하시오.

┌─ 보기 ┌─
| cross   turn off   ride   play |

1 2 3 4

1 _____ a bike here.

2 _____ the water.

3 _____ tennis together.

4 Look at the red light! _____ the street.

C 다음 문장에서 어법상 틀린 부분을 찾아 바르게 고쳐 문장을 다시 쓰시오. (단, 단어 수는 그대로 둘 것)

1 Let's waits in line.

→ _____

2 Not cut your fingernails too short.

→ _____

3 Let's don't fight again.

→ _____

4 Brushes your teeth after eating.

→ _____

5 Doesn't sit on the table.

→ _____

02 감탄문

1 감탄문

놀람, 기쁨, 슬픔 등의 감정을 표현하는 문장으로 '정말 ~이구나!', '정말 ~하구나!'라는 뜻이며, what이나 how 로 시작한다.

It is a very nice day. → **What** a nice day it is!

They are very pretty girls. → **What** pretty girls they are!

The bike is very expensive. → **How** expensive the bike is!

He runs very fast. → **How** fast he runs!

⊕ PLUS 감탄문의 「주어 + 동사」 생략
반드시 쓸 필요가 없는 경우에는 주어와 동사를 생략할 수 있다.
What a great idea (**it is**)!   How slow (**it is**)!

2 what 감탄문

1 명사를 강조하는 감탄문이다.

> What + a[an] + 형용사 + 명사(+ 주어 + 동사)!

He is a very clever boy. → **What a clever boy** he is!

It is a very tall building. → **What a tall building** it is!

This is a very easy question. → **What an easy question** this is!

2 강조하는 명사가 복수이거나 셀 수 없는 명사일 경우는 a 또는 an을 쓰지 않는다.

These are very cute puppies. → **What cute puppies** these are!

It is very soft cream. → **What soft cream** it is!

They are very interesting books. → **What interesting books** they are!

3 how 감탄문

형용사나 부사를 강조하는 감탄문이다.

> How + 형용사/부사(+ 주어 + 동사)!

She is very beautiful. → **How beautiful** she is!

This is very delicious. → **How delicious** this is!

She works very hard. → **How hard** she works!

He walks very slowly. → **How slowly** he walks!

Grammar Check Up

A 다음 괄호 안에서 알맞은 것을 고르시오.

1 (How / What) diligent she is!

2 (How / What) an honest boy he is!

3 (How / What) boring the movie is!

4 What (long / a long) bridge this is!

5 What (a tall / tall) trees these are!

B 다음 밑줄 친 부분을 강조하는 감탄문으로 바꿔 쓸 때, 빈칸에 알맞은 말을 쓰시오.

1 He is <u>handsome</u>. → _____ he is!

2 It is <u>an old building</u>. → _____ it is!

3 The game is <u>exciting</u>. → _____ the game is!

4 The old bread is <u>hard</u>. → _____ the old bread is!

5 This is <u>fresh juice</u>. → _____ this is!

C 다음 문장에서 어법상 틀린 부분을 찾아 바르게 고쳐 문장을 다시 쓰시오.

1 What a wonderful world is it!

→ _____

2 What lucky the man is!

→ _____

3 What expensive sweater this is!

→ _____

4 How a cheap watch it is!

→ _____

5 What a good students they are!

→ _____

A 다음 우리말과 의미가 같도록 괄호 안의 말을 이용하여 문장을 완성하시오.

1 매일 운동해라. (do exercise)

→ _____ every day.

2 다시는 거짓말하지 마라. (tell a lie)

→ _____ again.

3 그는 정말 용감하구나! (brave)

→ _____ he is!

4 길에 쓰레기를 버리지 말자. (let, throw)

→ _____ trash on the street.

5 그것은 정말 놀라운 소식이구나! (surprising news)

→ _____ it is!

B 다음 문장을 괄호 안의 지시대로 바꿔 쓰시오.

1 She is a very good singer. (감탄문)

→ _____

2 You do your homework after dinner. (명령문)

→ _____

3 You come home too late. (부정 명령문)

→ _____

4 Make a model airplane together. (청유문)

→ _____

5 This work was very hard. (감탄문)

→ _____

C 다음 친구들의 나쁜 습관에 대한 그림을 보고, [보기]의 단어를 이용하여 친구들에게 조언하는 문장을 완성하시오. (단, 명령문을 사용할 것)

┌─ 보기 ┐
| eat   surf   use   skip   go   get   careful |
└──┘

Mike   Jenny   Lucas

Mike	(1) _____	the Internet until late at night.
	(2) _____	to bed and _____ up early.
Jenny	(3) _____	snacks at night.
	(4) _____	breakfast.
Lucas	(5) _____	your smartphone when you walk.
	(6) _____	when you cross the street.

D 다음 우리말과 의미가 같도록 괄호 안의 말을 이용하여 대화를 완성하시오.

A Look at the Eiffel Tower.

B (1) _____ (beautiful) it is! (그것은 정말 아름답구나!)

A It's 324 meters tall.

B Wow! (2) _____ (tall) it is! (그것은 정말 높은 탑이구나!)

A Yeah. It is the tallest in Paris. Alexandre Gustave Eiffel built it in 1889.

B Oh, really? (3) _____ (old) it is! (그것은 정말 오래된 탑이구나!)

A Yes. (4) _____ (take pictures) in front of the Eiffel Tower.
(우리 에펠탑 앞에서 사진 찍자.)

[01-03] 다음 우리말과 의미가 같도록 빈칸에 들어갈 말로 알맞은 것을 고르시오.

01

도서관에서는 크게 말하지 마.
→ _____ loudly in the library.

① Speak
② To speak
③ Speaking
④ Speaks
⑤ Don't speak

02

지하철을 타자.
→ _____ the subway.

① Take
② Takes
③ Do take
④ Be take
⑤ Let's take

03

그는 정말 훌륭한 의사구나!
→ _____ an excellent doctor he is!

① How
② What
③ Why
④ It
⑤ That

[04-05] 다음 밑줄 친 부분 중 어법상 틀린 것을 고르시오.

04
① Stay calm.
② Don't crying.
③ Let's go camping.
④ What a sad movie it is!
⑤ How strong the man is!

05
① Be creative.
② Let's not do the dishes.
③ Studying English every day.
④ Don't eat too much sugar.
⑤ Do your homework right now.

[06-08] 다음 빈칸에 공통으로 들어갈 말로 알맞은 것을 고르시오.

06

• _____ not eat out. I'll cook dinner.
• _____ open the windows. It is too hot in the room.

① Let's
② Don't
③ Let's not
④ Be
⑤ Do

07 고난도

• _____ is your address?
• _____ a funny story it is!

① How
② What
③ Why
④ It
⑤ That

08 고난도

• _____ dirty the room is!
• _____ often do you exercise?

① How
② What
③ Why
④ It
⑤ That

[09-10] 다음 두 문장의 의미가 같도록 빈칸에 들어갈 말로 알맞은 것을 고르시오.

09

You must not use too much water.
= _____ too much water.

① Use
② Not use
③ To use
④ Using
⑤ Don't use

10

Shall we go to the movies?
= _____ to the movies.

① Go
② Going
③ Do go
④ Let's go
⑤ Let goes

[11-13] 다음 밑줄 친 부분 중 어법상 틀린 것을 고르시오.

11

①Do careful! ②How ③fast ④the car ⑤is!

12

①What ②a cold day ③it is! ④Let's ⑤go not out.

13

①What ②a huge pumpkins ③those are!
④Let's ⑤take a picture.

[14-15] 다음 중 빈칸에 들어갈 말이 나머지와 다른 것을 고르시오.

내신 빈출
14
① _____ a lazy boy he is!
② _____ big trees they are!
③ _____ a wonderful idea it is!
④ _____ sweet ice cream it is!
⑤ _____ noisy the girl is!

내신 빈출
15
① _____ quickly she speaks!
② _____ nice cars they are!
③ _____ crowded the bus is!
④ _____ lovely the flowers are!
⑤ _____ expensive the ring is!

[16-17] 다음 빈칸에 들어갈 말로 알맞은 것을 고르시오.

16

We just have 5 minutes before the movie starts. _____

① Let's not hurry up.
② Don't come too early.
③ Take a rest.
④ Be on time.
⑤ Let's run.

17

It is raining heavily. _____

① Stay home.
② Don't be lazy.
③ Let's jump rope.
④ Let's make a note.
⑤ Don't skip breakfast.

[18-19] 다음 중 어법상 옳은 것을 고르시오.

18 ① Do patient.
② What an poor man he is!
③ Let's go to see a doctor.
④ Be watch out for the car.
⑤ What colorful the shirt is!

내신 빈출
19 ① Does not wake him up.
② How soft scarves they are!
③ What clean the room is!
④ What a cute teddy bear it is!
⑤ Don't watches TV too long.

[20-21] 다음 우리말을 어법에 알맞게 영작한 것을 고르시오.

20

그 작은 소녀는 정말 사랑스러워 보이는구나!

① How a lovely the little girl looks!
② What a lovely the little girl looks!
③ How lovely the little girl looks!
④ What lovely the little girl looks!
⑤ How lovely looks the little girl!

21

아무것도 사지 말자.

① Let's buy anything.
② Let's buy not anything.
③ No let's buy anything.
④ Let's not buy anything.
⑤ Not let's buy anything.

[22-23] 다음 중 어법상 틀린 것으로 알맞게 짝지어진 것을 고르시오.

내신 빈출
22

ⓐ How a beautiful park it is!
ⓑ Let's take a rest.
ⓒ Pass me the salt, please.
ⓓ Don't runs in the classroom.

① ⓐ, ⓑ   ② ⓐ, ⓓ
③ ⓑ, ⓒ   ④ ⓐ, ⓒ, ⓓ
⑤ ⓑ, ⓒ, ⓓ

23
ⓐ Do quiet in the library.
ⓑ Don't go out late at night.
ⓒ Lets not worry too much.
ⓓ What a great goal is it!

① ⓐ, ⓑ   ② ⓑ, ⓒ
③ ⓑ, ⓓ   ④ ⓐ, ⓒ, ⓓ
⑤ ⓑ, ⓒ, ⓓ

[24-25] 다음 중 어법상 옳은 문장의 개수를 고르시오.

24
ⓐ Let's ask for the bill.
ⓑ Not drink too much soda.
ⓒ How a tiny puppy it is!
ⓓ What a wise person he is!

① 없음   ② 1개   ③ 2개   ④ 3개   ⑤ 4개

고난도
25
ⓐ Finishes the report by ten.
ⓑ Don't touch the hot water.
ⓒ What expensive sneakers they are!
ⓓ How rude your words are!

① 없음   ② 1개   ③ 2개   ④ 3개   ⑤ 4개

[26-28] 다음 우리말과 의미가 같도록 괄호 안의 말을 이용하여 영작하시오.

26
이번 주말에 소풍 가자. (go on a picnic)

→ _____

27
길이 정말 좁구나! (narrow, the road)

→ _____

28
그는 정말 용감한 군인이구나! (brave, soldier)

→ _____

[29-31] 다음 그림을 보고, 괄호 안의 말을 바르게 배열하시오.

29

(listen to, in class, the teacher)
→ _____

30

(play, too long, don't, computer games)
→ _____

31

(a, cat, what, is, cute, it)
→ _____

32 다음은 애플파이를 만드는 방법에 관한 글이다. 괄호 안의 말을 바르게 배열하여 글을 완성하시오.

> For a delicious apple pie, we should follow these steps.
> First, (1) (the, ingredients, mix, together).
> Second, cook for 15 minutes in the oven.
> And, (2) (the, apple pie, don't, touch, hot).

(1) _____

(2) _____

34 다음 대화의 밑줄 친 ①~⑤ 중 어법상 틀린 것을 2개 찾아 기호를 쓰고, 바르게 고쳐 문장을 다시 쓰시오.

> A: ① What a messy room it is!
> B: Yes. ② Lets clean the room.
> A: Okay. ③ Look at the socks on the floor.
> ④ What dirty they are! ⑤ Put them in the washing machine.

(1) _____ → _____

(2) _____ → _____

33 다음 빈칸에 들어갈 알맞은 문장을 [조건]에 맞게 영작하시오.

> Minho likes soccer and you like it, too.
> You say to Mihno, "_____"

ㅏ 조건 ㅏ
- Let's ~.를 사용할 것
- play, after school을 사용할 것
- 5단어로 쓸 것

→ _____

35 다음 글을 읽고, 괄호 안의 말을 이용하여 빈칸에 들어갈 명령문을 완성하시오.

> I got up late in the morning. So, I was late for school today. The teacher said to me, "_____" (late, again)

→ _____

MEMO

MEMO

2022 교육과정

강남 학원가의

입소문셀러

너무 유명한 교재!
주변 친구들 학원에서도 다 이거 푼대요.
학교 내신 시험에 자주 나오는 유형이
많아서 좋아요.
*D학원 신○○ 학생

학원 선생님 추천 교재라서
믿고 구매했어요.
*B학원 김○○ 학생

고쟁이 끝에 내신 1등급이 온다!

1,000개 이상의 내신 시험지 완벽 분석

내신 / 평가원 / 교육청 기출문제까지
철저하게 분석하여
학교 시험 대비 최적화

심화 유형서에 최적화된 문항 수

교과서 수준의 기본 문항부터
고난도 문항까지 모두 수록

개념 흐름을 한눈에 '개념 정리' 수록

선수학습과의 연결을 통해
개념의 흐름을 보여주어
문제 해결력 상승

• 이투스북 도서는 전국 서점 및 온라인 서점에서 구매하실 수 있습니다.
• 이투스북 온라인 서점 | www.etoosbook.com

이투스북

중학 국어의 문을 두드려라!

똑똑한 독해
중학 국어

똑독

중학 국어 비문학 독해+어휘

똑똑한 독해

똑독

중학 국어
비문학
독해+어휘

실전편

3

이투스북

1 비문학 독해의 기본이 되는 독해력과 어휘력을 동시에 습득
2 중학교 국어·도덕·사회·과학·음악·미술 교과서 연계 배경지식 강화
3 수능형·서술형·논술형 등 다양한 유형의 문제로 단계별 실력 향상

똑똑한 독해
똑독
중학 국어
문법
기본편

똑독 중학 국어 문법

똑똑한 독해
똑독
중학 국어
어휘
1

똑독 중학 국어 어휘

개념 학습과 문제 풀이의
1DAY 구성으로
계획적인 학습 가능

중학교 국어 교과서와
100% 연계된
개념 학습

족보닷컴을 활용하여
출제한 문제로
내신 시험과 수행 평가 대비

- 이투스북 도서는 전국 서점 및 온라인 서점에서 구매하실 수 있습니다.
- 이투스북 온라인 서점 | www.etoosbook.com

이투스북

GRAMMAR MASTER

Beginner
Level

WORKBOOK

ETOOS book

GRAMMAR MASTER

WORKBOOK

Beginner
Level

Practice 01 셀 수 있는 명사

01 -1 다음 명사의 복수형을 쓰시오.

1 notebook _____   2 knife _____
3 puppy _____   4 tooth _____
5 day _____   6 man _____
7 dish _____   8 roof _____
9 city _____   10 bus _____
11 piano _____   12 story _____

01 -2 다음 빈칸에 a나 an 중에서 알맞은 것을 골라 쓰시오.

1 He wears _____ cap.
2 My mom eats _____ orange every day.
3 My father is _____ science teacher.
4 _____ lion is in the zoo.
5 I have _____ onion.
6 He needs _____ fork.
7 I want _____ hamburger.
8 _____ umbrella is on the table.
9 _____ ant crawls on the ground.   *crawl: 기어가다
10 He picks up _____ carrot.
11 The hen lays _____ egg every day.   *hen: 암탉
12 There is _____ cup in the box.

01 -3 다음 괄호 안에서 알맞은 것을 고르시오.

1 Two (pig / pigs) are on the farm.
2 I need only one (potato / potatoes).
3 She has three (piggy bank / piggy banks).
4 My uncle has ten (sheeps / sheep).
5 Brush your (tooth / teeth).
6 There are four (mouses / mice) in the basement.
7 Many red and yellow (leafs / leaves) are on the street.

01-4 다음 문장의 밑줄 친 부분을 바르게 고쳐 쓰시오.

1 Five <u>child</u> play basketball. _____

2 Three beautiful <u>fishes</u> are in the fishbowl. _____

3 My little brother is three <u>feets</u> tall. _____

4 I need a pair of <u>scissor</u>. _____

5 Three <u>shelfs</u> are in my room. _____

6 We have five <u>class</u> today. _____

7 There are three <u>womans</u> in the store. _____

8 The farmer has five <u>deers</u>. _____

01-5 다음 우리말과 의미가 같도록 괄호 안의 말을 이용하여 문장을 완성하시오.

1 나는 달걀 한 개를 먹는다. (egg)

→ I eat _____.

2 저 세 마리의 쥐들을 봐. (mouse)

→ Look at the _____.

3 많은 사슴들이 동물원에 있다. (many, deer)

→ _____ are in the zoo.

4 나에게 좋은 생각이 하나 있다. (good, idea)

→ I have _____.

5 그는 손목시계 세 개를 가지고 있다. (watch)

→ He has _____.

6 그녀는 운동화 한 켤레를 신고 있다. (pair, sneaker)

→ She wears _____.

7 네 개의 고구마가 바구니 안에 있다. (sweet potato)

→ _____ are in the basket.

8 우리는 신선한 공기가 필요하다. (fresh, air)

→ We need _____.

Practice 02 셀 수 없는 명사

02-1 다음 빈칸에 a나 an을 쓰거나 필요 없을 경우 × 표시를 하시오.

1 I drink _____ water every morning.

2 _____ cucumber is in the refrigerator.

3 My uncle lives in _____ New York.

4 Her name is _____ Alice.

5 I need _____ salt and sugar.

6 She likes _____ tea.

7 Many people want _____ peace.

8 He has _____ expensive car.

9 My father is _____ taxi driver.

10 Your kids need _____ love.

11 I have _____ new computer.

12 Pour some water into _____ empty bottle.

02-2 다음 괄호 안의 말을 이용하여 문장을 완성하시오.

1 She drinks two _____ every day. (glass, juice)

2 Billy needs three _____. (sheet, paper)

3 I have three _____. (can, soda)

4 My brother eats a _____ every morning. (slice, cheese)

5 He wants a _____. (cup, tea)

6 Two _____ are on the table. (bottle, water)

7 My sister eats a _____ for dinner. (bowl, soup)

8 We need five _____. (loaf, bread)

9 Three _____ are on the plate. (piece, pizza)

10 Olivia buys three _____ every week. (carton, milk)

11 Two _____ are in the bathroom. (bar, soap)

02-3 다음 괄호 안에서 알맞은 것을 고르시오.

1 I love (cola / colas).

2 Everyone wants (a happiness / happiness).

3　Put some (sugar / sugars) in my coffee.

4　He is from (a Busan / Busan).

5　The kid wants (two cup of cocoas / two cups of cocoa).

6　Emily is (an English / English) teacher.

7　Give (a meat / a piece of meat) to the dog.

02-4 다음 문장의 밑줄 친 부분을 바르게 고쳐 쓰시오.

1　Take out three <u>slice of cakes</u> from the refrigerator.　_____

2　We have lots of <u>times</u>.　_____

3　My friend is from <u>the Paris</u>.　_____

4　I need five <u>pieces of papers</u>.　_____

5　She drinks a lot of <u>sodas</u>.　_____

6　Billy and Thomas are my <u>friend</u>.　_____

7　My grandmother needs a <u>pair of glass</u>.　_____

02-5 다음 우리말과 의미가 같도록 괄호 안의 말을 이용하여 문장을 완성하시오.

1　내 남동생은 돼지고기를 좋아한다. (pork)

　　→ My little brother likes _____.

2　나에게 바지 한 벌을 사 줘. (pair)

　　→ Buy _____ for me.

3　어린이들은 많은 사랑이 필요하다. (lot)

　　→ Children need _____.

4　그들은 약간의 돈이 필요하다. (some)

　　→ They need _____.

5　설탕 두 스푼을 냄비에 넣어라. (spoonful)

　　→ Put _____ in the pot.

6　나는 매일 밥 세 그릇을 먹는다. (bowl, rice)

　　→ I eat _____ every day.

7　그녀는 매일 아침 당근 주스 두 잔을 마신다. (glass, carrot juice)

　　→ She drinks _____ every morning.

Chapter Test

01 다음 중 명사의 복수형이 알맞게 짝지어진 것을 <u>모두</u> 고르면?

① pencils, maps, potatos
② knifes, buses, boxes
③ children, deer, fish
④ leaves, zoos, classes
⑤ apples, sandwiches, citys

02 다음 중 빈칸에 들어갈 말이 나머지와 <u>다른</u> 것은?

① It is _____ baby elephant.
② Subin has _____ red bicycle.
③ He is _____ famous actor.
④ I eat _____ apple every morning.
⑤ There are 24 hours in _____ day.

[03-04] 다음 빈칸에 들어갈 말로 알맞지 <u>않은</u> 것을 모두 고르시오.

03

A _____ is under the bed.

① photo   ② eraser   ③ book
④ key   ⑤ water

04

Two _____ are in the field.

① womans   ② wolves   ③ deers
④ sheep   ④ children

05 다음 (A)~(C)의 각 네모 안에서 알맞은 것끼리 짝지은 것은?

- (A) A love / Love is a wonderful thing.
- Michael wears (B) glass / glasses .
- Two (C) bar / bars of chocolate are on his desk.

	(A)		(B)		(C)
①	A love	–	glass	–	bar
②	A love	–	glass	–	bars
③	A love	–	glasses	–	bars
④	Love	–	glasses	–	bar
⑤	Love	–	glasses	–	bars

06 다음 우리말을 어법에 알맞게 영작한 것은?

우리는 소금 두 스푼이 필요하다.

① We need two salt.
② We need two salts.
③ We need two spoonful of salt.
④ We need two spoonfuls of salt.
⑤ We need two spoonfuls of salts.

07 다음 우리말과 의미가 같도록 괄호 안의 말을 배열할 때 세 <u>번째</u> 오는 단어는?

장갑 한 켤레를 사라. (a, gloves, buy, of, pair)

① a   ② gloves   ③ buy
④ of   ⑤ pair

08 다음 중 어법상 틀린 것은?

① He is an artist.

② It is a old house.

③ It is a good idea.

④ She is from Brazil.

⑤ Give some water to me.

09 다음 중 어법상 옳은 것으로 알맞게 짝지어진 것은?

ⓐ I need new bag.

ⓑ She uses a pair of scissors.

ⓒ A lot of fish are in the river.

ⓓ I need two bottle of ketchups.

ⓔ There are four men in the book club.

① ⓐ, ⓑ, ⓒ   ② ⓐ, ⓑ, ⓓ   ③ ⓑ, ⓒ, ⓓ

④ ⓑ, ⓒ, ⓔ   ⑤ ⓒ, ⓓ, ⓔ

10 다음 수진이의 오답노트 중 수진이가 고친 내용이 틀린 것은?

① Three tomatos are in the basket.

→ tomato처럼 -o로 끝나는 명사는 -es를 붙여서 복수형을 만드니까 tomatoes로 고쳐야 해.

② I make a sandwich with two slice of cheese.

→ 치즈가 두 장이고 cheese의 복수형은 cheeses이니까 two slices of cheeses로 써야 해.

③ A New York is a big city.

→ New York과 같은 고유명사는 셀 수 없는 명사니까 앞에 a를 쓸 수 없어.

④ Many people want a freedom.

→ freedom과 같은 추상명사는 셀 수 없는 명사니까 앞에 a를 쓸 수 없어.

⑤ Add three pieces of honey into a blender.

→ honey는 a piece of가 아니라 a spoonful of로 수량을 나타내야 해.

[11-12] 다음 우리말과 의미가 같도록 어법상 틀린 부분을 찾아 바르게 고쳐 쓰시오.

11
> 나는 영어를 좋아하고 Tom은 한국어를 좋아한다.
> → I like an English and Tom likes Korean.

_____ → _____

12
> 나는 점심으로 피자 두 조각과 콜라 한 캔을 먹는다.
> → I have two piece of pizza and a can of coke for lunch.

_____ → _____

[13-14] 다음 우리말과 의미가 같도록 괄호 안의 지시대로 문장을 완성하시오.

13
> 그는 커피 한 잔을 원한다. (4단어로)

→ He wants _____ .

14
> 냉장고에서 오렌지 주스 한 병을 꺼내라. (5단어로)

→ Take out _____
from the refrigerator.

15 다음 글에서 어법상 틀린 부분을 3개 찾아 바르게 고쳐 쓰시오.

> Sophie is my best friend. She is from the France. She is a teacher. She loves childs. She swims every day for her health. She eats a slice of salad for dinner. She keeps in shape.

(1) _____ → _____

(2) _____ → _____

(3) _____ → _____

Practice **01** **인칭대명사**

01-1 다음 밑줄 친 부분을 알맞은 대명사로 바꿔 쓰시오.

1 <u>Michael</u> is good at math. _____

2 <u>Jennifer</u> is a nice nurse. _____

3 <u>The cat</u> is very cute. _____

4 <u>My friend and I</u> swim well. _____

5 <u>James and Jim</u> are from Los Angeles. _____

6 <u>Sue and you</u> are my best friends. _____

7 Jake likes <u>Mina</u>. _____

8 This is <u>Juliet's</u> bag. _____

9 I live with <u>Katie and Sally</u>. _____

10 We smile at <u>Peter</u>. _____

11 <u>My birthday</u> is May 5. _____

12 They feed <u>the cats and dogs</u> in the park. _____

01-2 다음 괄호 안에서 알맞은 것을 고르시오.

1 This is (our / us) most popular item.

2 (Me / My) dress is red.

3 (It / Its) is a funny story.

4 Look at (him / his) broken car.

5 I have a puppy. (It's / Its) eyes are dark brown.

6 Wash (you / your) dirty hands right now.

7 I have many books. I read (their / them) every night.

01-3 다음 괄호 안의 말을 이용하여 문장을 완성하시오.

1 I meet _____ every day. (he)

2 Sometimes Jack stays with _____. (I)

3 Everyone hates _____. (she)

4 This is _____ backpack. (he)

5 That is _____ house. (we)

6 He misses _____ very much. (you)

7 _____ plays the piano in his free time. (he)

8   Those are _____ boats. (they)

9   We need _____ time. (you)

10 _____ neck is short. (it)

11 Mr. Johnson teaches English to _____. (we)

12 They know _____ address. (I)

01 -4 다음 문장의 밑줄 친 부분을 바르게 고쳐 문장을 다시 쓰시오.

1   <u>Its</u> very interesting.   _____

2   <u>Him</u> father is a firefighter.   _____

3   My grandparents visit <u>we</u> every Saturday.   _____

4   She often calls <u>their</u>.   _____

5   This is <u>you</u> computer.   _____

6   I like <u>them</u> long ears.   _____

7   I listen to <u>hers</u> songs sometimes.   _____

01 -5 다음 우리말과 의미가 같도록 괄호 안의 말을 이용하여 문장을 완성하시오.

1   나는 그들을 많이 그리워한다. (miss)
   → _____ a lot.

2   우리의 숙제는 매우 어렵다. (homework)
   → _____ is very difficult.

3   그 개는 그것의 꼬리를 흔든다. (tail)
   → The dog wags _____.   *wag: (개가 꼬리를) 흔들다

4   우리는 너를 아주 많이 사랑해. (love)
   → _____ very much.

5   나의 선생님들은 나를 도와주신다. (help)
   → _____ teachers _____.

6   많은 사람이 그녀의 그림들을 좋아한다. (painting)
   → Many people _____.

7   그들은 그들의 교복을 입는다. (wear)
   → _____ school uniforms.

02-1 다음 그림의 상황에 맞도록 [보기]에서 알맞은 말을 골라 문장을 완성하시오. (단, 중복 사용 가능)

보기				
this	that	these	those	it

1 _____ are my cookies.
2 _____ is my uncle's cabin.
3 _____ is rainy outside.
4 _____ is my new smartphone.
5 _____ are my balloons.
6 _____ is Wednesday today.

02-2 다음 우리말과 의미가 같도록 [보기]에서 알맞은 말을 골라 문장을 완성하시오. (단, 중복 사용 가능)

보기				
this	that	these	those	it

1 이것은 나의 모자이다.   → _____ is my cap.
2 저분은 나의 선생님이시다.   → _____ is my teacher.
3 오늘은 날씨가 화창하다.   → _____ is nice today.
4 이것들은 그의 신발이다.   → _____ are his shoes.
5 저것들은 사슴들이다.   → _____ are deer.
6 오늘은 월요일이다.   → _____ is Monday today.
7 이 수건은 너무 더럽다.   → _____ towel is so dirty.
8 저 시계들은 값이 싸다.   → _____ watches are cheap.
9 나는 이 컵들을 원한다.   → I want _____ cups.
10 저 절은 매우 오래됐다.   → _____ temple is very old.

02-3 다음 괄호 안에서 알맞은 것을 고르시오.

1 (This / These) apple is fresh and sweet.

2 (That / Those) baby tiger looks cute.

3 (This / These) rooms have big windows.

4 (It / That) is windy and snowy.

5 Look at (this / those) nice cars.

6 (This / These) blue jeans are very expensive.

7 Please write your name on (that / those) sheet.

02-4 다음 문장에서 어법상 틀린 부분을 찾아 바르게 고쳐 문장을 다시 쓰시오.

1 These watch is wrong. _____

2 Those is my grandmother. _____

3 That is 5 km from here to the bank. _____

4 I need those bike. _____

5 This are her cats. _____

6 That boxes are very heavy. _____

7 This is stormy here in Boston. _____

02-5 다음 우리말과 의미가 같도록 괄호 안의 말을 바르게 배열하시오.

1 이 소년은 나의 아들이다. (boy, is, my son, this)

→ _____

2 저 꽃들은 너를 위한 것이다. (those, are, for you, flowers)

→ _____

3 저것은 쉬운 문제이다. (an, problem, easy, that, is)

→ _____

4 밖이 어둡다. (dark, is, outside, it)

→ _____

5 많은 어린이는 이 책들을 좋아한다. (like, books, these, many children)

→ _____

6 저것들은 나의 오래된 장난감들이다. (are, toys, those, old, my)

→ _____

7 저분들은 용감한 군인들이다. (brave, are, those, soldiers)

→ _____

Chapter Test

[01-02] 다음 빈칸에 들어갈 말로 알맞지 <u>않은</u> 것을 고르시오.

01

> Is this _____ pencil?

① us ② his ③ her
④ your ⑤ their

02

> Those _____ are too expensive.

① pants ② gloves ③ camera
④ flowers ⑤ sunglasses

03 다음 밑줄 친 부분을 대명사로 바꿀 때 알맞지 <u>않은</u> 것은?

① <u>The little girl</u> is my sister. (→ She)
② I love <u>my friends</u>. (→ them)
③ The gift is for <u>my brother and me</u>. (→ us)
④ <u>Justin and Mark</u> are tall. (→ They)
⑤ <u>The rabbit's</u> ears are long. (→ Their)

04 다음 우리말을 어법에 알맞게 영작할 때 필요하지 <u>않</u>은 것은?

> 이 사람은 나의 사촌이다.

① cousin ② he ③ is
④ this ⑤ my

05 다음 밑줄 친 부분과 쓰임이 <u>다른</u> 것은?

> I know <u>her</u> phone number.

① It is <u>her</u> jewel case.
② <u>Her</u> mother is a doctor.
③ She always cleans <u>her</u> room.
④ Kevin is <u>her</u> brother.
⑤ I will meet <u>her</u> in the park.

06 다음 빈칸에 들어갈 말로 알맞게 짝지어진 것은?

> Julia and I are best friends. I meet
> _____ every day. _____ know
> each other well.

① her - You ② her - We
③ she - We ④ them - We
⑤ them - They

07 다음 중 어법상 <u>틀린</u> 것을 <u>모두</u> 고르면?

① I like this socks.
② It is winter in Australia.
③ We love he very much.
④ Welcome to my house.
⑤ This is her grandfather.

08 다음 중 밑줄 친 It의 쓰임이 같은 것끼리 짝지어진 것은?

> ⓐ <u>It</u> is windy and cold.
> ⓑ <u>It</u> is his new kite.
> ⓒ <u>It</u> is 500 meters to school.
> ⓓ <u>It</u> is December 24.
> ⓔ <u>It</u> is my favorite color.

① ⓐ, ⓑ ② ⓐ, ⓔ
③ ⓑ, ⓔ ④ ⓐ, ⓑ, ⓒ
⑤ ⓑ, ⓓ, ⓔ

09 다음 우리말을 어법에 알맞게 영작한 것은?

> 저것이 Anna의 안경이니?

① Is it Anna's glasses?
② Is that Anna glasses?
③ Is that Anna's glasses?
④ Are those Anna glasses?
⑤ Are those Anna's glasses?

10 다음 중 어법상 옳은 문장의 개수는?

> ⓐ This is Sunday today.
> ⓑ Are this your shoes?
> ⓒ Those seats are for kids.
> ⓓ This is my first visit to Seoul.
> ⓔ Can you fix these watch?

① 1개　② 2개　③ 3개　④ 4개　⑤ 5개

11 다음 빈칸에 공통으로 들어갈 알맞은 말을 쓰시오.

> A: What time is _____ now?
> _____ is light outside.
> B: _____ is around 6 a.m.

→ _____

[12-13] 다음 밑줄 친 부분을 대신하여 빈칸에 들어갈 대명사를 쓰시오.

12
> Hi, I'm Jacob. Do you remember _____ ?

→ _____

13
> Sophie and David were born on the same day. _____ birthday is July 17.

→ _____

14 다음 우리말과 의미가 같도록 빈칸에 알맞은 말을 쓰시오.

> A: Is this (1) _____ bag?
> (이것은 Jenny의 가방이니?)
> B: No. It's (2) _____ bag.
> (아니. 그것은 내 가방이야.)

(1) _____

(2) _____

15 다음 밑줄 친 부분 중 어법상 틀린 것을 2개 찾아 바르게 고쳐 쓰시오.

> A: Look at these picture.
> B: Who is this boy? Is it you?
> A: No. This is my father.
> B: Really? You look just like his!

(1) _____ → _____

(2) _____ → _____

Practice **01** **be동사의 현재형**

01 -1 다음 주어에 맞는 be동사의 현재형을 쓰시오.

1 I _____   2 The dogs _____
3 You _____   4 The student _____
5 John _____   6 That _____
7 Sue and I _____   8 It _____
9 We _____   10 You and your father _____
11 Jenny _____   12 Those crayons _____

01 -2 다음 [보기]와 같이 빈칸에 알맞은 be동사를 쓰고, 「주어 + be동사」를 줄여 문장을 다시 쓰시오.

┌─ 보기 ┐
He is my brother. → He's my brother.
└──────────────────────────────────────┘

1 She _____ sad.   → _____
2 They _____ in the living room.   → _____
3 I _____ thirsty.   → _____
4 It _____ hot and cloudy.   → _____
5 We _____ proud of you.   → _____
6 You _____ a kind teacher.   → _____
7 He _____ always late for school.   → _____
8 I _____ 13 years old.   → _____
9 That _____ a good idea.   → _____
10 They _____ my best friends.   → _____

01 -3 다음 괄호 안에서 알맞은 것을 고르시오.

1 (This / These) is your present.
2 Mia and James (is / are) from America.
3 (I / It) is a great picture.
4 I (am / are) smart and brave.
5 That monkey (is / are) very cute.
6 These watermelons (is / are) very big.
7 (My grandmother / My grandparents) is still young.

01-4 다음 문장의 밑줄 친 부분을 바르게 고쳐 쓰시오.

1 It <u>am</u> an exciting story. _____

2 The actor <u>are</u> handsome and kind. _____

3 Billy and I <u>am</u> tired. _____

4 Vegetables <u>is</u> good for us. _____

5 My aunt <u>am</u> a famous designer. _____

6 These skirts <u>is</u> too long. _____

7 John and I <u>is</u> very popular. _____

8 Some beautiful flowers <u>is</u> on the table. _____

01-5 다음 우리말과 의미가 같도록 괄호 안의 말을 이용하여 문장을 완성하시오.

1 이 스마트폰은 매우 빠르다. (this smartphone)
→ _____ very fast.

2 저 운동화는 너를 위한 것이다. (those sneakers)
→ _____ for you.

3 Juliet은 내 짝꿍이다. (Juliet)
→ _____ my partner.

4 많은 쿠키들이 접시 위에 있다. (many cookies)
→ _____ on the plate.

5 거북이 몇 마리가 모래 위에 있다. (some turtles)
→ _____ on the sand.

6 약국이 이 근처에 있다. (the pharmacy)
→ _____ near here.

7 피아노 한 대가 교실에 있다. (a piano)
→ _____ in the classroom.

8 Tom과 그의 친구들은 강당에 있다. (Tom and his friends)
→ _____ in the auditorium.

be동사의 부정문과 의문문

02 -1 다음 문장을 부정문으로 바꿔 쓰시오. (단, 줄임말로 쓰지 말 것)

1 He is smart and wise. → _____

2 You are in our club. → _____

3 Julie is from Canada. → _____

4 Daniel is a genius. → _____

5 Ella and I are in the garden. → _____

6 She is a top ballerina. → _____

7 They are in the same class. → _____

8 The cake is in the refrigerator. → _____

02 -2 다음 [보기]와 같이 밑줄 친 부분을 줄여 문장을 다시 쓰시오.

┌─ 보기 ┤
It is not my watch. → It's not my watch. / It isn't my watch.
└─

1 She is not my favorite singer.

→ _____

2 I am not hungry now.

→ _____

3 They are not good for our health.

→ _____

4 You are not honest.

→ _____

5 We are not late for school.

→ _____

02 -3 다음 문장을 의문문으로 바꿔 쓰고, 그에 대한 대답을 완성하시오.

1 They are in Paris, France.

→ _____ No, _____.

2 He is angry at me.

→ _____ No, _____.

3 It is far from here.

→ _____ Yes, _____.

4 You are good at math.

→ _____ Yes, _____.

5 Her hair is long and black.

→ _____ Yes, _____.

02 -4 다음 괄호 안에서 알맞은 것을 고르시오.

1 This (is not / not is) a parrot. *parrot: 앵무새

2 (Is / Am) he in the hospital?

3 It (isn't / aren't) cold.

4 (Is / Are) Italy in Europe?

5 David and Calvin (isn't / aren't) musicians.

6 (Is / Are) those trees old?

7 (Is / Are) Betty and her twin sister 11 years old?

8 I (am not / amn't) a good cook.

02 -5 다음 괄호 안의 말과 be동사를 이용하여 문장을 완성하시오. (단, 줄임말로 쓰지 말 것)

1 _____ a doctor. (Billy, not)

2 _____ kangaroos? (these)

3 _____ interesting. (the book, not)

4 _____ clever? (the students)

5 _____ clear. (the water, not)

6 _____ in New York? (the actors)

02 -6 다음 우리말과 의미가 같도록 괄호 안의 말을 이용하여 영작하시오. (단, 줄임말로 쓰지 말 것)

1 이 수건은 더럽지 않다. (this towel, dirty)

→ _____

2 그는 마술사니? (a magician)

→ _____

3 그녀는 교실에 없다. (in the classroom)

→ _____

4 이 요리는 매우 맵니? (this dish, very spicy)

→ _____

5 그들은 극장에 있니? (at the movie theater)

→ _____

6 그 수영장은 크지 않다. (the pool, large)

→ _____

7 너의 휴대전화가 침대 밑에 있니? (your cell phone, under the bed)

→ _____

8 나는 이번 주에 바쁘지 않다. (busy, this week)

→ _____

03 -1 다음 문장을 last year를 사용하여 바꿔 쓸 때, 빈칸에 알맞은 말을 쓰시오.

1 She is in New Zealand. → _____ last year.

2 He is 150 cm tall. → _____ last year.

3 They are college students. → _____ last year.

4 Christmas is wonderful. → _____ last year.

5 We are baseball players. → _____ last year.

6 Brad is 12 years old. → _____ last year.

7 Jane and I are classmates. → _____ last year.

03 -2 다음 문장을 부정문으로 바꿔 쓰시오. (단, 줄임말로 쓸 것)

1 I was eight years old last year.

→ _____

2 Jenny and I were cheerleaders two years ago.

→ _____

3 The vegetables were fresh an hour ago.

→ _____

4 It was snowy and stormy yesterday.

→ _____

5 The bus was crowded this morning.

→ _____

03 -3 다음 문장을 의문문으로 바꿔 쓰고, 그에 대한 대답을 완성하시오.

1 They were at the movie theater.

→ _____ No, _____.

2 His dad was tired last night.

→ _____ Yes, _____.

3 The park was very clean.

→ _____ No, _____.

4 The caps were on sale.

→ _____ Yes, _____.

5 You were upset yesterday.

→ _____ No, _____.

03-4 다음 괄호 안에서 알맞은 것을 고르시오.

1 My puppy (was / were) sick yesterday.

2 The room (was not / not was) messy.

3 (Were / Was) your parents surprised at the news?

4 Jimmy and his friend (wasn't / weren't) together yesterday.

5 (Was / Were) his answer right?

6 Many old houses (was / were) in the village.

7 (Was / Were) it foggy last night?

03-5 다음 빈칸에 들어갈 알맞은 말을 [보기]에서 골라 쓰시오. (단, 중복 사용 가능)

┌─ 보기 ─
│   was   were   wasn't   weren't
└

1 It _____ rainy yesterday. It was sunny.

2 The movie _____ funny. I was not sleepy.

3 The apples _____ fresh. They were delicious.

4 The soldiers _____ scared. They were brave.

5 Was the pot hot? - No, it _____ .

6 _____ the cookies sweet? - Yes, they were.

03-6 다음 우리말과 의미가 같도록 괄호 안의 말을 이용하여 영작하시오. (단, 줄임말로 쓰지 말 것)

1 그녀의 배낭은 비싸지 않았다. (her backpack, expensive)

→ _____

2 Jessy와 너는 구내식당에 있었니? (Jessy, and, in the cafeteria)

→ _____

3 그 책들은 지루하지 않았다. (the books, boring)

→ _____

4 너는 어제 한가했니? (free, yesterday)

→ _____

5 시장이 여기서 멀었니? (the market, far from here)

→ _____

6 그 원숭이들은 우리 안에 있지 않았다. (the monkeys, in the cage)

→ _____

7 너의 아버지는 위층에 계셨니? (your father, upstairs)

→ _____

04 -1 다음 빈칸에 There is나 There are 중에서 알맞은 것을 골라 쓰시오.

1 _____ many cars in the parking lot.

2 _____ a lot of candles on the table.

3 _____ some milk in the bottle.

4 _____ two pieces of pizza on the plate.

5 _____ some chocolate in the refrigerator.

6 _____ five boys in the playground.

7 _____ a cup of tea on your desk.

04 -2 다음 괄호 안의 지시대로 문장을 바꿔 쓰시오.

1 There are many onions in the basket. (부정문)

→ _____

2 There is a cat on the roof. (과거형)

→ _____

3 There are many mountains in our village. (과거 부정문)

→ _____

4 There is a shirt on the bed. (부정문)

→ _____

5 There is a pencil in the pencil case. (과거 부정문)

→ _____

04 -3 다음 문장을 의문문으로 바꿔 쓰고, 그에 대한 대답을 완성하시오.

1 There are many people on the bus.

→ _____   No, _____.

2 There was an egg in the basket.

→ _____   Yes, _____.

3 There is a picture on the wall.

→ _____   No, _____.

4 There were two birds in the cage.

→ _____   Yes, _____.

5 There were lots of books on the shelf.

→ _____   No, _____.

04 -4 다음 문장의 밑줄 친 부분을 바르게 고쳐 쓰시오.

1   There <u>is</u> my favorite toys in the box.   _____
2   There <u>aren't</u> any water in the pond.   _____
3   There <u>is</u> a concert last night.   _____
4   There <u>are</u> some money in the piggy bank.   _____
5   <u>Are there</u> a math test yesterday?   _____
6   There <u>is</u> some famous restaurants in my neighborhood.   _____
7   <u>Were there</u> a library near here at that time?   _____

04 -5 다음 우리말과 의미가 같도록 괄호 안의 말과 There is[are] 구문을 이용하여 문장을 완성하시오.

1   길 건너편에 약국이 하나 있다. (a pharmacy)
    → _____ across the street.

2   실험실에는 두 명의 과학자들이 있다. (two scientists)
    → _____ in the lab.

3   바닥에 개미가 많이 있었다. (many ants)
    → _____ on the floor.

4   농구 팀에는 5명의 선수들이 있니? (five players)
    → _____ on a basketball team?

5   지갑에는 돈이 하나도 없었다. (any money)
    → _____ in the wallet.

04 -6 다음 우리말과 의미가 같도록 괄호 안의 말을 바르게 배열하시오.

1   우리 마당에는 커다란 연못이 있었다. (a big pond, in our yard, was, there)
    → _____

2   세계에는 약 230개의 국가가 있다. (are, about 230 countries, there, in the world)
    → _____

3   어항에는 물고기가 한 마리도 없다. (in the fishbowl, there, any fish, not, are)
    → _____

4   파티에 많은 사람들이 있었니? (many people, at the party, there, were)
    → _____

5   작년에는 이곳에 식당이 없었다. (any restaurants, here, there, were, not, last year)
    → _____

01 다음 빈칸에 are를 쓸 수 없는 것은?

① They _____ good doctors.

② The twins _____ popular in school.

③ His eye color _____ green.

④ Lucy and I _____ best friends.

⑤ My parents _____ in the kitchen now.

[02-03] 다음 빈칸에 들어갈 말로 알맞게 짝지어진 것을 고르시오.

02

> · Kevin and I _____ cousins.
> · His name _____ Jimin.
> · I _____ fourteen years old.

① is – are – am   ② am – is – is

③ is – are – is   ④ are – is – am

⑤ are – am – are

03

> A: Is Dorothy in London?
> B: No, she _____. She _____ in Rome now.

① is – is   ② isn't – is

③ is – was   ④ isn't – isn't

⑤ isn't – wasn't

04 다음 우리말을 어법에 알맞게 영작한 것은?

> 그 나무 아래에는 벤치 한 개가 있었다.

① It is a bench under the tree.

② There is a bench under the tree.

③ There isn't a bench under the tree.

④ There was a bench under the tree.

⑤ That is a bench under the tree.

05 다음 질문에 대한 대답으로 알맞은 것은?

> Are you high school students?

① Yes, I am.

② Yes, I was.

③ Yes, you are.

④ No, we aren't.

⑤ No, we weren't.

06 다음 빈칸에 들어갈 be동사가 [보기]와 같은 것은?

> ┌ 보기 ┐
> Jim _____ in Paris three years ago.

① It _____ my turn now.

② These dogs _____ very smart.

③ The basketball players _____ tall.

④ There _____ red roses on the table.

⑤ I _____ so sad at the news yesterday.

07 다음 중 어법상 틀린 것을 모두 고르면?

① Were the movie moving?

② There are many festivals in fall.

③ Is there a bakery near here?

④ We weren't late for the meeting.

⑤ There aren't any ice in the bottle.

08 다음 밑줄 친 There[there]의 의미가 나머지와 다른 것은?

① Is there a zoo in Seoul?

② There was a cake in the box.

③ Are there many sheep in the farm?

④ They lived there from 2010.

⑤ There are five rooms in the house.

09 다음 대화 중 가장 자연스럽지 <u>않은</u> 것은?

① A: Was it sunny this morning?

B: Yes, it was.

② A: Is your father a police officer?

B: No, he isn't.

③ A: Are these oranges fresh?

B: Yes, they are.

④ A: Are those flowers for her?

B: Yes, they are.

⑤ A: Were you at home yesterday?

B: No, I weren't.

12

이 책들은 흥미롭지 않다. (interesting)

→ These books _____.

13 다음 빈칸에 알맞은 be동사를 쓰시오.

A: (1) _____ you at the library an hour ago?

B: No, I (2) _____ . I was at Luna's house.

(1) _____

(2) _____

10 다음 ①~⑤ 중 어법상 <u>틀린</u> 문장은?

①Paul and I are classmates. ②Paul is American. ③He were in Los Angeles last year. He came to Korea with his family a month ago. ④There are many beautiful beaches in Los Angeles. ⑤So, he is good at surfing.

14 다음 밑줄 친 문장에서 어법상 <u>틀린</u> 부분을 바르게 고쳐 쓰시오.

Look at the dog! <u>It's</u> legs are very short.

_____ → _____

15 다음 괄호 안의 말을 바르게 배열할 때 <u>세 번째</u> 오는 단어를 쓰시오.

[11-12] 다음 우리말과 의미가 같도록 괄호 안의 말을 이용하여 문장을 완성하시오.

11

벽에 몇 점의 그림들이 있었다. (some pictures)

→ _____ on the wall.

A: _____ ?

(in, your, the living room, are, parents)

B: Yes, they are.

_____

Practice 01 일반동사의 현재형

01-1 다음 동사의 3인칭 단수형을 쓰시오.

1 do _____ 2 pay _____
3 have _____ 4 eat _____
5 take _____ 6 fry _____
7 miss _____ 8 climb _____
9 make _____ 10 mix _____
11 study _____ 12 catch _____

01-2 다음 괄호 안의 말을 이용하여 현재형 문장을 완성하시오.

1 Mom _____ coffee every day. (drink)
2 My father _____ to work by subway. (go)
3 We _____ TV in the living room. (watch)
4 Some birds _____ in the sky. (fly)
5 My mom and dad _____ glasses. (wear)
6 Mike _____ computer games for an hour a day. (play)
7 I sometimes _____ with my little brother. (fight)
8 She _____ broken things in the yard. (fix)
9 He _____ the windows every morning. (open)
10 Jennifer _____ rope every evening. (jump)
11 My class _____ at 4 p.m. (finish)
12 He _____ novels on weekends. (read)

01-3 다음 괄호 안에서 알맞은 것을 고르시오.

1 My sister (take / takes) a shower every morning.
2 We (eat / eats) cereal and milk for breakfast.
3 (They / He) study in the library.
4 School (start / starts) at 9:00.
5 Victoria usually (have / has) lunch at noon.
6 (Jessy / Her friends) helps us every Sunday.
7 My grandfather (get / gets) up too early.
8 (The man / The men) work at the bank.

01-4 다음 문장의 밑줄 친 부분을 바르게 고쳐 쓰시오. (단, 현재형으로 쓸 것)

1 The kids <u>plays</u> soccer in the park. _____

2 Mr. Lee <u>haves</u> a daughter and two sons. _____

3 Julie <u>go</u> to church every Sunday. _____

4 Spring <u>come</u> after winter. _____

5 The baby <u>crys</u> every night. _____

6 Katie and her sister <u>swims</u> very well. _____

7 The bakery <u>open</u> at 7:30 in the morning. _____

8 The teachers <u>teaches</u> geography. _____

01-5 다음 우리말과 의미가 같도록 괄호 안의 말을 이용하여 문장을 완성하시오.

1 Anne은 홍콩에 산다. (live)

→ _____ in Hong Kong.

2 나의 아빠는 매일 아침 조깅을 하신다. (dad, jog)

→ _____ every morning.

3 지구는 태양의 주위를 돈다. (the earth, go around)

→ _____ the sun.

4 여름에는 비가 많이 온다. (it, rain)

→ _____ a lot in summer.

5 내 여동생은 비누로 손을 씻는다. (wash)

→ _____ her hands with soap.

6 David는 한국어를 잘한다. (speak)

→ _____ Korean well.

7 나의 고양이들은 텐트 안에서 잠을 잔다. (sleep)

→ _____ in a tent.

8 나의 부모님은 새 침대를 원하신다. (want)

→ _____ a new bed.

일반동사 현재형의 부정문과 의문문

02 -1 다음 문장을 부정문으로 바꿔 쓸 때, 빈칸에 알맞은 말을 쓰시오. (단, 줄임말로 쓸 것)

1 I have much time.

→ I _____ much time.

2 Martin likes baseball.

→ Martin _____ baseball.

3 We know your phone number.

→ We _____ your phone number.

4 Hannah loves comic books.

→ Hannah _____ comic books.

5 Katie and Sally do yoga every evening.

→ Katie and Sally _____ yoga every evening.

6 They listen to the teachers carefully.

→ They _____ to the teachers carefully.

7 It seems all right to me.

→ It _____ all right to me.

8 My brother writes a letter to Santa.

→ My brother _____ a letter to Santa.

02 -2 다음 문장을 의문문으로 바꿔 쓰고, 그에 대한 대답을 완성하시오.

1 Water boils at 100°C.

→ _____ Yes, _____.

2 David and his brother do their homework after dinner.

→ _____ No, _____.

3 The sun sets in the west.

→ _____ Yes, _____.

4 Her dad works at the bank.

→ _____ Yes, _____.

5 Mrs. Park has enough money.

→ _____ No, _____.

6 You buy clothes on the Internet.

→ _____ No, _____.

7 Sue and her sister walk to school.

→ _____ Yes, _____.

8 He washes the dishes after a meal.

→ _____ No, _____.

02 -3 다음 괄호 안에서 알맞은 것을 고르시오.

1 My brother (does not / not does) eat cheese.

2 (Do / Does) you and your friends like lemonade?

3 Nancy doesn't (remember / remembers) your name.

4 We (don't / doesn't) go to bed late.

5 (Do / Does) he drive a car?

6 Does your little brother (read / reads)?

7 (Do / Does) Nick and John practice skating?

8 The bear (don't / doesn't) run fast.

02 -4 다음 문장에서 어법상 **틀린** 부분을 찾아 바르게 고쳐 쓰시오. (단, 주어는 고치지 말 것)

1 I doesn't have any questions.　　　_____ → _____

2 Does it snows a lot in winter?　　　_____ → _____

3 Do your mom work at the post office?　　_____ → _____

4 My daughter don't do her work.　　　_____ → _____

5 Does you use chopsticks?　　　_____ → _____

6 Mina doesn't has many friends.　　　_____ → _____

7 My mother and I loves pop music.　　_____ → _____

8 Do your child take a shower every day?　_____ → _____

02 -5 다음 우리말과 의미가 같도록 괄호 안의 말을 이용하여 문장을 완성하시오.

1 내 아들들은 공포 영화를 좋아하지 않는다. (sons, like)

→ _____ horror movies.

2 나의 아빠는 아침을 거르지 않으신다. (dad, skip)

→ _____ breakfast.

3 달은 지구의 주위를 도나요? (the moon, go around)

→ _____ the earth?

4 너는 매일 운동을 하니? (exercise)

→ _____ every day?

5 나는 일기를 쓰지 않는다. (keep)

→ _____ a diary.

6 내 여동생은 안경을 쓰지 않는다. (sister, wear)

→ _____ glasses.

7 그는 매일 저녁 산책을 가니? (go for a walk)

→ _____ every evening?

Chapter Test

01 다음 중 동사의 원형과 3인칭 단수 현재형이 <u>잘못</u> 짝 지어진 것을 <u>모두</u> 고르면?

① cry – cryes

② do – does

③ teach – teaches

④ worry – worries

⑤ watch – watchs

02 다음 빈칸에 들어갈 말로 알맞은 것은?

> I _____ a sister, but I have a brother.

① have

② has

③ have not

④ don't have

⑤ doesn't have

03 다음 대화의 밑줄 친 ①~⑤ 중 어법상 <u>틀린</u> 것은?

> A: ①Does Kate ②enjoys winter sports?
> B: Yes, ③she ④does. She ⑤likes snowboarding.

04 다음 빈칸에 들어갈 수 <u>없는</u> 것끼리 알맞게 짝지어진 것은?

> _____ doesn't like Chinese food.

> ⓐ Rebecca   ⓑ My uncle
> ⓒ Eric and I   ⓓ The student
> ⓔ My grandparents

① ⓐ, ⓒ   ② ⓑ, ⓓ   ③ ⓒ, ⓓ

④ ⓒ, ⓔ   ⑤ ⓓ, ⓔ

05 다음 대화의 빈칸에 들어갈 말로 알맞은 것은?

> A: Do you and your sister have breakfast?
> B: _____ We eat oatmeal for breakfast.

① Yes, I do.   ② No, I don't.

③ Yes, we do.   ④ No, we don't.

⑤ Yes, they do.

06 다음 우리말을 어법에 알맞게 영작할 때 필요하지 <u>않</u> <u>은</u> 것은?

> 그 서점은 일요일에 열지 않는다.

① do   ② does   ③ not

④ open   ⑤ bookstore

07 다음 중 어법상 <u>틀린</u> 것은?

① I clean my room every day.

② Do we need our passports?

③ She doesn't use paper cups.

④ Does her parents live in London?

⑤ My brother and I go to bed early.

08 다음 중 밑줄 친 부분의 쓰임이 나머지와 <u>다른</u> 것은?

① <u>Do</u> you have a sister?

② <u>Does</u> he play the piano well?

③ I <u>do</u> not know about the man.

④ Jake <u>does</u> the dishes after dinner.

⑤ Lucy <u>does</u> not like fast food.

09 다음 빈칸에 들어갈 말로 알맞게 짝지어진 것은?

> • I _____ have many friends.
> • _____ Junsu learn Japanese?
> • Ryan always _____ an umbrella.

① don't – Do – carry
② doesn't – Does – carries
③ don't – Do – carrys
④ doesn't – Does – carrys
⑤ don't – Does – carries

10 다음 중 어법상 옳은 문장의 개수는?

> ⓐ Does Peter have a winter coat?
> ⓑ Emma like cheesecake.
> ⓒ They lives in this apartment.
> ⓓ Do you goes to the movies on often?
> ⓔ The shop closes at 5 p.m. on Mondays.

① 1개   ② 2개   ③ 3개   ④ 4개   ⑤ 5개

11 다음 대화의 빈칸에 들어갈 알맞은 말을 쓰시오.

> A: _____ the players practice swimming every day?
> B: No, they _____. They _____ three times a week.

12 다음 [보기]에서 빈칸에 들어갈 알맞은 말을 골라 쓰시오. (단, 필요하면 형태를 바꿀 것)

> ┌ 보기 ─────────────────
> fly   go   take   play

> I live with my family. We (1) _____ to the park on Sundays. My mom and I (2) _____ badminton, and my sister (3) _____ a kite. My dad (4) _____ pictures of us. We have a lot of fun!

(1) _____   (2) _____

(3) _____   (4) _____

13 다음은 민호와 유나가 좋아하는 것과 싫어하는 것을 나타낸 표이다. 표의 내용과 일치하도록 글을 완성하시오.

	Minho	Yuna
cats	☺	☺
chocolate	☹	☺
math	☹	☹

☺: like   ☹: not like

Minho and Yuna like cats. (1) Yuna _____ chocolate, but Minho _____ chocolate. (2) Minho and Yuna _____ math.

14 다음 우리말과 의미가 같도록 괄호 안의 말을 이용하여 영작하시오.

> A: 너의 삼촌은 서울에 사시니? (your uncle)
> B: No, he doesn't. He lives in Busan.

→ _____

15 다음 글의 주어 I를 Lily로 고쳐 문장을 다시 쓰시오.

> I come from Canada. I don't speak Korean well. But I have many Korean friends.

→ Lily _____.
She _____.
But she _____.

05 일반동사 2

Practice 01 **일반동사의 과거형**

01 -1 다음 동사의 과거형을 쓰시오.

1 do	_____	**2** run	_____
3 visit	_____	**4** drop	_____
5 give	_____	**6** try	_____
7 write	_____	**8** tie	_____
9 use	_____	**10** make	_____
11 study	_____	**12** get	_____

01 -2 다음 괄호 안의 말을 이용하여 과거형 문장을 완성하시오.

1 I _____ to the zoo last Sunday. (go)

2 He _____ a lot of pictures there. (take)

3 She _____ an email to me. (send)

4 We _____ a funny movie. (watch)

5 Jake _____ new jeans yesterday. (buy)

6 The scarf _____ soft and smooth. (feel)

7 The man _____ strange. (look)

8 Lots of people _____ the event. (join)

9 She _____ a gold medal. (win)

10 They _____ a very big pizza for dinner. (eat)

11 Jack _____ with his brother last night. (fight)

12 My son _____ the windows. (break)

01 -3 다음 괄호 안에서 알맞은 것을 고르시오.

1 My brother (liked / likeds) hamburgers.

2 Sue (visits / visited) her grandparents last week.

3 They (knowed / knew) the answers.

4 My mom (talked / talkeds) on the phone an hour ago.

5 I (played / plaied) soccer after school.

6 Our summer vacation (starts / started) yesterday.

7 She (meets / met) her friend 30 minutes ago.

8 The tears (runned / ran) down her cheeks.

01-4 다음 문장에서 어법상 <u>틀린</u> 부분을 찾아 바르게 고쳐 쓰시오.

1 I swimed yesterday.   _____ → _____

2 It raineds a lot last night.   _____ → _____

3 He wears sunglasses yesterday. _____ → _____

4 Marie teaches math last year.   _____ → _____

5 The player hitted a home run yesterday. _____ → _____

6 My father reads the newspaper last night. _____ → _____

7 Angela works for the company last year. _____ → _____

8 The school bus stoped suddenly. _____ → _____

01-5 다음 우리말과 의미가 같도록 괄호 안의 말을 이용하여 문장을 완성하시오.

1 우리 팀은 어제 경기에서 졌다. (team, lose)

→ _____ the game yesterday.

2 나의 강아지는 소파 위에서 잠을 잤다. (puppy, sleep)

→ _____ on the sofa.

3 그는 케이크를 5등분으로 잘랐다. (cut, the cake)

→ _____ into fifths.

4 나는 숙제로 그림을 그렸다. (draw, the picture)

→ _____ for homework.

5 그녀는 어제 나의 휴대전화를 사용했다. (use, my cell phone)

→ _____ yesterday.

6 나는 어젯밤에 퍼즐을 맞췄다. (put together)

→ _____ a puzzle last night.

7 그들은 지난주에 그 소식을 들었다. (hear, the news)

→ _____ last week.

8 그는 자신의 딸에게 인형을 주었다. (give)

→ _____ a doll to his daughter.

일반동사 과거형의 부정문과 의문문

02-1 다음 문장을 부정문으로 바꿔 쓸 때, 빈칸에 알맞은 말을 쓰시오. (단, 줄임말로 쓸 것)

1 The printer broke.

 → The printer _____.

2 I knew the song.

 → I _____ the song.

3 He answered my question.

 → He _____ my question.

4 They sat on the bench in the park.

 → They _____ on the bench in the park.

5 Marvin and Kelly did their homework.

 → Marvin and Kelly _____ their homework.

6 My dad drove a car yesterday.

 → My dad _____ a car yesterday.

7 I found my watch under the desk.

 → I _____ my watch under the desk.

8 They built a new house.

 → They _____ a new house.

02-2 다음 문장을 의문문으로 바꿔 쓰고, 그에 대한 대답을 완성하시오.

1 You read a comic book yesterday.

 → _____ Yes, _____.

2 Karl bought a cap for his brother.

 → _____ No, _____.

3 They searched for information on the Internet.

 → _____ No, _____.

4 Your dad made a cake for your mom.

 → _____ Yes, _____.

5 The cat jumped over the fence last night.

 → _____ Yes, _____.

6 Many birds sang this morning.

 → _____ No, _____.

7 They lived in Chicago last year.

 → _____ Yes, _____.

8 She took a rest last night.

 → _____ No, _____.

02 **-3** 다음 문장에서 어법상 <u>틀린</u> 부분을 찾아 바르게 고쳐 쓰시오.

1 He didn't said anything.   _____ → _____
2 Do you get up early yesterday morning?   _____ → _____
3 She didn't meets her twin sister.   _____ → _____
4 Did Martin rides his bike last week?   _____ → _____
5 I don't come here a year ago.   _____ → _____
6 Does Jerry go skiing last winter?   _____ → _____

02 **-4** 다음 우리말과 의미가 같도록 괄호 안의 말을 이용하여 문장을 완성하시오.

1 Cathy는 어제 학교에 가지 않았다. (go)
→ _____ to school yesterday.

2 나는 오늘 저녁에 나의 개를 산책시키지 않았다. (walk)
→ _____ my dog this evening.

3 너는 두 시간 전에 운동을 했니? (exercise)
→ _____ two hours ago?

4 나의 누나는 입학시험에 합격하지 못했다. (sister, pass)
→ _____ the entrance exam.

5 Daniel은 오늘 그 책을 빌렸니? (borrow)
→ _____ the book today?

6 너는 지난주에 수학 시험을 봤니? (take)
→ _____ a math test last week?

02 **-5** 다음 우리말과 의미가 같도록 괄호 안의 말을 바르게 배열하시오.

1 그 기차는 제시간에 도착했니? (the train, did, arrive, on time)
→ _____

2 그는 어제 세차를 하지 않았다. (did, his car, not, he, wash, yesterday)
→ _____

3 나의 아빠는 그 컴퓨터를 고치지 않으셨다. (my dad, fix, not, the computer, did)
→ _____

4 너는 어제 열쇠들을 잃어버렸니? (you, lose, the keys, did, yesterday)
→ _____

5 우리는 우리의 최선을 다하지 않았다. (we, do, not, our best, did)
→ _____

6 그녀는 네 도움이 필요하지 않았다. (help, she, did, your, not, need)
→ _____

Chapter Test

01 다음 중 동사의 현재형과 과거형이 같은 것을 <u>모두</u> 고르면?

① run   ② read

③ know   ④ put

⑤ hear

02 다음 중 동사의 과거형을 만드는 방법이 같은 것끼리 짝지어진 것은?

① hate – make

② study – clean

③ drop – chat

④ plan – listen

⑤ visit – drink

03 다음 빈칸에 들어갈 말로 알맞게 짝지어진 것은?

> I first _____ Lucas in elementary school. Soon, we _____ best friends.

① meet – become

② met – become

③ meet – became

④ met – became

⑤ met – becomed

04 다음 우리말을 어법에 알맞게 영작할 때 필요하지 <u>않</u>은 것은?

> Sophia는 그 편지를 쓰지 않았다.

① did   ② the letter

③ wrote   ④ not

⑤ write

05 다음 밑줄 친 부분을 바르게 고칠 때, 알맞지 <u>않은</u> 것은?

① I <u>make</u> cookies last night. (→ made)

② Paul <u>moves</u> house last month. (→ moved)

③ I <u>eat</u> fish this morning. (→ ate)

④ We <u>go</u> camping last weekend. (→ went)

⑤ He <u>buys</u> a coat yesterday. (→ buyed)

06 다음 대화의 빈칸에 들어갈 말로 알맞은 것은?

> A: Did Mia go to the library today?
> B: _____ She stayed at home all day.

① Yes, she does.

② Yes, she did.

③ No, she did.

④ No, she doesn't.

⑤ No, she didn't.

07 다음 빈칸에 들어갈 말로 알맞지 <u>않은</u> 것은?

> My sister _____ the book last week.

① read   ② reads

③ didn't read   ④ didn't buy

⑤ bought

08 다음 우리말을 어법에 알맞게 영작한 것은?

① 나는 어젯밤에 잠을 잘 못 잤다.

   → I didn't slept well last night.

② 그녀는 아까 손을 베었다.

   → She cut her hand a minute ago.

③ 너는 아침 식사를 했니?

   → Did you had breakfast?

④ 그 선생님은 나의 이름을 알지 못했다.

   → The teacher didn't knew my name.

⑤ 우리는 지난 주말에 동물원에 갔다.

   → We go to the zoo last weekend.

09 다음 대화의 빈칸에 들어갈 말로 알맞게 짝지어진 것은?

> A: Did it _____ a lot last night?
> B: Yes, it _____. Let's go out and make a snowman!

① snow – did
② snow – didn't
③ snows – did
④ snowed – did
⑤ snowed – didn't

10 다음 중 어법상 옳은 것으로 알맞게 짝지어진 것은?

> ⓐ Did you sang songs on the stage?
> ⓑ We saw a rainbow in the afternoon.
> ⓒ They didn't visited the museum.
> ⓓ I drank milk every morning.
> ⓔ He bought a ring for Julia.

① ⓐ, ⓒ   ② ⓐ, ⓓ
③ ⓑ, ⓓ   ④ ⓑ, ⓔ
⑤ ⓒ, ⓔ

[11-12] 다음 우리말과 의미가 같도록 괄호 안의 말을 이용하여 문장을 완성하시오.

11
> 그는 작년에 학교에서 영어를 가르쳤다. (teach)

→ _____ at school last year.

12
> 오늘 아침에 비가 그쳤다. (stop)

→ _____ this morning.

13 다음 우리말과 의미가 같도록 괄호 안의 말을 이용하여 영작하시오.

> A: 네가 이 사진들을 찍었니? (these photos)
> B: No, I didn't. My dad took them.

→ _____

14 다음 [보기]에서 빈칸에 들어갈 알맞은 말을 골라 문장을 완성하시오. (단, 중복 사용 불가능, 필요하면 형태를 바꿀 것)

> ┤ 보기 ├
> have   ride   eat   go   see

> Heejin and I _____ to the amusement park last month. There were a lot of people there. We _____ a roller coaster and _____ cotton candy. We _____ a dolphin show, too. We _____ so much fun!

15 다음 우리말과 의미가 같도록 문장을 바르게 고쳐 다시 쓰시오.

> Jack은 나에게 그의 비밀을 말해 주지 않았다.

Jack told his secret to me.

→ _____

Practice **01** 현재진행형

---

01 -1 다음 괄호 안의 말을 이용하여 현재진행형 문장을 완성하시오.

1 The cat _____ fish. (eat)

2 The students _____ the classroom. (clean)

3 My sister _____ in the park. (run)

4 It _____ heavily outside. (rain)

5 My mom and dad _____ chairs. (move)

6 Amy _____ Chinese. (learn)

7 Two little girls _____ hands. (hold)

01 -2 다음 문장을 부정문으로 바꿔 쓰시오. (단, 줄임말로 쓸 것)

1 My mom is reading a magazine.

→ _____

2 He is peeling apples. *peel: 껍질을 벗기다

→ _____

3 The kids are making noise.

→ _____

4 My dad is smiling at me.

→ _____

5 Two puppies are sitting on the sofa.

→ _____

01 -3 다음 문장을 의문문으로 바꿔 쓰고, 그에 대한 대답을 완성하시오.

1 She is writing a letter.

→ _____ No, _____ .

2 They are hiding under the bed.

→ _____ No, _____ .

3 Tommy is riding a bike.

→ _____ No, _____ .

4 The farmers are sleeping under the tree.

→ _____ Yes, _____ .

5 Minhee is looking out the window.

→ _____ Yes, _____ .

01-4 다음 괄호 안에서 알맞은 것을 고르시오.

1 Mike is (playing / plaing) the guitar.
2 I am (tieing / tying) my shoelaces.
3 It (is not / not is) snowing outside.
4 (Is / Does) Angela listening to music?
5 They (know / are knowing) my secret.
6 (Are / Do) you wearing a seat belt?
7 Harry is (waited / waiting) for the next train.

01-5 다음 문장의 밑줄 친 부분을 바르게 고쳐 쓰시오.

1 The man is fix the radio now. _____
2 Mr. James not is driving a car. _____
3 Are the students read the textbook? _____
4 Do you worrying about your future? _____
5 He is planing a big party for his wife. _____
6 They are touch their noses. _____
7 Dora drew a picture right now. _____

01-6 다음 우리말과 의미가 같도록 괄호 안의 말을 이용하여 문장을 완성하시오.

1 그는 바닥에 누워 있는 중이다. (lie)
   → _____ on the floor.
2 우리는 숙제를 하고 있지 않다. (do)
   → _____ our homework.
3 그들은 수학 문제를 풀고 있니? (solve)
   → _____ the math problem?
4 나의 아이는 수영장에서 수영을 하고 있지 않다. (kid, swim)
   → _____ in the pool.
5 Anne은 주스 한 잔을 마시고 있니? (drink)
   → _____ a glass of juice?
6 열쇠는 문 옆에 있는 끈에 매달려 있다. (key, hang)
   → _____ on a string by the door.
7 나는 신문을 읽고 있지 않다. (read)
   → _____ the newspaper.

02-1 다음 괄호 안의 말을 이용하여 미래형 문장을 완성하시오.

1 We _____ a party tonight. (will, have)
2 It _____ tomorrow. (be going to, rain)
3 He _____ you later. (will, call)
4 I _____ my puppy. (be going to, wash)
5 My parents _____ to Jeju Island. (be going to, travel)
6 She _____ coffee. (be going to, order)

02-2 다음 문장을 부정문으로 바꿔 쓸 때, 빈칸에 알맞은 말을 쓰시오. (단, 줄임말로 쓸 것)

1 Alvin will study music in Germany.
→ Alvin _____ music in Germany.
2 I am going to watch a movie with him.
→ I _____ a movie with him.
3 We will visit the art gallery this week.
→ We _____ the art gallery this week.
4 She is going to cook dinner for you.
→ She _____ dinner for you.
5 Tim and Jim are going to join us.
→ Tim and Jim _____ us.
6 We are going to plant a tree this afternoon.
→ We _____ a tree this afternoon.

02-3 다음 문장을 의문문으로 바꿔 쓰고, 그에 대한 대답을 완성하시오.

1 He will be a great pianist.
→ _____ Yes, _____.
2 Tommy is going to have lunch at 1:00.
→ _____ No, _____.
3 They will buy a gift for their mom.
→ _____ No, _____.
4 The young men are going to work here.
→ _____ Yes, _____.
5 Jessica is going to see a dentist.
→ _____ Yes, _____.
6 He will change his plans for summer vacation.
→ _____ No, _____.

02 -4 다음 괄호 안에서 알맞은 것을 고르시오.

1 It (wills / will) be windy and stormy.
2 (Are / Do) you going to buy a smartphone?
3 He (will water / will waters) the garden tomorrow.
4 She is going to (take / takes) a rest.
5 They (will not wash / will wash not) their hands.
6 They (are not going / not are going) to sell their house.
7 I (am going / am going to) write an email to Helen.

02 -5 다음 문장의 밑줄 친 부분을 바르게 고쳐 쓰시오.

1 He will dances on the stage tomorrow. _____
2 We are going not to eat out. _____
3 They help you with your homework tomorrow. _____
4 Are you going bake cookies? _____
5 She will drive not a car. _____
6 I am going to running on the track. _____
7 Eva will is 5 years old next year. _____

02 -6 다음 우리말과 의미가 같도록 괄호 안의 말을 이용하여 문장을 완성하시오.

1 내가 너에게 문자를 보낼게. (be going to, send)
→ _____ a text message to you.

2 그 상점은 다음 주에 문을 열 것이다. (store, will, open)
→ _____ next week.

3 그녀는 시험을 보지 않을 것이다. (be going to, take)
→ _____ a test.

4 너는 내일 바쁘니? (will, be)
→ _____ busy tomorrow?

5 그들은 거기에 버스를 타고 갈 거니? (be going to, go)
→ _____ there by bus?

6 Jake는 그 나무를 베지 않을 것이다. (will, cut)
→ _____ the tree.

7 나는 전화를 받지 않을 것이다. (be going to, answer)
→ _____ the phone.

01 다음 중 동사의 원형과 -ing형이 <u>잘못</u> 짝지어진 것을 <u>모두</u> 고르면?

① live – liveing   ② die – dying

③ play – playing   ④ sing – singing

⑤ swim – swiming

[02-03] 다음 빈칸에 들어갈 말로 알맞은 것을 고르시오.

02
> The designer _____ for a model now.

① look   ② looks

③ looking   ④ is looking

⑤ are looking

03
> We _____ eat Chinese food tomorrow.

① go to   ② going to

③ are going   ④ be going to

⑤ are going to

04 다음 빈칸에 들어갈 말로 알맞게 짝지어진 것은?

> · I _____ again next year.
> · I _____ a short hair cut.

① try – want

② will try – want

③ will try – am wanting

④ will try – wanting

⑤ try – am wanting

05 다음 우리말을 어법에 알맞게 영작한 것은?

① 나는 지금 공원에서 조깅을 하고 있다.

　　→ I jogging at the park now.

② 나는 그 소문을 믿지 않을 것이다.

　　→ I will not believe the rumor.

③ Emma는 내년에 해외여행을 갈 것이다.

　　→ Emma will travels abroad next year.

④ 그는 공항에 가는 중이다.

　　→ He is going to go to the airport.

⑤ 우리는 오늘 밤 그 호텔에 머물지 않을 것이다.

　　→ We are going not to stay in the hotel tonight.

06 다음 중 밑줄 친 부분의 쓰임이 나머지와 <u>다른</u> 것은?

① She <u>is going to</u> buy new scarves.

② It <u>is going to</u> be windy tomorrow.

③ We <u>are going to</u> the concert.

④ They <u>are going to</u> go camping.

⑤ Jack <u>is going to</u> be an adult next year.

07 다음 대화의 빈칸에 들어갈 말로 알맞은 것은?

> A: _____ a comic book?
> B: No, I'm not. I'm studying English.

① Do you read

② Do you reading

③ Are you reading

④ Are you read

⑤ Did you read

08 다음 중 어법상 <u>틀린</u> 것은?

① Emily will not stay up late.

② The theater will open next month.

③ I'm going to say sorry to her.

④ Is he going to join the bowling club?

⑤ I won't watching horror movies anymore.

09 다음 대화 중 가장 자연스럽지 <u>않은</u> 것은?

① A: Will you eat out tonight?
   B: No, I won't. I'm going to make pasta.
② A: Is your dad doing the laundry now?
   B: No, he isn't. He is taking a shower.
③ A: Are you going to buy fruit?
   B: Yes, I do. I need some apples.
④ A: Are Lucy and Kevin climbing the mountain?
   B: No, they aren't. They're studying.
⑤ A: The play will start soon. Hurry up!
   B: Yes, I'm coming.

10 다음 중 어법상 옳은 문장의 개수는?

ⓐ Are you going work tonight?
ⓑ I am having a friend in London.
ⓒ She won't changes her mind.
ⓓ My brother is flying a drone in the park.
ⓔ Ted are going to fix the roof this weekend.

① 1개   ② 2개   ③ 3개   ④ 4개   ⑤ 5개

11 다음 대화의 빈칸에 들어갈 알맞은 말을 쓰시오.

A: Will it snow on Christmas Day?
B: No, _____. It will be sunny.

→ _____

12 다음 우리말과 의미가 같도록 괄호 안의 말을 바르게 배열하시오.

우리는 너를 기다리지 않을 것이다.
(not, wait, to, we, going, are)

→ _____ for you.

13 다음 글에서 밑줄 친 부분을 바르게 고쳐 쓰시오.

Daniel and I ⓐare travel in Los Angeles now. We ⓑgoing to visit Disneyland tomorrow. We will go on the rides. And we will see a parade of characters. It'll be fun!

ⓐ → _____
ⓑ → _____

14 다음 우리말과 의미가 같도록 괄호 안의 말을 이용하여 문장을 완성하시오.

그들은 지금 영어로 말하고 있지 않다. (speak)

→ They _____ in English now.

15 다음 우리말과 의미가 같도록 [조건]에 맞게 영작하시오.

A: 너는 이 모자를 살 거니?
B: Yes, I am. I like the color.

┌ 조건 ┐
• be동사를 사용할 것
• buy와 this cap을 사용할 것
• 7단어로 쓸 것

→ _____

Practice **01** | **조동사 can, may**

01-1 다음 우리말과 의미가 같도록 can 또는 can't와 괄호 안의 말을 이용하여 문장을 완성하시오.

1 개구리는 물과 땅에서 살 수 있다. (live)

→ Frogs _____ in water and on land.

2 Richard는 수영을 잘하지 못한다. (swim)

→ Richard _____ well.

3 너는 젓가락을 사용할 수 있니? (use)

→ _____ you _____ chopsticks?

4 펭귄은 하늘을 날 수 없다. (fly)

→ Penguins _____ in the sky.

5 제게 소금 좀 건네주시겠어요? (pass)

→ _____ you _____ me the salt?

6 그는 이 상자를 혼자 옮길 수 없다. (move)

→ He _____ this box alone.

01-2 다음 우리말과 의미가 같도록 may와 괄호 안의 말을 이용하여 문장을 완성하시오.

1 너는 내 사전을 사용해도 된다. (use) → You _____ my dictionary.

2 그는 내 모자를 써도 된다. (wear) → He _____ my cap.

3 제가 창문을 열어도 될까요? (open) → _____ I _____ the window?

4 그녀가 여기에 머물러도 될까요? (stay) → _____ she _____ here?

5 우리는 회사에 늦을지도 모른다. (be) → We _____ late for work.

6 제가 메시지를 남겨도 될까요? (leave) → _____ I _____ a message?

01-3 다음 대화의 빈칸에 알맞은 말을 쓰시오.

1 A: Can you make spaghetti?

B: _____ I make it very well.

2 A: _____ borrow your pen?

B: Yes, you may. I have many pens.

3 A: May she eat this bread?

B: _____ It is not for her. It is for John.

4 A: Can I use your book?

B: _____ I'm using it now.

5 A: May I swim here?

B: _____ The water is deep.

01 -4 다음 괄호 안에서 알맞은 것을 고르시오.

1 He (cans / can) bake cookies.

2 You may (be / are) very busy next week.

3 She (cannot play / not can play) the cello.

4 My dad (mays / may) do volunteer work.

5 (May / Are) we visit you tomorrow?

6 Can your little sister (read / to read)?

7 Jessica can't (dance / dances) well.

8 Sam may (remember not / not remember) her.

01 -5 다음 문장의 밑줄 친 부분의 의미를 괄호 안에서 고르시오.

1 <u>May</u> I turn on the air conditioner?　(허가 / 추측)

2 <u>Can</u> he pass the test?　(가능 / 허가)

3 You <u>can</u> watch TV now.　(가능 / 허가)

4 My mom <u>may</u> be free.　(허가 / 추측)

5 You <u>cannot</u> go there by car.　(가능 / 허가)

6 He <u>may</u> sit in my seat.　(허가 / 추측)

7 It <u>may</u> not be good for your health.　(허가 / 추측)

8 You <u>may</u> not go outside now.　(허가 / 추측)

01 -6 다음 문장의 밑줄 친 부분을 바르게 고쳐 쓰시오.

1 Mrs. White can <u>makes</u> furniture.　_____

2 You may <u>to go</u> home early.　_____

3 <u>Cans he play</u> tennis?　_____

4 <u>May ask I</u> a question?　_____

5 Your cell phone <u>may is</u> on the bed.　_____

6 My dad <u>can eat not</u> spicy food.　_____

7 <u>Can have we</u> some more cookies?　_____

8 She <u>not may be</u> rich.　_____

Practice 02 조동사 must, have to

02-1 다음 빈칸에 must 또는 must not을 이용하여 문장을 완성하시오.

1 You are always late. You _____ be on time.
2 He is sick. He _____ take medicine.
3 The baby is sleeping. You _____ make any noise.
4 It is very cold and windy. You _____ go out.
5 I'm very hungry. I _____ eat something.
6 She left the house an hour ago. She _____ be at home.

02-2 다음 문장의 밑줄 친 부분을 have to를 이용하여 바꿔 쓰시오. (단, 필요하면 형태를 바꿀 것)

1 Victoria must wash her hands often.
→ Victoria _____ her hands often.
2 We must pick up the trash on the street.
→ We _____ the trash on the street.
3 I must cook dinner today.
→ I _____ dinner today.
4 She must study hard for the test.
→ She _____ hard for the test.
5 Jason must go to the dentist.
→ Jason _____ to the dentist.
6 You must wash your dad's car.
→ You _____ your dad's car.

02-3 다음 빈칸에 have to 또는 don't have to를 이용하여 문장을 완성하시오. (단, 필요하면 형태를 바꿀 것)

1 Tomorrow is Sunday. She _____ get up early.
2 Her foot hurts badly. She _____ go to the doctor.
3 We have enough cheese. We _____ buy any cheese.
4 My computer is broken. I _____ fix it.
5 We don't have much time. We _____ hurry.
6 Cindy looks slim. She _____ lose weight.

02 -4 다음 괄호 안에서 알맞은 것을 고르시오.

1 You must (clean / to clean) the bathroom.

2 He (musts / has to) buy new pants.

3 She (must / have) stay up late tonight.

4 He (don't has to / doesn't have to) call me.

5 Lisa (must / has) to arrive on time.

6 We (don't have to / doesn't have to) study math today.

02 -5 다음 우리말과 의미가 같도록 괄호 안의 말을 이용하여 문장을 완성하시오. (단, 필요하면 형태를 바꿀 것)

1 그는 선생님들께 공손해야 한다. (must, be polite)

→ _____ to teachers.

2 그녀는 오늘 그 일을 끝낼 필요가 없다. (have to, finish)

→ _____ the work today.

3 그들은 입구 앞에 주차해서는 안 된다. (must, park)

→ _____ in front of the entrance.

4 그녀는 안전 규칙을 따라야 한다. (have to, follow)

→ _____ the safety rule.

5 너는 너무 걱정할 필요가 없다. (have to, worry)

→ _____ too much.

6 우리는 미래를 위한 계획을 세워야 한다. (have to, make)

→ _____ plans for the future.

02 -6 다음 우리말과 의미가 같도록 괄호 안의 말을 바르게 배열하시오.

1 그는 커피를 너무 많이 마셔서는 안 된다. (must, he, drink, too much coffee, not)

→ _____

2 너는 우산을 가져갈 필요가 없다. (don't, you, take, your umbrella, have to)

→ _____

3 우리는 안전벨트를 매야 한다. (have to, wear, we, seat belts)

→ _____

4 그들이 그것을 일주일 이내에 배달해야 하나요? (have to, deliver, they, it, do, within a week)

→ _____

5 Amy는 그에게 이메일을 보내야 한다. (Amy, to him, send, must, an email)

→ _____

6 그녀는 도서관에 책을 몇 권 반납해야 한다. (she, return, some books, has to, to the library)

→ _____

Chapter Test

[01-02] 다음 빈칸에 들어갈 말로 알맞은 것을 고르시오.

01

> It's sunny and warm today. You _____ go on a picnic.

① must
② may
③ cannot
④ must not
⑤ don't have to

02

> Mary's eyes aren't very good. She _____ wear glasses.

① can't
② have to
③ must
④ must not
⑤ doesn't have to

[03-04] 다음 [보기]와 밑줄 친 부분의 쓰임이 같은 것을 고르시오.

03

┌ 보기 ┐
> Can I have some water?

① She <u>can</u> draw a picture.
② I <u>can</u> swim in the deep sea.
③ <u>Can</u> you play basketball well?
④ You <u>can</u> take a picture here.
⑤ The birds <u>can</u> fly so well.

04

┌ 보기 ┐
> He <u>may</u> be our teacher.

① <u>May</u> I try on the shoes?
② We <u>may</u> have snow today.
③ You <u>may</u> take a break now.
④ We <u>may</u> leave the classroom.
⑤ <u>May</u> I have your name?

05 다음 빈칸에 공통으로 들어갈 말로 알맞은 것은?

> · She _____ be in her room now.
> · He _____ finish his homework by 7.

① will
② may
③ have to
④ must
⑤ don't have to

06 다음 질문에 대한 대답으로 알맞은 것은?

> A: May I use your camera?
> B: _____

① Yes, I may.
② Yes, you may to.
③ No, I may not.
④ No, you may not.
⑤ No, you don't have to.

[07-08] 다음 밑줄 친 부분 중 어법상 틀린 것을 고르시오.

07
① <u>Can</u> I <u>visit</u> you this Sunday?
② He <u>have to</u> stay home.
③ We <u>must not walk</u> on the grass.
④ <u>May</u> I <u>park</u> the car here?
⑤ You <u>don't have to agree</u> with him.

08
① He <u>must carry</u> this desk.
② I <u>can't find</u> my cell phone.
③ <u>Can</u> Jenny <u>speaks</u> Korean?
④ <u>May</u> I <u>play</u> computer games now?
⑤ You <u>must not pick</u> the flowers.

09 다음 우리말을 어법에 알맞게 영작한 것은?

> 너는 시간을 낭비해서는 안 된다.

① You will not waste your time.
② You cannot waste your time.
③ You have to not waste your time.
④ You must not waste your time.
⑤ You don't have to waste your time.

10 다음 중 어법상 옳은 문장의 개수는?

> ⓐ Can I bring my cat?
> ⓑ The rumor may is true.
> ⓒ He don't has to move to Seoul.
> ⓓ The children must not play here.

① 없음　② 1개　③ 2개　④ 3개　⑤ 4개

11 다음 두 문장의 의미가 같도록 빈칸에 알맞은 말을 쓰시오.

> Amy must answer the question.
> = Amy _____ _____ answer the question.

12 다음 대화의 빈칸에 들어갈 알맞은 조동사를 쓰시오.

> A: _____ I go to school every day?
> B: No, you don't have to go to school on weekends.

13 다음 글에서 어법상 <u>틀린</u> 부분을 찾아 바르게 고쳐 쓰시오.

> We can't meet you on Friday. We has to work. We must finish the project by Friday.

_____ → _____

14 다음은 민수와 Judy가 할 수 있는 것과 할 수 없는 것을 나타낸 표이다. 표의 내용과 일치하도록 문장을 완성하시오.

	drive a car	make cookies	play tennis
Minsu	○	×	×
Judy	×	○	○

Minsu (1) _____.
But he can't make cookies. Judy can play tennis. But she (2) _____
_____.

15 다음 우리말과 의미가 같도록 [조건]에 맞게 영작하시오.

> ┤조건├
> • 조동사 have to를 사용할 것
> • listen to, words, carefully를 사용할 것
> • 9단어로 쓸 것

너는 그들의 말을 주의 깊게 들을 필요가 없다.

→ _____

Practice 01 형용사

01 -1 다음 문장에서 형용사를 <u>모두</u> 찾아 밑줄을 그으시오.

1 I am hungry and thirsty.
2 The parrots are green.
3 The artist is famous.
4 She has brown hair and blue eyes.
5 The subway is fast.
6 He wants something cold.
7 She is a kind person.
8 He is wearing a black jacket.

01 -2 다음 빈칸에 many와 much 중 알맞은 형용사를 골라 쓰시오.

1 The girl didn't have _____ money.
2 We have _____ mountains in our country.
3 There are _____ coins in my piggy bank.
4 My brother drinks too _____ soda.
5 You don't have _____ time.
6 Emma has _____ skirts.
7 There is too _____ rice in the pot.
8 My brother has _____ friends at school.

01 -3 다음 빈칸에 some과 any 중 알맞은 형용사를 골라 쓰시오.

1 Would you have _____ dessert?
2 There is _____ snow on the bench.
3 Do you have _____ questions?
4 Jack had _____ free tickets.
5 The players need _____ water.
6 Are there _____ tomatoes in the box?
7 Amy didn't have _____ sleep last night.
8 I bought _____ paint for the kitchen.

01 -4 다음 괄호 안에서 알맞은 것을 고르시오.

1 He has a (car new / new car).

2 This is (great a book / a great book).

3 I want (rare something / something rare). *rare: 희귀한, 진귀한

4 The chef needed (any / some) butter.

5 My uncle has (many / much) sheep.

6 Insu doesn't have (any / some) classes today.

7 Will there be (many / much) traffic?

01 -5 다음 문장의 밑줄 친 부분을 바르게 고쳐 쓰시오.

1 Watch out for the knife sharp.　　　　　　　_____

2 Would you like any bread?　　　　　　　　_____

3 There are much toys in the box.　　　　　　_____

4 We have many homework today.　　　　　　_____

5 Did he need some time?　　　　　　　　　_____

6 Tell me new something.　　　　　　　　　_____

7 The song sounds beautifully.　　　　　　　_____

01 -6 다음 우리말과 의미가 같도록 괄호 안의 말을 바르게 배열하시오.

1 그 학생들은 피곤해 보인다. (tired, look, the students)
　→ _____

2 이것은 오래된 절이다. (is, old, an, this, temple)
　→ _____

3 나는 꽃을 조금 샀다. (some, I, flowers, bought)
　→ _____

4 저렴한 것이 있나요? (have, you, do, anything, cheap)
　→ _____

5 우리는 어린이날에 특별한 무언가를 한다. (something, do, we, special, for Children's Day)
　→ _____

6 나는 서점에서 많은 학생들을 보았다. (saw, students, I, many, at the bookstore)
　→ _____

7 이 거리에는 병원이 한 군데도 없다. (there, hospital, any, on this street, isn't)
　→ _____

02-1 다음 형용사의 부사형을 쓰시오.

1	wise	_____	2 healthy	_____
3	strange	_____	4 warm	_____
5	quiet	_____	6 good	_____
7	real	_____	8 polite	_____
9	happy	_____	10 lucky	_____

02-2 다음 우리말과 의미가 같도록 [보기]에서 알맞은 말을 골라 문장을 완성하시오.

┌─ 보기 ┐
high   highly   hard   hardly   late   lately   near   nearly
└──────┘

1 • 그는 열심히 공부한다.   → He studies _____.
  • 그는 거의 공부하지 않는다.   → He _____ studies.

2 • 그 기차는 늦게 도착했다.   → The train arrived _____.
  • 나는 최근에 그를 보지 못했다.   → I haven't seen him _____.

3 • 비행기가 하늘 높이 날고 있다.   → A plane is flying _____ up in the sky.
  • Harry는 매우 비범한 소년이다.   → Harry is a _____ unusual boy.

4 • 그들은 런던 근처에 살고 있다.   → They live _____ London.
  • 여기까지 오는 데 거의 두 시간이 걸렸다. → It took _____ two hours to get here.

02-3 다음 괄호 안의 말을 이용하여 문장을 완성하시오.

1 I eat apple pie for dessert. (usually)
  → _____

2 My father is busy. (often)
  → _____

3 Ava is selfish. (never)
  → _____

4 They must get up at 6:00. (always)
  → _____

5 We see her there. (often)
  → _____

02-4 다음 괄호 안에서 알맞은 것을 고르시오.

1 The baby is smiling at me (bright / brightly).
2 The cheetah runs (very fast / fast very).
3 He (often tells / tells often) a lie.
4 Injun plays basketball (good / well).
5 (Sad / Sadly), the king died.
6 She closed the door (quiet / quietly).
7 I (never will / will never) give up.

02-5 다음 문장의 밑줄 친 부분을 바르게 고쳐 쓰시오.

1 The announcer speaks clear.   _____
2 It is raining very heavy.   _____
3 My father came home lately last night.   _____
4 My mom can make a cake very good.   _____
5 They make never mistakes.   _____
6 You always can quit the job.   _____
7 He threw the ball highly into the air.   _____

02-6 다음 우리말과 의미가 같도록 괄호 안의 말을 바르게 배열하시오.

1 나는 때때로 학교에 지각한다. (am, late, sometimes)
  → I _____ for school.
2 운이 좋게도, 나는 시험에 통과했다. (passed, luckily, I)
  → _____ the test.
3 그녀는 항상 아침에 우유를 조금 마신다. (drinks, always, milk, some)
  → She _____ in the morning.
4 선생님들은 보통 우리에게 친절하시다. (are, kind, usually, to, us)
  → The teachers _____.
5 나는 결코 너를 잊지 않을 것이다. (never, will, you, forget)
  → I _____.
6 이 경기는 나에게 아주 중요하다. (important, me, is, very, to)
  → This match _____.

Chapter Test

01 다음 중 두 단어의 관계가 나머지와 <u>다른</u> 것은?

① sad – sadly

② slow – slowly

③ lone – lonely

④ easy – easily

⑤ careful – carefully

02 다음 우리말과 의미가 같도록 빈칸에 들어갈 말로 알맞은 것은?

우리는 이 요리법을 위해 몇 개의 사과가 필요하다.

→ We need _____ apples for this recipe.

① any ② some

③ many ④ much

⑤ a lot of

[03-04] 다음 빈칸에 들어갈 말로 알맞지 <u>않은</u> 것을 고르시오.

03
They are _____ students.

① good ② kind

③ smart ④ well

⑤ diligent

04
We can't see _____ birds on the tree.

① any ② much

③ many ④ lots of

⑤ a lot of

[05-06] 다음 밑줄 친 부분 중 어법상 <u>틀린</u> 것을 고르시오.

05 ① He can <u>speak fastly</u>.

② The train <u>moved slowly</u>.

③ She is drinking <u>some coffee</u>.

④ We don't have <u>any problems</u>.

⑤ Mina and I studied <u>really hard</u>.

06 ① They <u>are always</u> noisy.

② He <u>writes sometimes</u> to me.

③ <u>Many people</u> like online shopping.

④ There's <u>nothing wrong</u> with the camera.

⑤ My brother doesn't have <u>much interest</u> in art.

07 다음 빈칸에 들어갈 말로 알맞게 짝지어진 것은?

· The bus came ten minutes _____.

· When did you see him _____?

① late – late ② late – lately

③ lately – late ④ lately – later

⑤ lately – lately

08 다음 중 밑줄 친 부분의 쓰임이 나머지와 <u>다른</u> 것은?

① We arrived <u>early</u> the next day.

② Why don't you go home <u>early</u>?

③ He went out <u>early</u> in the morning.

④ My family eats dinner <u>early</u>.

⑤ He is in his <u>early</u> twenties.

09 다음 중 어법상 틀린 것으로 알맞게 짝지어진 것은?

> ⓐ Water and oil don't mix easy.
> ⓑ The water bottle is nearly empty.
> ⓒ I want some information about the car.
> ⓓ He goes often to New York on business.

① ⓐ, ⓑ   ② ⓐ, ⓓ
③ ⓑ, ⓓ   ④ ⓐ, ⓒ, ⓓ
⑤ ⓑ, ⓒ, ⓓ

10 다음 중 어법상 옳은 문장의 개수는?

> ⓐ Suddenly, the lights went off.
> ⓑ Judy always is kind to everyone.
> ⓒ We planted much trees in the garden.
> ⓓ I don't have any schedule.

① 없음   ② 1개   ③ 2개   ④ 3개   ⑤ 4개

[11-12] 다음 우리말과 의미가 같도록 괄호 안의 말을 이용하여 문장을 완성하시오.

11
> 하늘에는 구름 한 점 없었다.
> (hardly, a cloud, in the sky)

→ There _____.

12
> 나는 수업 시간에 거의 잠들었다.
> (in class, nearly, fall asleep)

→ I _____.

13 다음 표를 보고, 알맞은 빈도부사를 이용하여 질문에 대한 대답을 완성하시오.

	Mon	Tue	Wed	Thu	Fri
Mina	🚌	🚌	🚌	🚌	🚌
Tom	🚇	🚌	🚇	🚇	🚇

Q: How do they go to school?

(1) Mina _____ by bus.

(2) Mina _____ by subway.

(3) Tom _____ by subway.

14 다음 글을 읽고, 어법상 틀린 부분을 찾아 바르게 고쳐 쓰시오.

> Sally works very hard. She came home late again today. Sometimes she goes to work on weekends. So, she hard meets her friends. She really misses them.

_____ → _____

15 다음 우리말과 의미가 같도록 [조건]에 맞게 문장을 완성하시오.

> ┌ 조건 ┐
> • 알맞은 수량 형용사를 사용할 것
> • too, stress, be good for를 사용할 것
> • 7단어로 쓸 것

너무 많은 스트레스는 네 건강에 좋지 않다.

→ _____
your health.

Practice **01** 장소를 나타내는 전치사

01 -1 다음 [보기]에서 그림에 알맞은 말을 골라 쓰시오.

┌─ 보기 ┐
| next to   in   under   on   in front of   behind   over |

1 _____ 2 _____ 3 _____ 4 _____

5 _____ 6 _____ 7 _____

01 -2 다음 우리말과 의미가 같도록 [보기]에서 알맞은 말을 골라 문장을 완성하시오.

┌─ 보기 ┐
| at   next to   in   under   on   in front of   behind |

1 Mike는 내 옆에 앉았다.   → Mike sat _____ me.
2 나는 책을 책상 위에 놓았다.   → I put the book _____ the desk.
3 모퉁이에 약국이 있다.   → There is a pharmacy _____ the corner.
4 Julie는 그녀의 방에 있다.   → Julie is _____ her room.
5 그 소년은 나무 뒤에 숨었다.   → The boy hid _____ the tree.
6 그는 선물을 침대 아래에 두었다.   → He put the present _____ the bed.
7 우리는 매표소 앞에서 만났다.   → We met _____ the box office.

01 -3 다음 괄호 안에서 알맞은 것을 고르시오.

1 The children made the sandcastle (at / in) the beach.
2 My aunt lives (at / in) Los Angeles.
3 He stood behind (I / me).
4 There is a great picture (on / at) the wall.
5 I gave a presentation (front / in front of) my class.
6 The restaurant is (next / next to) the theater.
7 There is a small bench (on / under) the street lamp.
8 Some birds are flying (over / on) the tree.

01 -4 다음 우리말과 의미가 같도록 괄호 안의 말을 이용하여 문장을 완성하시오.

1 나는 바닥에 컵을 떨어뜨렸다. (the floor)

→ I dropped the cup _____.

2 그는 버스 정류장에서 버스를 기다리고 있다. (the bus stop)

→ He is waiting for a bus _____.

3 우리는 교회 앞에서 노래를 했다. (the church)

→ We sang songs _____.

4 상어는 바다 아래 2,000피트에서 산다. (the sea)

→ The shark lives 2,000 feet _____.

5 그는 소파 뒤에서 열쇠를 발견했다. (the sofa)

→ He found the key _____.

6 나는 침대 옆에 알람 시계를 두었다. (the bed)

→ I put the alarm clock _____.

7 야구는 한국에서 인기 있는 스포츠다. (Korea)

→ Baseball is a popular sport _____.

01 -5 다음 괄호 안의 말을 바르게 배열하여 문장을 완성하시오.

1 (stood, the students, in front of)

→ The teacher _____.

2 (in, many vegetables, the box)

→ There are _____.

3 (under, slept, the tree)

→ The rabbit _____.

4 (next to, the one, the school)

→ My house is _____.

5 (footsteps, her, heard, behind)

→ She _____.

6 (get, the airport, at, a taxi)

→ You can _____.

7 (a mark, your shirt, on)

→ There is _____.

02-1 다음 빈칸에 in, at, on 중 알맞은 전치사를 골라 쓰시오.

1 I visited New York _____ 2020.

2 She did her homework until late _____ night.

3 The airplane will leave _____ 11:00.

4 He usually walks his dog _____ the evening.

5 My birthday is _____ May 6.

6 We always go skiing _____ winter.

7 I wrote a letter to my mom _____ Parents' Day.

02-2 다음 빈칸에 before와 after 중 알맞은 전치사를 골라 쓰시오.

1 Summer comes _____ spring.

2 She always prays _____ going to bed.

3 Tuesday comes _____ Wednesday.

4 We must arrive there _____ departure time. *departure time: 출발 시간

5 There's a rainbow _____ rain.

6 My mother washes the dishes _____ dinner.

7 It is dark _____ sunrise. *sunrise: 일출

02-3 다음 빈칸에 for와 during 중 알맞은 전치사를 골라 쓰시오.

1 My mom was sick _____ a week.

2 He studies science _____ two hours.

3 She watches TV _____ her free time.

4 I'll take a trip to China _____ the holiday season.

5 Catherine was very busy _____ the weekend.

6 Let's take a break _____ 10 minutes.

7 We must not talk _____ the exam.

02 -4 다음 괄호 안에서 알맞은 것을 고르시오.

1 The farmers work hard (for / during) summer.
2 I give some chocolate to my friends (in / on) Valentine's Day.
3 My mom drinks coffee (in / at) the morning.
4 She doesn't eat lunch (at / on) noon.
5 I looked for my cell phone (for / during) an hour.
6 These flowers bloom (on / in) spring.

02 -5 다음 [보기]에서 빈칸에 들어갈 알맞은 말을 골라 문장을 완성하시오.

| 보기 |
| on   in   for   at   during |

1 The evening news starts _____ 8:00.
2 He was very sleepy _____ the class.
3 Korea's Independence Day is _____ August 15.
4 I cleaned my house _____ two hours.
5 School starts _____ March.

02 -6 다음 우리말과 의미가 같도록 괄호 안의 말을 이용하여 문장을 완성하시오.

1 학교는 3시에 끝난다. (ends, 3 p.m.)
   → School _____.
2 나는 금요일에 친구들과 영화를 보러 갈 것이다. (go to the movies, Friday)
   → I'll _____ with my friends.
3 나의 아빠는 식사 전에 물을 드신다. (drinks water, meals)
   → My dad _____.
4 나는 2주 동안 그 그림을 그렸다. (drew, the picture, two weeks)
   → I _____.
5 나뭇잎은 가을에 색이 변한다. (change, color, autumn)
   → Leaves _____.
6 나의 엄마는 보통 점심 식사 후에 체육관에 가신다. (go to the gym, lunch)
   → My mom usually _____.

Chapter Test

[01-02] 다음 빈칸에 들어갈 말로 알맞은 것을 고르시오.

01

I go fishing with my father _____ Saturday.

① at　　　② in　　　③ on
④ for　　　⑤ next to

02

The car stopped _____ the traffic light.

① in　　　② at　　　③ on
④ to　　　⑤ over

03 다음 빈칸에 공통으로 들어갈 말로 알맞은 것은?

· We have a shop _____ London.
· The dance was popular _____ 2020.

① on　　　② at　　　③ in
④ for　　　⑤ under

[04-05] 다음 중 어법상 틀린 것을 고르시오.

04 ① I often feel tired at night.
② He first visited Canada in 2021.
③ She came back to Korea on May 5.
④ I waited for a bus during an hour.
⑤ Would you like some coffee after dinner?

05 ① I arrived at a port.
② He was hiding behind a door.
③ Turn right in the end of the street.
④ I met James in front of the station.
⑤ A subway runs under this street.

[06-07] 다음 빈칸에 들어갈 말로 알맞게 짝지어진 것을 고르시오.

06

He's always _____ home _____ the afternoon.

① at – on　　　② at – in
③ at – at　　　④ on – in
⑤ in – for

07

The man will arrive _____ Seoul _____ 2 o'clock.

① in – at　　　② in – on
③ at – on　　　④ at – in
⑤ on – at

08 다음 그림을 보고, 빈칸에 들어갈 말로 알맞은 것을 고르시오.

The soccer ball is _____ the chair.

① in　　　② on
③ under　　　④ next to
⑤ in front of

09 다음 우리말을 어법에 알맞게 영작한 것은?

> 나의 아버지는 저녁 식사 후에 TV를 보신다.

① My father watches TV in dinner.
② My father watches TV for dinner.
③ My father watches TV before dinner.
④ My father watches TV after dinner.
⑤ My father watches TV during dinner.

10 다음 중 어법상 옳은 문장의 개수는?

> ⓐ The dog is lying under the table.
> ⓑ Hang the picture on the wall.
> ⓒ The match starts in 6 o'clock.
> ⓓ My parents live at New Zealand now.

① 없음　② 1개　③ 2개　④ 3개　⑤ 4개

11 다음 괄호 안의 말을 이용하여 대화를 완성하시오.

> A: How long did you read the book?
> B: I read it ＿＿＿＿＿＿＿. (two hours)

12 다음 우리말과 의미가 같도록 알맞은 전치사와 괄호 안의 말을 이용하여 문장을 완성하시오.

> 공연 전에 우리 집에서 만나자.
> (meet, my house, the show)

→ Let's ＿＿＿＿＿＿＿＿＿＿＿＿.

13 다음 지도를 보고, 괄호 안의 말을 이용하여 대화를 완성하시오.

> A: Where is the hospital?
> B: Go straight and turn right.
>   It's ＿＿＿＿＿＿＿＿＿＿.
>   (the post office)

14 다음 글을 읽고, 어법상 틀린 부분을 찾아 바르게 고쳐 쓰시오.

> My family goes to the park every Sunday. My dad and I play badminton together. My mom sits in the bench under a tree and reads a book.

＿＿＿＿＿＿ → ＿＿＿＿＿＿

15 다음 우리말과 의미가 같도록 [조건]에 맞게 영작하시오.

> ┤조건├
> • 알맞은 전치사를 사용할 것
> • park, the store를 사용할 것
> • 7단어로 쓸 것

가게 앞에 주차하지 마시오.

→ ＿＿＿＿＿＿＿＿＿＿＿＿

Practice 01 의문사 who, what

01 -1 다음 [보기]에서 빈칸에 들어갈 알맞은 말을 골라 쓰시오. (단, 중복 사용 가능)

┌─ 보기 ┐
| what who whose |
└────────────────────┘

1 _____ invented the TV?
2 _____ is your favorite singer?
3 _____ house is that?
4 _____ did he miss?
5 _____ does he do for a living?
6 _____ car is this?
7 _____ helped you?
8 _____ did you do yesterday?
9 _____ sneakers are those?
10 _____ movie did you watch?

01 -2 다음 밑줄 친 부분을 묻는 의문문이 되도록 빈칸에 알맞은 의문사를 쓰시오.

1 I used Yujin's umbrella.
→ _____ umbrella did you use?

2 We invited Edward and Jamie.
→ _____ did you invite?

3 They are looking for Mark's cap.
→ _____ cap are they looking for?

4 My dad plays badminton every morning.
→ _____ does your dad play every morning?

5 My sister drew the picture.
→ _____ drew the picture?

6 I wear a small size.
→ _____ size do you wear?

7 He called his girlfriend yesterday.
→ _____ did he call yesterday?

01-3 다음 괄호 안에서 알맞은 것을 고르시오.

1 (What / Who) did you eat for lunch?
2 (Who / Whose) textbook is this?
3 (What / Whose) does the chef need?
4 (What / Who) lives in this house?
5 (What / Who) are your plans for the party?
6 (Who / What) did you send it to?
7 (Whose / What) size are these shoes?

01-4 다음 빈칸에 who, what, whose 중 알맞은 의문사를 골라 대화를 완성하시오.

1 A: _____ do frogs eat?　　　B: They eat insects.
2 A: _____ discovered America?　　　B: Christopher Columbus discovered it.
3 A: _____ dictionary is it?　　　B: It is my dictionary.
4 A: _____ day is it today?　　　B: It's Friday.
5 A: _____ can play the piano?　　　B: I can play it.
6 A: _____ is your role model?　　　B: My father is my role model.
7 A: _____ turn is it?　　　B: It's my turn.

01-5 다음 우리말과 의미가 같도록 괄호 안의 말을 이용하여 문장을 완성하시오.

1 화장실에는 누가 있니? (be)
→ _____ in the bathroom?

2 너의 전화번호는 뭐니? (be)
→ _____ your phone number?

3 너는 건강을 위해 어떤 운동을 하니? (exercise)
→ _____ you do for your health?

4 그것은 누구의 배낭이니? (backpack)
→ _____ is it?

5 누가 그 비밀을 말했니? (tell)
→ _____ the secret?

6 너는 어제 누구를 만났니? (meet)
→ _____ yesterday?

02-1 다음 우리말과 의미가 같도록 빈칸에 알맞은 의문사를 쓰시오.

1 너는 왜 나에게 화가 났니?　　　→ _____ are you angry at me?
2 너는 그 중국 음식점에 언제 갔니? → _____ did you go to the Chinese restaurant?
3 박쥐는 어디에 사니?　　　　　→ _____ do bats live?
4 너는 종이비행기를 어떻게 접니? → _____ do you fold a paper airplane?
5 너는 왜 그렇게 피곤해 보이니? → _____ do you look so tired?
6 그는 휴가 동안 어디에 머물 거니? → _____ will he stay during his vacation?

02-2 다음 밑줄 친 부분을 묻는 의문문이 되도록 빈칸에 알맞은 의문사를 쓰시오.

1 I took a science test <u>yesterday</u>.
→ _____ did you take a science test?

2 You can go there <u>by subway or taxi</u>.
→ _____ can I go there?

3 I became a teacher <u>because I like children</u>.
→ _____ did you become a teacher?

4 <u>About a thousand</u> people lost their homes.
→ _____ people lost their homes?

5 I hang my clothes <u>in the closet</u>.
→ _____ do you hang your clothes?

6 It leaves <u>at ten</u>.
→ _____ does the airplane leave?

02-3 다음 괄호 안에서 알맞은 것을 고르시오.

1 A: (Where / Why) did you skip dinner?　　　　　　B: Because I was not hungry.
2 A: (Where / When) does she work?　　　　　　　B: She works at a post office.
3 A: (When / Why) did they build the bridge?　　　B: They built it in 2000.
4 A: (How far / How old) is the bus stop from here? B: It's 50 meters from here.
5 A: (How much / How often) do you eat out?　　　B: I eat out twice a week.
6 A: (Where / Why) does he go every morning?　　B: He goes to the gym.

02-4 다음 우리말과 의미가 같도록 괄호 안의 말을 이용하여 문장을 완성하시오.

1 너의 엄마는 왜 케이크를 만드셨니? (mom, make)

→ _____ a cake?

2 너는 언제 그 책을 도서관에 반납할 거니? (will, return)

→ _____ the book to the library?

3 그는 어디서 그 멋진 휴대전화를 샀니? (buy)

→ _____ the nice cell phone?

4 너는 그것에 대해 어떻게 알게 되었니? (know)

→ _____ about that?

5 우리는 왜 하루에 8시간 정도 잠을 자야만 할까? (must, sleep)

→ _____ about eight hours a day?

6 그녀는 방과 후에 어디서 공부하니? (study)

→ _____ after school?

7 그들은 몇 시에 점심을 먹니? (time, have)

→ _____ lunch?

02-5 다음 우리말과 의미가 같도록 괄호 안의 말을 바르게 배열하시오.

1 너희들은 어제 어디서 만났니? (where, did, meet, you, yesterday)

→ _____

2 그 사고는 어떻게 일어났니? (the accident, did, how, happen)

→ _____

3 너는 왜 Tim을 놀렸니? (why, you, did, tease, Tim)

→ _____

4 너는 언제 행복하다고 느끼니? (do, feel, you, when, happy)

→ _____

5 개는 왜 꼬리를 흔들까? (wag, does, a dog, why, its tail)

→ _____

6 너는 보통 언제 기상하니? (usually, when, you, get up, do)

→ _____

7 너는 그 어려운 문제를 어떻게 풀었니? (you, did, the difficult problem, how, solve)

→ _____

Chapter Test

[01-02] 다음 대화의 빈칸에 들어갈 말로 알맞은 것을 고르시오.

01
> A: _____ is the supermarket?
> B: It is across the street.

① Who   ② What
③ When   ④ How
⑤ Where

02
> A: _____ do you do your homework?
> B: I do my homework after dinner.

① Who   ② What
③ When   ④ How
⑤ Where

[03-04] 다음 밑줄 친 부분 중 쓰임이 틀린 것을 고르시오.

03
① <u>Who</u> plays the piano?
② <u>What</u> is the weather here?
③ <u>Why</u> did he go to the hospital?
④ <u>Where</u> will she go this afternoon?
⑤ <u>When</u> did you move into this house?

04
① <u>How old</u> is the temple?
② <u>How tall</u> is the building?
③ <u>How many</u> guests were there?
④ <u>How often</u> do you meet her?
⑤ <u>How much</u> tickets do you want?

05 다음 빈칸에 들어갈 말이 나머지와 <u>다른</u> 것은?

① _____ is your camera?
② _____ is on the table?
③ _____ is he going now?
④ _____ did you buy the book?
⑤ _____ does she go on Sundays?

06 다음 빈칸에 공통으로 들어갈 말로 알맞은 것은?

> • _____ was the test today?
> • _____ far is the park from here?

① Who   ② How
③ What   ④ When
⑤ Where

07 다음 대화 중 가장 자연스럽지 <u>않은</u> 것은?

① A: How much is this speaker?
   B: It's 200 dollars.
② A: What are you doing now?
   B: I'm baking.
③ A: Whose fault is it?
   B: It's your fault.
④ A: When does Jane come here?
   B: She comes here by car.
⑤ A: Who wrote this letter?
   B: My brother wrote it.

08 다음 질문에 대한 대답으로 알맞은 것은?

> Why were you absent from school?

① I go to school every day.
② Because I had a bad cold.
③ I always go to school by bus.
④ I was absent from school yesterday.
⑤ It was 400 meters from here to the school.

09 다음 대답에 대한 질문으로 알맞은 것은?

> I play computer games twice a week.

① Why do you play computer games?
② When do you play computer games?
③ Where do you play computer games?
④ How often do you play computer games?
⑤ How long do you play computer games?

10 다음 우리말을 어법에 알맞게 영작한 것은?

> 우리가 얼마나 오래 기다려야 하나요?

① Why do we have to wait?
② When do we have to wait?
③ How do we have to wait?
④ How often do we have to wait?
⑤ How long do we have to wait?

11 다음 두 문장의 의미가 같도록 빈칸에 알맞은 말을 쓰시오.

> A: When does the bakery open?
> = _____ _____ does the bakery open?
> B: It opens at 8 o'clock.

12 다음 빈칸에 알맞은 말을 써서 대화를 완성하시오.

> A: (1) _____ is that man?
> B: He is my uncle, David.
> A: Oh, (2) _____ is his job?
> B: He is a computer engineer.

(1) _____

(2) _____

13 다음 그림을 보고, 괄호 안의 말을 바르게 배열하시오.

> A: I'm looking for a shirt.
> B: (color, like, what, you, do)?
> A: I want a black shirt.

→ _____

14 다음 대화에서 쓰임이 틀린 부분을 찾아 바르게 고쳐 쓰시오.

> A: How many pens do you have?
> B: I have five pens. I'll give you one.
> A: Thanks. When did you buy them?
> B: At the store next to the school.

_____ → _____

15 다음 우리말과 의미가 같도록 [조건]에 맞게 영작하시오.

> ┌ 조건 ┐
> • 「How+형용사/부사」를 사용할 것
> • water, drink, every day를 사용할 것
> • 8단어로 쓸 것

너는 매일 얼마나 많은 물을 마시니?

→ _____

Practice 01 접속사 and, but, or, so

01 -1 다음 우리말과 의미가 같도록 [보기]에서 알맞은 말을 골라 문장을 완성하시오. (단, 중복 사용 가능)

┌ 보기 ┐
and   or   so   but

1 우리는 소파에 앉아서 축구 경기를 시청했다.
→ We sat on the sofa _____ watched the soccer game.

2 Cathy는 똑똑하지만 이기적이다.
→ Cathy is smart _____ selfish.

3 나는 도서관이나 영어 학원에 가야 한다.
→ I must go to the library _____ English academy.

4 나는 아침을 걸러서 지금 매우 배가 고프다.
→ I skipped breakfast, _____ I'm very hungry now.

5 그는 일찍 일어났지만 학교에 지각했다.
→ He got up early, _____ he was late for school.

6 너는 개나 고양이 중 뭐가 더 좋니?
→ Do you prefer dogs _____ cats?

01 -2 다음 [보기]에서 알맞은 말을 골라 두 문장을 한 문장으로 연결하시오.

┌ 보기 ┐
and   or   so   but

1 She ate snacks every night. She gained weight. * gain weight: 체중이 늘다
→ She ate snacks every night, _____.

2 We went to the beach. We collected seashells.
→ We went to the beach, _____.

3 It is sunny now. It will rain soon.
→ It is sunny now, _____.

4 I bought a shirt. My sister bought blue jeans.
→ I bought a shirt, _____.

5 Do you go to school by bus? Do you go to school on foot?
→ Do you go to school by bus _____?

01 -3 다음 괄호 안에서 알맞은 것을 고르시오.

1 They need some food (and / so) money.
2 Jenny is kind, (so / but) she has many friends.
3 I want Korean food (but / or) Italian food for lunch.
4 He has math class on Monday, Tuesday, (and / so) Friday.
5 I did my homework, (and / but) my brother didn't.
6 Is the baby a boy (or / and) a girl?

01 -4 다음 우리말과 의미가 같도록 밑줄 친 부분을 바르게 고쳐 쓰시오.

1 그녀의 방은 작지만 예쁘다.
  → Her room is small <u>or</u> pretty. _____

2 너는 그것을 이메일이나 팩스로 보낼 수 있다.
  → You can send it by email <u>but</u> fax. _____

3 그 이야기는 사실일까, 혹은 거짓일까?
  → Is the story true <u>and</u> false? _____

4 너는 네 이름과 전화번호를 적어야 한다.
  → You must write down your name <u>so</u> your phone number. _____

5 나는 오늘 아침에 늦게 일어나서, 아침 식사를 하지 못했다.
  → I got up late this morning, <u>but</u> I didn't eat breakfast. _____

01 -5 다음 우리말과 의미가 같도록 알맞은 접속사와 괄호 안의 말을 이용하여 문장을 완성하시오.

1 너는 설거지를 하거나 거실을 청소해야 한다. (wash the dishes, clean the living room)
  → You must _____.

2 단 음식은 맛있지만, 너무 많은 설탕은 우리의 건강에 좋지 않다. (delicious, too much sugar, bad)
  → Sweets _____ for our health.

3 나는 어제 야근해서 오늘 피곤하다. (I, feel, tired)
  → I worked overtime yesterday, _____ today.

4 식탁 위에는 포크와 나이프 그리고 접시가 있다. (a fork, a knife, a plate)
  → There are _____ on the table.

5 그는 매우 재능이 있어서 다른 경쟁자들을 쉽게 이겼다. (he, beat, the other competitors)
  → He was so talented, _____ easily.

Practice **02** 접속사 when, because

02 -1 다음 우리말과 의미가 같도록 빈칸에 when과 because 중 알맞은 접속사를 골라 쓰시오.

1 그 문제는 어렵기 때문에 나는 그것을 풀 수가 없다.

→ I can't solve the problem _____ it is difficult.

2 그가 16살이었을 때 그는 서점에서 일했다.

→ He worked at a bookstore _____ he was sixteen years old.

3 나는 한가할 때 만화책을 읽는다.

→ _____ I have free time, I read comic books.

4 오늘은 파도가 거칠기 때문에 배들이 출항해서는 안 된다.

→ _____ the waves are rough today, the ships must not sail.

5 길을 건널 때는 길 양쪽을 잘 살펴라.

→ Look both ways carefully _____ you cross the street.

6 비가 오고 있었기 때문에 우리는 택시를 탔다.

→ We took a taxi _____ it was raining.

02 -2 다음 두 문장을 괄호 안의 말을 이용하여 한 문장으로 연결하시오.

1 Anne was very angry. Her sister drew on her report. (because)

→ Anne was very angry _____.

2 I was good at math. I was an elementary school student. (when)

→ I was good at math _____.

3 I arrived at the bus stop. Someone called my name. (when)

→ _____, someone called my name.

4 I don't have enough money. I can't buy the sneakers. (because)

→ _____, I can't buy the sneakers.

5 My dog barked loudly. I woke up. (when)

→ _____, I woke up.

6 She looks pale. She has a bad cold. (because of)

→ She looks pale _____.

02-3 다음 괄호 안에서 알맞은 것을 고르시오.

1 He is blind (when / because) he lost his sight from a fever.
2 She got hurt (when / because) the movie theater was too dark.
3 (When / Because) he scored, he was offside.
4 (Because / Because of) the concert, the neighbors couldn't sleep.
5 (Because / Because of) it costs too much, I will not buy it.
6 (When / Because) I visit London, I always carry an umbrella.

02-4 다음 우리말과 의미가 같도록 괄호 안의 말을 바르게 배열하시오.

1 우리가 그 소식을 들었을 때 우리는 충격을 받았다. (heard, the, we, when, news)
→ _____, we were shocked.

2 너무 더웠기 때문에 나는 에어컨을 틀었다. (too, was, because, it, hot)
→ _____, I turned on the air conditioner.

3 나는 충치가 두 개 있기 때문에 치과에 가야 한다. (I, because, decayed teeth, have, two)
→ _____, I must go to the dentist.

4 그는 화가 나면 음악을 듣는다. (angry, when, is, he)
→ _____, he listens to music.

5 태풍 때문에 비가 많이 내리고 있다. (the, because, typhoon, of)
→ It is raining heavily _____.

02-5 다음 우리말과 의미가 같도록 괄호 안의 말을 이용하여 문장을 완성하시오.

1 우리는 약을 복용할 때 주의해야 한다. (take, medicine)
→ We have to be careful _____.

2 그가 무례하기 때문에 우리는 그를 싫어한다. (rude)
→ We don't like him _____.

3 내가 그 사고를 보았을 때 나는 차를 운전해서 출근 중이었다. (see, the accident)
→ I was driving to work _____.

4 안 좋은 날씨 때문에 촬영이 지연되었다. (the bad weather)
→ Filming was delayed _____.

5 그 상자는 너무 무거워서 내가 옮길 수 없다. (the box, very heavy)
→ _____, I can't move it.

Chapter Test

[01-02] 다음 빈칸에 들어갈 말로 알맞은 것을 고르시오.

01

> My father gets up early _____ makes breakfast.

① or ② and
③ but ④ so
⑤ because

02

> I had a stomachache _____ I ate too much yesterday.

① so ② or
③ but ④ and
⑤ because

[03-04] 다음 밑줄 친 부분 중 쓰임이 틀린 것을 고르시오.

03
① He went to the store and bought a cap.
② We can order pizza by telephone or Internet.
③ She can sing well, so she can't dance.
④ I will play tennis or take a rest this weekend.
⑤ It got dark, so I went home.

04
① Mary and Bob are in the same class.
② I will be a lawyer when I grow up.
③ I'll tell her when she comes home.
④ He stayed up late because he had to study.
⑤ I was sleeping because you called me.

[05-06] 다음 빈칸에 공통으로 들어갈 말로 알맞은 것을 고르시오.

05

> • We need a table, two chairs, _____ a desk.
> • She had coffee _____ cake for dessert.

① or ② and
③ but ④ when
⑤ so

06

> • _____ does your school start?
> • My brother plays the guitar _____ he feels good.

① So[so] ② And[and]
③ But[but] ④ When[when]
⑤ Because[because]

07 다음 밑줄 친 부분 중 어법상 틀린 것은?

> I ①will go ②to bed ③when I ④will finish ⑤my work.

08 다음 중 빈칸에 들어갈 말이 나머지와 다른 것은?
① I ate some cake _____ I was hungry.
② I can't buy the bag _____ it's too expensive.
③ She wore a coat _____ it was very cold.
④ He must study hard _____ he has a test tomorrow.
⑤ The plane can't take off _____ heavy snow.

09 다음 빈칸에 들어갈 말로 알맞게 짝지어진 것은?

> · The wind is very strong, _____
> I won't go out tonight.
> · She looked happy _____ I met her.

① so – when   ② so – but

③ but – because   ④ but – when

⑤ because – when

10 다음 중 어법상 옳은 문장의 개수는?

> ⓐ She was crying when I saw her.
> ⓑ Did you put the wallet on the sofa or on the table?
> ⓒ He is short, but he plays basketball very well.
> ⓓ I was late again because the traffic jam.

① 없음   ② 1개   ③ 2개   ④ 3개   ⑤ 4개

[11-12] 다음 우리말과 의미가 같도록 알맞은 접속사와 괄호 안의 말을 이용하여 문장을 완성하시오.

11

> Sally는 돈이 좀 있어서 자전거를 샀다.
> (some money, buy, a bike)

→ Sally had _____.

12

> 준호는 감기에 걸리면 따뜻한 물을 마신다.
> (warm water, has, a cold)

→ Junho drinks _____.

13 다음 대화를 읽고, 빈칸에 알맞은 말을 쓰시오.

> Tom: Can I use your cell phone?
> Mina: I'm sorry, but you can't. It's broken.

→ Tom can't use Mina's cell phone
_____ _____ _____.

14 다음 글을 읽고, 어법상 틀린 부분을 찾아 바르게 고쳐 쓰시오.

> Yesterday, I came to Busan with my family. We took many pictures. When we went to the beach, I bought a present for you there. When I will see you tomorrow, I'll give it to you.

_____ → _____

15 다음 두 문장을 우리말과 의미가 같도록 [조건]에 맞게 한 문장으로 연결하시오.

> · Many people grow plants at home.
> · Many people keep pets at home.

┌ 조건 ┐
· 알맞은 접속사를 사용할 것
· 9단어로 쓸 것

많은 사람들이 집에서 식물을 기르거나 반려동물을 키운다.

→ _____

_____

명령문, 청유문, 감탄문

Practice 01 명령문, 청유문

01-1 다음 우리말과 의미가 같도록 [보기]에서 알맞은 말을 골라 문장을 완성하시오. (단, 중복 사용 가능)

┌ 보기 ┐
| save | be | turn | close |

1 창문을 닫아라.

→ _____ the window.

2 시간을 잘 지키자.

→ _____ on time.

3 TV를 켜자.

→ _____ on the TV.

4 돈을 절약해라.

→ _____ your money.

5 학급 친구들에게 친절하게 대해라.

→ _____ kind to your classmates.

6 컴퓨터를 꺼라.

→ _____ off your computer.

01-2 다음 문장을 부정문으로 바꿔 쓰시오.

1 Drink a lot of cola.

→ _____ a lot of cola.

2 Add more oil.

→ _____ more oil.

3 Let's report it to the police.

→ _____ it to the police.

4 Take pictures here.

→ _____ here.

5 Let's wash the car.

→ _____ the car.

6 Let's go there.

→ _____ there.

01 -3 다음 괄호 안에서 알맞은 것을 고르시오.

1 (Let / Let's) order pizza by phone.
2 Let's (not waste / waste not) our time.
3 (Do / Does) your best.
4 Let's (be / is) nice to our neighbors.
5 (Do / Be) quiet in the classroom.
6 (Not / Don't) put your clothes on the bed.

01 -4 다음 밑줄 친 부분을 바르게 고쳐 쓰시오.

1 Do be confident. _____
2 Don't wakes up your father. _____
3 Let sell those books. _____
4 Takes off your cap indoors. _____
5 Let's not talking about him. _____
6 Don't angry at him. _____

01 -5 다음 우리말과 의미가 같도록 괄호 안의 말을 이용하여 문장을 완성하시오.

1 버스를 타지 말자. (take)
→ _____ the bus.

2 같은 실수를 하지 마. (make)
→ _____ the same mistake.

3 이 책을 그에게 줘. (give)
→ _____ this book to him.

4 피부에 자외선 차단제를 바르자. (put)
→ _____ sunscreen on your skin.

5 네 꿈을 포기하지 마. (give up)
→ _____ your dream.

6 강아지들을 쓰다듬어 봐. (pat)
→ _____ the puppies.

Practice 02 감탄문

02-1 다음 빈칸에 What과 How 중 알맞은 것을 골라 쓰시오.

1 _____ an exciting game it is!
2 _____ brave the young man is!
3 _____ sweet peaches they are!
4 _____ comfortable the chair is!
5 _____ a sad book it is!
6 _____ smooth silk cloth this is!
7 _____ hard he tries!
8 _____ fast she types!
9 _____ a long river it is!
10 _____ big the box is!

02-2 다음 밑줄 친 부분을 강조하는 감탄문으로 바꿔 쓰시오.

1 They are very noisy kids.
   → _____ they are!

2 The model is very skinny.
   → _____ the model is!

3 It is a very beautiful rainbow.
   → _____ it is!

4 The turtle moves very slowly.
   → _____ the turtle moves!

5 It is very happy news.
   → _____ it is!

6 The street is very crowded.
   → _____ the street is!

7 It is a very lovely day.
   → _____ it is!

8 The white dress is very elegant.
   → _____ the white dress is!

◦ 🗐 Answers p.38

02 -3 다음 괄호 안에서 알맞은 것을 고르시오.

1 (How / What) busy you are!

2 (How / What) lazy my sister is!

3 (What / What an) expensive gifts they are!

4 (How / What) delicious this cake is!

5 (How / What a) nice shirt it is!

02 -4 다음 우리말과 의미가 같도록 괄호 안의 말을 이용하여 문장을 완성하시오.

1 너의 할아버지께서는 정말 건강하시구나! (healthy)

→ _____ your grandfather is!

2 너는 정말 재미있구나! (humorous)

→ _____ you are!

3 그것은 정말 유용한 도구이구나! (useful, tool)

→ _____ it is!

4 이것은 정말 딱딱한 빵이구나! (hard, bread)

→ _____ this is!

5 그녀는 정말 예의 바른 소녀이구나! (polite, girl)

→ _____ she is!

6 그 남자는 정말 잘 생겼구나! (handsome)

→ _____ the man is!

02 -5 다음 우리말과 의미가 같도록 괄호 안의 말을 바르게 배열하시오.

1 이 초콜릿은 정말 달콤하구나! (sweet, how, is, this chocolate)

→ _____

2 그것은 정말 큰 버섯이구나! (what, it, mushroom, a, is, big)

→ _____

3 그것은 정말 단정한 필체이구나! (is, neat, handwriting, what, it)

→ _____

4 파도가 정말 거세구나! (rough, are, the waves, how)

→ _____

5 그것들은 정말 멋진 그림들이구나! (nice, what, they, pictures, are)

→ _____

6 너의 배낭은 정말 무겁구나! (your backpack, how, is, heavy)

→ _____

Chapter Test

[01-02] 다음 우리말과 의미가 같도록 빈칸에 들어갈 말로 알맞은 것을 고르시오.

01

밤에 늦게까지 깨어 있지 마라.
→ _____ stay up late at night.

① Do   ② Not
③ Don't   ④ Let's
⑤ Let's not

02

캥거루는 정말 높이 뛰는구나!
→ _____ high the kangaroo jumps!

① It   ② What
③ Why   ④ How
⑤ That

[03-04] 다음 중 어법상 틀린 것을 고르시오.

03
① How big elephants they are!
② Let's go and exercise.
③ How delicious these apples are!
④ Come back home by 6 o'clock.
⑤ What deep snow it is!

04
① Don't be disappointed.
② Let's don't buy it.
③ Let's eat out tonight.
④ What a kind girl she is!
⑤ How brave the boy is!

05 다음 중 빈칸에 들어갈 말이 나머지와 다른 것은?

① _____ thin boys they are!
② _____ a nice car you have!
③ _____ hard he works!
④ _____ exciting sports these are!
⑤ _____ a wonderful day it is!

06 다음 빈칸에 공통으로 들어갈 말로 알맞은 것은?

· _____ does she go to work?
· _____ heavy the stone is!

① Who   ② How
③ What   ④ When
⑤ Where

07 다음 밑줄 친 부분 중 어법상 틀린 것은?

①No ②put ③too ④much sugar ⑤in my coffee.

08 다음 중 어법상 옳은 것은?

① Not eat between meals.
② Lets keep a diary in English.
③ Comes in and have some tea.
④ Don't forget the shopping list.
⑤ Let's talk not about her.

09 다음 문장을 감탄문으로 알맞게 바꿔 쓴 것은?

> It is a very interesting book.

① How interesting book is it!
② What interesting book it is!
③ How an interesting book it is!
④ What is it an interesting book!
⑤ What an interesting book it is!

10 다음 중 어법상 옳은 것으로 알맞게 짝지어진 것은?

> ⓐ Look at the pictures on the wall.
> ⓑ How wonderful is the party!
> ⓒ Don't use your cell phone in class.
> ⓓ What a dry desert these are!

① ⓐ, ⓑ   ② ⓐ, ⓒ
③ ⓑ, ⓓ   ④ ⓐ, ⓒ, ⓓ
⑤ ⓑ, ⓒ, ⓓ

11 다음 대화의 괄호 안의 말을 바르게 배열하시오.

> A: My sister cleans her room every morning.
> B: (she, diligent, how, is)!

→ _____

12 다음 우리말과 의미가 같도록 어법상 <u>틀린</u> 부분을 찾아 바르게 고쳐 쓰시오.

> 균형 잡힌 식사를 하자.
> → Let's to eat balanced meals.

_____ → _____

13 다음 그림을 보고, 빈칸에 알맞은 말을 쓰시오.

→ _____ _____ in the river.

14 다음 글을 읽고, 괄호 안의 말을 이용하여 빈칸에 알맞은 말을 쓰시오.

> You are in a car. Tony drives the car, but he isn't careful. He drives too fast. You say, "Tony, _____." (careful)

→ _____ _____

15 다음 글을 읽고, 빈칸에 들어갈 알맞은 말을 [조건]에 맞게 영작하시오.

> I found an old doll in my toy box yesterday. Her name is Mary. She was my best friend. She is still very pretty. Happily, I said, "_____"

| 조건 |
• what 감탄문을 사용할 것
• pretty, this를 사용할 것
• 6단어로 쓸 것

→ _____

MEMO

MEMO

GRAMMAR MASTER

Beginner

ANSWERS

Chapter 01 명사

Practice 01 셀 수 있는 명사
본문 13쪽

Grammar Check Up

A 1 An   2 a
   3 A   4 An
   5 a

B 1 thieves   2 benches
   3 men   4 fish
   5 toys   6 radios
   7 foxes   8 mice
   9 bushes   10 cities

C 1 women   2 deer
   3 puppies   4 classes
   5 tomatoes

D 1 dishes   2 peaches
   3 teeth   4 children
   5 pianos

Practice 02 셀 수 없는 명사
본문 15쪽

Grammar Check Up

A New York, luck, money, art, London, happiness

B 1 peace   2 Time
   3 America   4 tea

C 1 a slice of   2 three spoonfuls of
   3 two loaves of   4 Three bowls of

D 1 salts → salt
   2 an English → English
   3 pizzas → pizza

Writing Exercise
본문 16~17쪽

A 1 a hot dog   2 butter
   3 an apple   4 an onion
   5 milk   6 a fork

B 1 This city has lots of churches.
   2 Brush your teeth three times a day.
   3 Her family lives in Seattle.
   4 I always put two spoonfuls of sugar in my coffee.
   5 He puts a lot of photos on the wall.

C (1) Two children   (2) a cup of coffee
   (3) Two glasses of milk   (4) Three puppies

D (1) two pieces[slices] of pizza
   (2) a glass of coke

Actual Test
본문 18~22쪽

01 ①   02 ④   03 ⑤   04 ②   05 ⑤
06 ④   07 ⑤   08 ⑤   09 ④   10 ④
11 ②   12 ③   13 ③   14 wolfs → wolves
15 piece → pair   16 scissor → scissors   17 ⑤
18 ②   19 ④   20 ④   21 ③, ④   22 ③, ⑤
23 ②, ⑤   24 ②   25 ③
26 I need three bottles of water.
27 Tommy eats five pieces of cake.
28 Lots of mice live in the village.
29 ten pairs of shoes   30 two sheets[pieces] of paper
31 a loaf of bread   32 eyes, teeth, wings, legs
33 (1) ③, sheep and deer (2) ④, children
34 I have a sandwich, an egg, a mango, and an apple.
35 (1) a[one] bowl of chicken soup
    (2) wants two slices of pizza
    (3) wants three loaves of bread

01 명사의 첫소리가 자음이면 a를 쓰고 모음이면 an을 쓰므로, ①에는 a가 들어가고 나머지에는 모두 an이 들어간다.

02 ④는 셀 수 없는 명사이고, 나머지는 모두 셀 수 있는 명사이다

03 mouse의 복수형은 mice이다.

04 deer는 단수형과 복수형의 형태가 같다.

05 watch의 복수형은 watches이다.

06 salad는 셀 수 없는 명사이므로 복수형으로 쓸 수 없고, 셀 수 없는 명사의 수량을 나타낼 때는 단위 표현을 복수형으로 써야 한다.

07 orange는 첫소리가 모음인 명사로 an과 함께 쓰여야 하므로 빈칸에 알맞지 않다.

08 a pair of ~는 '~ 한 쌍, ~ 한 켤레' 등의 의미로 짝을 이루는 명사와 함께 쓰인다. 한 쌍을 이루는 명사는 항상 복수형으로 써야 하므로 glass는 glasses(안경)가 되어야 한다.

09 cheese는 셀 수 없는 명사이므로 복수형으로 쓸 수 없고, 단위 표현 slice를 복수형으로 써야 한다.

10 빈칸 앞에 수를 나타내는 three가 있으므로 빈칸에는 복수형이 들어가야 한다. child의 복수형은 children이다.

11 bottle과 함께 쓰일 수 있는 명사는 water, juice, milk 등의 액체류이다. water, juice, milk는 셀 수 없는 명사이므로 복수형으로 쓸 수 없다.

12 love는 추상적인 개념을 나타내는 명사로 셀 수 없으므로 복수형으로 쓸 수 없다.

13 셀 수 없는 명사의 수량을 나타낼 때는 단위 표현을 복수형으로 만든

다. 따라서 spoonful은 spoonfuls가 되어야 한다.

14 wolf는 -f로 끝나므로 f를 ves로 고쳐서 복수형을 만든다.

15 '~ 한 쌍, ~ 한 켤레'라는 의미로 한 쌍을 이루는 명사의 수를 나타내는 단위 표현은 a pair of이다. a piece of는 '~ 한 조각'이라는 의미이다.

16 '가위'는 한 쌍을 이루는 명사이므로 항상 복수형으로 쓴다.

17 butter는 셀 수 없는 명사이므로 복수형으로 쓸 수 없다.

18 sheep은 단수형과 복수형이 같으므로 sheeps는 sheep이 되어야 한다.

19 paper, pizza에 모두 사용될 수 있는 단위 표현은 a piece of이며, 앞에 three와 two가 있으므로 pieces가 들어가야 한다.

20 fish는 단수형과 복수형이 같으므로 빈칸에는 모두 fish가 들어가야 한다.

21 ③ sugar는 셀 수 없는 명사이므로 복수형으로 쓸 수 없다.
④ apple은 첫소리가 모음으로 시작하는 셀 수 있는 명사이므로 an, the, 소유격을 앞에 쓰거나 복수형으로 써야 한다.

22 ③ foot의 복수형은 feet이므로 feets는 feet가 되어야 한다.
⑤ juice는 셀 수 없는 명사이므로 앞에 A를 쓸 수 없다.

23 ① a winter → winter, winter는 셀 수 없는 명사이므로 앞에 a를 쓸 수 없다.
③ dishs → dishes, dish의 복수형은 dishes이다.
④ a milk → a glass of milk, '우유 한 잔'은 단위 표현과 함께 a glass of milk로 쓴다.

24 ⓐ a Vancouver → Vancouver, Vancouver는 고유명사로 셀 수 없는 명사이므로 앞에 a를 쓸 수 없다.
ⓒ a hour → an hour, hour는 자음인 'h'로 시작하지만 발음상 첫소리가 모음으로 시작하므로 앞에 an을 붙인다.
ⓓ a egg → an egg, egg는 발음상 첫소리가 모음으로 시작하므로 앞에 an을 붙인다.

25 ⓐ a boots → a pair of boots, '부츠'와 같이 한 쌍을 이루는 명사는 항상 복수형으로 쓰고 a pair of로 수를 나타낸다.
ⓓ china → China, 국가명을 나타내는 고유명사는 첫 글자를 대문자로 쓴다.

26 '물 세 병'은 three bottles of water로 쓴다.

27 '케이크 다섯 조각'은 five pieces of cake로 쓴다.

28 '많은 쥐들'은 주어진 lots of 뒤에 mouse의 복수형 mice를 써서 나타낸다.

29 '신발 열 켤레'는 ten pairs of shoes로 쓴다.

30 '종이 두 장'은 단위 표현 sheet나 piece를 사용하여 two sheets[pieces] of paper로 쓴다.

31 '빵 한 덩이'는 단위 표현 loaf를 사용하여 a loaf of bread로 쓴다.

32 eye의 복수형 eyes, tooth의 복수형 teeth, wing의 복수형 wings, leg의 복수형 legs를 써서 글을 완성한다.

33 (1) sheep과 deer는 단수형과 복수형의 형태가 같다.
(2) child의 복수형은 children이다.

34 sandwich와 mango는 첫소리가 자음으로 시작하므로 앞에 a를 붙이고, egg와 apple은 첫소리가 모음으로 시작하므로 앞에 an을

붙인다.

35 (1) soup는 단위 표현 a bowl of를 써서 수량을 나타내므로 '치킨 수프 한 그릇'은 a[one] bowl of chicken soup로 쓴다.
(2) pizza의 수량을 나타낼 때는 단위 표현 a slice of의 복수형을 써서 나타내므로 '피자 두 조각'은 two slices of pizza로 쓴다.
(3) bread의 수량을 나타낼 때는 단위 표현 a loaf of의 복수형을 써서 나타내므로 '빵 세 덩이'는 three loaves of bread로 쓴다.

Chapter 02 대명사

Practice 01 인칭대명사
본문 25쪽

Grammar Check Up

A 1 She 2 I
3 They 4 You

B 1 my 2 us
3 you 4 them
5 its 6 their
7 we 8 it

C 1 She 2 We
3 They 4 It

D 1 They 2 it
3 us 4 my
5 your 6 His
7 Their 8 her

Practice 02 this, that, it
본문 27쪽

Grammar Check Up

A 1 This 2 Those
3 That 4 These

B 1 That 2 Those
3 these 4 It

C 1 This 2 those
3 It 4 it

D 1 this → these 2 This → It
3 That → Those 4 These → This

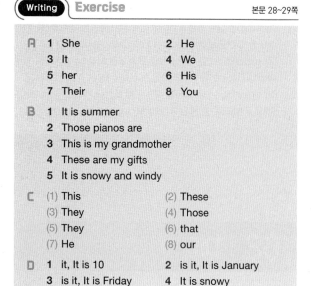

Writing **Exercise** 본문 28~29쪽

A 1 She 　　2 He
 3 It 　　4 We
 5 her 　　6 His
 7 Their 　　8 You

B 1 It is summer
 2 Those pianos are
 3 This is my grandmother
 4 These are my gifts
 5 It is snowy and windy

C (1) This 　　(2) These
 (3) They 　　(4) Those
 (5) They 　　(6) that
 (7) He 　　(8) our

D 1 it, It is 10 　　2 is it, It is January
 3 is it, It is Friday 　　4 It is snowy

Actual **Test** 본문 30~34쪽

01 ④	02 ④	03 ②	04 ②	05 ⑤
06 ③	07 ②	08 ③	09 ④	10 ②
11 ④	12 ④	13 ③	14 ④	15 ①
16 ①	17 ⑤	18 ②	19 ⑤	20 ④
21 ⑤	22 ③	23 ⑤	24 ③	25 ②, ④

26 This is my
27 I meet him
28 Those are their
29 Those twins
30 miss us
31 It is windy
32 ① We ② She ③ He ④ they
33 (1) this → these (2) that → it
34 (1) It is seven[7] (2) It is humid and hot (3) weather
35 (1) It is cloudy (2) It is nine[9] (3) They (4) their (5) It

01 '너와 나'는 '우리', 즉 1인칭 복수를 나타내는 대명사 we로 바꾼다.

02 멀리 있는 단수 명사를 가리키는 대명사는 that이다.

03 This나 your new bike를 대신해서 쓰일 수 있는 대명사는 it이다.

04 복수 명사인 books와 함께 쓰일 수 있는 지시형용사는 Those이다.

05 거리를 나타내는 문장의 주어로는 비인칭 주어 It이 쓰인다.

06 my sister는 3인칭 단수이고 여자이므로 대명사 She가 알맞다.

07 남자인 명사를 대신하면서 목적어 역할을 해야 하므로 him이 알맞다.

08 여자인 명사를 대신하면서 소유 관계를 나타내야 하므로 her가 알맞다.

09 사물인 명사를 대신하면서 소유 관계를 나타내야 하므로 its가 알맞다.

10 '이것들'은 This의 복수형인 These로 나타내야 하고, 동사도 is가 아닌 are가 되어야 한다.

11 the men은 3인칭 복수이므로 they로 대신할 수 있다.

12 빈칸은 동사 know의 목적어 자리이므로 목적격이 들어가야 한다. 따라서 주격인 we는 알맞지 않다.

13 빈칸이 명사 앞에 위치하므로 소유격이 들어가야 한다. 따라서 목적격인 him은 알맞지 않다.

14 첫 번째 빈칸은 butterfly를 대신하는 대명사 It을 써야 하고, 두 번째와 세 번째 빈칸은 날씨와 거리를 나타낼 때 사용하는 비인칭 주어 It을 써야 한다.

15 첫 번째 문장은 three sisters를 대신하므로 She를 3인칭 복수형 주격인 They로 고쳐야 하고, 두 번째 문장은 Jin's house가 단수이므로 These를 This로 고쳐야 한다.

16 첫 번째 빈칸은 단수 명사 앞에서 '이 ~'라는 의미로 쓰였으므로 this가 들어가야 알맞고, 두 번째 빈칸은 단수 명사 앞에서 '저 ~'라는 의미로 쓰였으므로 that이 들어가야 알맞다.

17 첫 번째 빈칸은 '이것들'이라는 의미로 This의 복수형 대명사 These가 들어가야 알맞고, 두 번째 빈칸은 '나의'라는 의미로 소유격인 my가 들어가야 알맞다.

18 동사 love의 목적어 자리이므로 I는 목적격 me가 되어야 한다.

19 뒤에 이어지는 명사가 단수이므로 These는 this가 되어야 한다.

20 날씨를 나타내므로 This는 비인칭 주어 It이 되어야 한다.

21 명사 앞에서 '너의'라는 소유의 의미를 나타내므로 you는 소유격인 your가 되어야 한다.

22 ③은 대명사로 쓰인 It으로 '그것'이라는 의미이고, 나머지는 모두 비인칭 주어로 쓰인 It이다.

23 '고양이'를 대신하면서 소유 관계를 나타내야 하므로 소유격 Its가 알맞다.

24 ⓐ That → Those, their crayons가 복수이므로 Those를 써야 한다.
 ⓑ she → her, '그녀의 목소리'라는 의미가 되어야 하므로 voice의 소유 관계를 나타내는 소유격 her를 써야 한다.
 ⓓ Its → It is[It's], '그것은 호화로운 호텔이다.'라는 문장에서 주어와 동사의 자리이므로 It is나 축약형 It's를 써야 한다. Its는 '그것의'라는 뜻의 소유격으로 뒤에 명사가 와야 한다.

25 ⓑ Him → His, '그의 이름'이라는 의미가 되어야 하므로 name의 소유 관계를 나타내는 소유격 His를 써야 한다.
 ⓓ it → them, 목적어 역할을 하면서 복수 명사 old games를 대신하므로 them을 써야 한다.

26 '이분', '이 사람'이라는 의미의 대명사 This를 주어로 쓰고, 동사와 소유격을 순서대로 배열한다.

27 「주어 + 동사 + 목적어」의 순서가 되도록 배열한다.

28 '저것들'이라는 의미의 Those를 주어로 쓰고, 동사와 소유격을 순서대로 배열한다.

29 '저 ~'라는 뜻으로 복수 명사 앞에 쓰이는 지시형용사는 those이다.

30 '우리를'은 we의 목적격 us로 쓴다.

31 날씨를 나타내는 문장에는 비인칭 주어 It을 쓴다.

32 ① 나를 포함한 여러 사람들이므로 1인칭 복수 대명사 We로 바꿔 쓸 수 있다.
 ② Ann은 3인칭 단수이고 여자이므로 대명사 She로 바꿔 쓸 수 있다.

③ James는 3인칭 단수이고 남자이므로 대명사 He로 바꿔 쓸 수 있다.

④ Ann and James는 3인칭 복수이므로 they로 바꿔 쓸 수 있다.

33 (1) this → these, pants는 복수이므로 지시형용사도 복수형인 these를 써야 한다.

(2) that → it, 명암을 나타내는 문장의 주어로는 비인칭 주어 It을 써야 한다.

34 (1) 시간을 나타내는 문장의 주어로 비인칭 주어 It을 쓰고 동사 is와 시간을 쓴다.

(2) 날씨를 나타내는 문장의 주어로 비인칭 주어 It을 쓰고 동사 is와 날씨를 나타내는 형용사 humid and hot을 쓴다.

(3) 날씨를 물을 때는 How is the weather ~?나 What is the weather like ~? 등으로 묻는다.

35 (1) 바로 다음 문장의 내용으로 보아 날씨를 나타내는 문장이 되어야 한다. 비인칭 주어 It을 쓰고 날씨가 흐리므로 동사 is와 형용사 cloudy를 쓴다.

(2) a.m.은 오전을 나타내므로 시간을 나타내는 문장이 되어야 한다. 비인칭 주어 It을 쓰고 벽시계가 9시를 가리키고 있으므로 동사 is와 nine[9]을 순서대로 쓴다.

(3) 3인칭 복수 명사 two dogs를 가리키는 주격으로 They를 쓴다.

(4) 내가 '그들의' 털을 빗질하는 것이므로 hair의 소유격 their를 써야 한다.

(5) 앞 문장의 their hair를 가리키는데 hair는 셀 수 없는 명사이므로 3인칭 단수 주격인 It을 써야 한다.

Chapter 03 be동사

Practice 01 be동사의 현재형
본문 37쪽

Grammar Check Up

A 1 am   2 is
   3 is   4 are
   5 are

B 1 It's   2 I'm
   3 He's   4 You're
   5 She's   6 We're
   7 They're

C 1 I   2 You
   3 She   4 We
   5 She   6 We

D 1 is   2 are
   3 is   4 are
   5 is

Practice 02 be동사의 부정문과 의문문
본문 39쪽

Grammar Check Up

A 1 He is not a violinist.
   2 I am not very busy.
   3 They are not in the library.
   4 It is not my house.

B 1 Is, is   2 Are, I am
   3 Is, isn't   4 Are, we aren't

C 1 are not, You're not, You aren't
   2 are not, We're not, We aren't
   3 is not, It's not, It isn't
   4 are not, They're not, They aren't
   5 is not, He's not, He isn't

D 1 Is he, he is
   2 Is it, it isn't
   3 Are they, they are
   4 Is the plate, it isn't
   5 Are we, you[we] aren't

Practice 03 be동사의 과거형
본문 41쪽

Grammar Check Up

A 1 was   2 was
   3 were   4 was
   5 were

B 1 weren't, were   2 weren't, were
   3 wasn't, was

C 1 Was he, he was
   2 Was it, it wasn't
   3 Were we, you[we] weren't
   4 Were the vegetables, they were
   5 Were you, I was[we were]

Practice 04 There is[are]
본문 43쪽

Grammar Check Up

A 1 are   2 is
   3 is   4 was
   5 were

B 1 There isn't   2 There was
   3 There aren't   4 There were

C 1 There wasn't, Was there
   2 There isn't, Is there
   3 There weren't, Were there

A 1 He is　　　　2 We aren't
3 There are　　　4 Is Jake, he isn't
5 Are there, there are

B 1 were, weren't alone, Were you alone
2 was, wasn't 6 years old, Was he 6 years old
3 were, weren't comfortable, Were the chairs comfortable
4 was, wasn't a lot of snow, Was there a lot of snow
5 were, weren't many stars, Were there many stars

C (1) was　　　　(2) is
(3) was　　　　(4) were
(5) was　　　　(6) am

D (1) Was there
(2) was, isn't, There is
(3) Were there
(4) there were, there aren't, There is
(5) Were there
(6) there weren't, there are

01 ④	02 ②	03 ③	04 ②	05 ①
06 ④	07 ③	08 ④	09 ③	10 ②
11 ④	12 ③	13 ⑤	14 ④	15 ④
16 ③	17 ③	18 ②	19 ④	20 ⑤
21 ⑤	22 ④	23 ①	24 ②	25 ④

26 It was　　　　27 Are there
28 is not[isn't]　　29 It was not[wasn't] rainy
30 was sick, is healthy
31 There is some money
32 (1) Were (2) weren't (3) There was
33 (1) was (2) it is snowy
　　(3) There were (4) there is
34 (1) Last month, she was with her family in her hometown.
　　(2) Now, she is alone in Korea.
35 (1) Was Jina, she was
　　(2) Was Nick, Yes, he was.
　　(3) Were Brian and Susan, No, they weren't.

01 '그녀와 나'는 복수이므로 are 또는 were가 알맞다.

02 am not은 줄여 쓸 수 없다.

03 주어가 We로 복수이고, now로 보아 현재의 일이므로 현재형 be동사 are로 고쳐야 알맞다.

04 be동사의 부정문은 be동사 뒤에 not을 쓰므로 was 뒤에 not이 들어가야 한다.

05 주어가 Its hair로 단수이므로 is가 알맞다.

06 주어가 The dictionaries로 복수이므로 are not이 알맞다.

07 주어가 They로 복수이고, yesterday로 보아 과거에 있었던 일이므로 과거형 be동사 were가 알맞다.

08 동사 are가 있으므로 빈칸에는 셀 수 있는 명사의 복수형이 들어가야 한다. ④ glass는 셀 수 있는 명사의 단수형이다.

09 동사 isn't가 있으므로 빈칸에는 셀 수 있는 명사의 단수형이나 셀 수 없는 명사가 들어가야 한다. ③ onions는 셀 수 있는 명사의 복수형이다.

10 '~이 있다'는 There is[are]로 나타낸다.

11 '~이 없다'는 There is[are] not ~으로 나타내는데, 주어가 복수이고 현재의 일이므로 aren't가 알맞다.

12 첫 번째 빈칸은 '~이 있다'는 There is[are] 의문문으로, 주어가 단수이므로 Is가 들어가야 알맞다. 두 번째 빈칸은 Lisa and Nancy는 복수이고, in 2021으로 과거를 나타내고 있으므로 were가 들어가야 알맞다.

13 Joan and Jim은 복수이므로 부정의 대답으로 No, they aren't.라고 답해야 한다.

14 ④를 제외한 나머지는 모두 주어가 복수이므로 are, were, aren't, weren't가 공통으로 들어갈 수 있지만, ④의 경우는 주어가 some water로 단수이므로 is, was, isn't, wasn't가 들어가야 한다.

15 It is의 줄임말은 It's이다. its는 it의 소유격이다.

16 질문의 주어가 the test로 단수 사물이고, 과거의 일이므로 Yes, it was. 또는 No, it wasn't.로 대답해야 한다.

17 Are there ~?에 대한 대답은 Yes, there are. 또는 No, there aren't.로 해야 한다.

18 '~이 있었다'는 There was[were]로 나타내는데, 주어가 단수이므로 There was를 써야 알맞다.

19 '이 접시들은'은 these plates로 표현하고, 이에 알맞은 be동사는 are인데, 부정문이므로 동사는 aren't가 되어야 한다.

20 첫 번째 빈칸은 주어가 you이므로 be동사 Are 또는 Were가 들어가야 알맞다. 두 번째 빈칸은 B가 No라고 부정의 대답을 하고 있고 주어가 we이므로 aren't 또는 weren't가 들어가야 한다.

21 ①~④는 There is[are] 구문의 there로 아무런 뜻이 없지만, ⑤의 there는 '저기에'라는 의미를 가진 부사로 쓰였다.

22 last year라는 과거를 나타내는 표현이 있으므로 Is를 과거형인 Was로 고쳐야 한다.

23 주어 Your brother는 3인칭 단수이므로 are를 is로 고쳐야 한다.

24 ⓐ is → are, 주어 a girl and a cat이 복수이므로 be동사는 are를 써야 한다.
ⓒ Is → Was, at that time은 '그때'라는 뜻으로 과거를 나타내므로 be동사는 과거형 Was를 써야 한다.
ⓓ Was → Were, 주어 Cindy and you가 복수이고 last night가 과거를 나타내므로 be동사는 과거형 Were를 써야 한다.

25 '태어났다'라는 의미는 「be동사 + born」의 형태로 나타내며 항상 과거형으로 쓰고, 주어가 복수이므로 Was를 Were로 고쳐야 한다.

26 last Sunday(지난주 일요일)라는 말로 보아 과거의 일이므로 동사를 was로 고쳐야 한다.

27 fish 앞에 many가 있는 것으로 보아 fish는 복수임을 알 수 있으므로 동사를 Are로 고쳐야 한다. fish는 단수형과 복수형의 형태가 같다.

28 Your sister는 3인칭 단수이므로 be동사 is를 써서 is not[isn't]으로 고쳐야 한다.

29 날씨를 표현할 때는 비인칭 주어 It을 쓴다. '어제'의 상태이므로 과거형으로 쓰고, 부정문이므로 동사는 was not[wasn't]이 알맞다.

30 '나의 아빠', 즉 My dad는 3인칭 단수이므로 동사는 과거일 때는 was, 현재일 때는 is를 쓴다.

31 '~이 있다'는 There is[are] 구문으로 나타내는데, some money는 셀 수 없는 명사이므로 be동사로 is를 쓴다.

32 (1) 주어가 복수이고, 과거의 일이므로 Were가 알맞다.
(2) Were there ~?에 대한 대답은 Yes, there were. 또는 No, there weren't.로 하는데 부정의 대답이므로 weren't가 알맞다.
(3) 주어가 단수이고, 과거의 일이므로 There was가 알맞다.

33 (1) 과거의 일이므로 be동사는 was를 쓴다.
(2) 날씨를 나타내는 비인칭 주어 It을 쓰고, 현재의 일이므로 be동사는 is를 쓴다.
(3) 주어가 복수이고 과거의 일을 나타내므로 be동사는 were를 써서 There were로 쓴다.
(4) 주어가 단수이고 현재의 일을 나타내므로 be동사는 is를 써서 there is로 쓴다.

34 (1) Last month라는 과거를 나타내는 표현이 있으므로 is를 was로 고쳐야 한다.
(2) Now라는 현재를 나타내는 표현이 있으므로 was를 is로 고쳐야 한다.

35 (1) be동사의 과거형 의문문은 be동사를 주어 앞에 써서 Was Jina ~?라고 물어야 하며, Yes의 긍정의 대답이므로 she was라고 이어 답하는 것이 알맞다.
(2) be동사의 과거형 의문문은 be동사를 주어 앞에 써서 Was Nick ~?이라고 물어야 하며, 긍정의 대답이 와야 하므로 Yes, he was.라고 답하는 것이 알맞다.
(3) be동사의 과거형 의문문은 be동사를 주어 앞에 써서 Were Brian and Susan ~?이라고 물어야 하고, 부정의 대답이 와야 하므로 No, they weren't.라고 답하는 것이 알맞다.

Chapter 04 일반동사1

Practice 01 일반동사의 현재형
본문 53쪽

Grammar Check Up

A
1	goes	2	carries
3	has	4	washes
5	keeps	6	buys
7	mixes	8	crosses

B
1	cleans	2	teach
3	dries	4	plays
5	smile		

C
1	rides	2	studies
3	read	4	freezes
5	finishes		

D
1	cries → cry	2	has → have
3	feel → feels	4	buies → buys
5	want → wants		

Practice 02 일반동사 현재형의 부정문과 의문문
본문 55쪽

Grammar Check Up

A
1	doesn't	2	Do
3	brush	4	get

B
1	don't play, play	2	doesn't eat, eats
3	doesn't do, does		

C
1	Does, try, does	2	Do, help, don't
3	Does, do, doesn't	4	Do, have, do

Writing Exercise
본문 56~57쪽

A
1	goes	2	learns
3	has	4	doesn't like
5	doesn't go		

B
1 doesn't listen, Does David listen, he does
2 don't clean up, Do the children clean up, they don't
3 doesn't bark, Does the dog bark, it doesn't
4 doesn't wear, Does your brother wear, he does

C
(1)	like	(2)	have
(3)	lives	(4)	has
(5)	eats	(6)	drinks
(7)	jumps	(8)	looks
(9)	love		

D 1 Do you like, I do, watch
   2 Does he live, he doesn't, lives
   3 Does Amy teach, she doesn't, teaches
   4 Do they work, they do, work

Actual Test

본문 58~62쪽

01 ②	02 ②	03 ④	04 ①	05 ③
06 ⑤	07 ③	08 ②	09 ④	10 ①, ④
11 ④	12 ④	13 ④	14 ⑤	15 ①
16 ②	17 ②	18 ②	19 ④	20 ③
21 ④	22 ③	23 ⑤	24 ④	25 ④

26 Does she know   27 We don't learn

28 Do you use   29 I do not[don't] have

30 Does Julie brush   31 Jake does not[doesn't] eat

32 (1) Do you clean, do
   (2) Do you wash, don't, washes the dishes
   (3) Does your brother walk, he does

33 (1) don't → doesn't (2) eats → eat (3) Do → Does

34 (1) gets up (2) reads (3) practices (4) watches
   (5) studies

35 (1) do volunteer work (2) wash the blankets
   (3) repairs

01 -x로 끝나는 동사의 3인칭 단수형은 -es를 붙이므로 fix의 3인칭 단수 현재형은 fixes이다.

02 We는 복수이므로 동사를 쓸 때 원형 그대로 써야 한다.

03 「자음 + y」로 끝나는 동사의 3인칭 단수형은 y를 i로 바꾸고 -es를 붙이므로 fly의 3인칭 단수형은 flies이다.

04 주어가 These books로 복수이므로 동사는 원형을 그대로 쓴다.

05 주어가 your father로 3인칭 단수이고 동사원형 eat이 쓰였으므로 일반동사 현재형의 의문문인 「Does + 주어 + 동사원형 ~?」의 형태가 되어야 한다.

06 일반동사 현재형의 의문문은 「Do[Does] + 주어 + 동사원형 ~?」으로 나타내는데, ⑤는 주어가 your parents로 복수이므로 Do가 들어가야 하고, 나머지는 모두 주어가 3인칭 단수이므로 Does가 들어가야 한다.

07 일반동사 현재형의 부정문은 「주어 + do[does] not + 동사원형 ~.」의 형태이므로 does 뒤에 not이 들어가야 알맞다.

08 주어가 I이므로 동사는 원형을 그대로 써서 take로 고쳐야 한다.

09 일반동사 현재형의 의문문은 「Do[Does] + 주어 + 동사원형 ~?」의 형태이므로 swim으로 고쳐야 한다.

10 ② don't → doesn't, 주어가 The horse로 3인칭 단수이므로 일반동사 현재형의 부정문은 「주어 + does not[doesn't] + 동사원형 ~.」으로 써야 알맞다.
   ③ know → knows, 주어가 Minhee로 3인칭 단수이므로 동사는 3인칭 단수형 knows로 써야 알맞다.
   ⑤ doesn't → don't, 주어가 The workers로 복수이므로 일반

동사 현재형의 부정문 「주어 + do not[don't] + 동사원형 ~.」으로 써야 알맞다.

11 주어가 The animals로 복수이므로 동사는 원형인 move로 고쳐야 한다.

12 주어가 3인칭 단수인 일반동사 현재형의 의문문은 「Does + 주어 + 동사원형 ~?」의 형태로 쓰므로 Does she have a brother?로 배열해야 알맞다. 따라서 세 번째 오는 단어는 have이다.

13 주어가 3인칭 단수이므로 일반동사 현재형의 의문문은 「Does + 주어 + 동사원형 ~?」으로 써야 한다.

14 주어가 3인칭 단수인 일반동사 현재형의 의문문 「Does + 주어 + 동사원형 ~?」에 대한 긍정의 대답은 「Yes, 주어 + does.」로, 부정의 대답은 「No, 주어 + doesn't.」로 한다.

15 첫 번째 빈칸은 주어가 you이므로 일반동사 현재형의 의문문은 「Do you + 동사원형 ~?」의 형태가 되어야 한다. 두 번째 빈칸은 이에 대한 긍정의 대답으로 Yes, I do.가 되어야 한다.

16 첫 번째 빈칸은 주어가 3인칭 단수이므로 일반동사 현재형의 의문문은 「Does + 주어 + 동사원형 ~?」의 형태가 되어야 한다. 두 번째 빈칸은 이에 대한 부정의 대답으로 「No, 주어 + doesn't.」가 되어야 한다.

17 첫 번째 빈칸은 do exercise(운동하다)에 해당하는 일반동사로 쓰인 do가 들어가야 하는데, 주어가 I이므로 원형 그대로 쓴다. 두 번째 빈칸은 주어가 They로 복수인 일반동사 현재형의 부정문 「주어 + do not[don't] + 동사원형 ~.」의 형태가 되어야 하므로 조동사 do가 들어가야 한다. 세 번째 빈칸은 주어가 the kids로 복수인 일반동사 현재형의 의문문 「Do + 주어 + 동사원형 ~?」의 형태가 되어야 하므로 조동사 Do가 들어가야 한다.

18 주어가 We로 복수이므로 일반동사 현재형의 부정문은 「주어 + do not[don't] + 동사원형 ~.」으로 써야 한다.

19 주어가 your father로 3인칭 단수이므로 일반동사 현재형의 의문문은 「Does + 주어 + 동사원형 ~?」으로 써야 한다.

20 주어가 he로 3인칭 단수인 일반동사 현재형의 의문문은 「Does + he + 동사원형 ~?」으로 써야 하므로 has를 have로 고쳐야 한다.

21 주어가 복수인 일반동사 현재형의 부정문은 「주어 + don't + 동사원형 ~.」으로 써야 하므로 likes를 like로 고쳐야 한다.

22 ③은 '~을 하다'라는 의미로 쓰인 일반동사 does이고, 나머지는 모두 의문문 또는 부정문을 만드는 데 사용된 조동사 do[does]이다.

23 주어가 your mom으로 3인칭 단수인 일반동사 현재형의 의문문에 대한 부정의 대답은 No, she doesn't.로 해야 한다.

24 주어가 3인칭 단수인 일반동사 현재형의 의문문은 「Does + 주어 + 동사원형 ~?」으로 써야 하므로 Do를 Does로 써야 한다.

25 (A) 주어가 3인칭 단수이므로 일반동사 sound의 현재형은 sounds가 알맞다.
   (B) 일반동사의 부정문은 don't 뒤에 동사원형이 와야 하므로 listen이 알맞다.
   (C) 주어가 3인칭 단수인 일반동사 현재형의 의문문은 「Does + 주어 + 동사원형 ~?」으로 써야 하므로 동사원형 begin이 알맞다.

26 주어가 she로 3인칭 단수이므로 일반동사 현재형의 의문문은 「Does + 주어 + 동사원형 ~?」으로 써야 한다.

27 주어가 We로 복수이므로 일반동사 현재형의 부정문은 「주어 +

don't + 동사원형 ~.」으로 써야 한다.

28 주어가 you로 2인칭이므로 일반동사 현재형의 의문문은 「Do + you + 동사원형 ~?」으로 써야 한다.

29 주어가 I로 1인칭이므로 일반동사 현재형의 부정문은 「주어 + do not[don't] + 동사원형 ~.」으로 써야 한다.

30 주어가 Julie로 3인칭 단수이므로 일반동사 현재형의 의문문은 「Does + 주어 + 동사원형 ~?」으로 써야 한다.

31 주어가 Jake로 3인칭 단수이므로 일반동사 현재형의 부정문은 「주어 + does not[doesn't] + 동사원형 ~.」으로 써야 한다.

32 (1) 대답을 I로 하였으므로 의문문은 「Do + you + 동사원형 ~?」이 되어야 하고, 긍정의 대답이므로 Yes, I do.로 답하는 것이 알맞다.
(2) 대답을 I로 하였으므로 의문문은 「Do + you + 동사원형 ~?」이 되어야 하고, 부정의 대답이므로 No, I don't.로 답해야 한다. 또한 일요일에 설거지를 하는 사람은 My brother이므로 wash의 3인칭 단수 현재형 washes를 써야 한다.
(3) 토요일에 개를 산책시키는 사람은 my brother이므로 Does your brother walk ~?로 묻고, 긍정의 대답이므로 Yes, he does.로 답해야 한다.

33 (1) 주어가 3인칭 단수인 일반동사 현재형의 부정문은 「주어 + does not[doesn't] + 동사원형 ~.」으로 써야 하므로 don't를 doesn't로 고쳐야 한다.
(2) 주어가 3인칭 단수인 일반동사 현재형의 부정문은 doesn't 뒤에 동사원형을 써야 하므로 eats를 eat으로 고쳐야 한다.
(3) 주어가 3인칭 단수인 일반동사 현재형의 의문문은 「Does + 주어 + 동사원형 ~?」으로 써야 하므로 Do를 Does로 고쳐야 한다.

34 주어가 Mina로 3인칭 단수이므로 각각 gets up, reads, practices, watches, studies로 바꿔야 한다.

35 (1) '자원봉사를 하다'는 do volunteer work로 나타낼 수 있고, 주어가 My dad and I로 복수이므로 동사는 원형 그대로 쓴다.
(2) '이불 빨래를 하다'는 wash the blankets로 나타낼 수 있고, 주어가 I로 1인칭이므로 동사는 원형 그대로 쓴다.
(3) 주어가 my dad로 3인칭 단수이므로 동사 repair의 3인칭 단수 현재형 repairs를 쓴다.

Chapter 05 일반동사 2

Practice 01 일반동사의 과거형 본문 65쪽

Grammar Check Up

A
1 arrived
2 cried
3 had
4 broke
5 knew
6 played
7 ran
8 taught

B
1 washed
2 sang

3 bought
4 cut
5 wore

C
1 dropped
2 went
3 slept
4 ate
5 saw

D
1 drove
2 invented
3 met
4 made
5 did

Practice 02 일반동사 과거형의 부정문과 의문문 본문 67쪽

Grammar Check Up

A
1 didn't
2 Did
3 didn't
4 Did
5 snow
6 take

B
1 didn't go, went
2 didn't eat, ate
3 didn't wash, washed

C
1 Did, help, didn't
2 Did, drive, didn't
3 Did, do, did

Writing Exercise 본문 68~69쪽

A
1 finished
2 didn't take
3 Did, read
4 bought
5 didn't make
6 Did, cry

B
1 Judy didn't listen, Did Judy listen, she did
2 He didn't study, Did he study, he didn't
3 They didn't send, Did they send, they didn't
4 Ms. Green didn't wear, Did Ms. Green wear, she did

C
(1) went
(2) set
(3) helped
(4) climbed
(5) ate
(6) told
(7) slept
(8) had

D
(1) had
(2) didn't sleep
(3) Did you see
(4) I didn't
(5) took

Actual Test 본문 70~74쪽

01 ②	02 ②	03 ②, ③	04 ③	05 ④
06 ④	07 ⑤	08 ②	09 ④	10 ①
11 ⑤	12 ③	13 ④	14 ⑤	15 ⑤
16 ③	17 ④	18 ⑤	19 ④	20 ⑤
21 ④	22 ⑤	23 ⑤	24 ⑤	25 ①
26 ran	27 Did Bill wear			

28 Did they visit the farm
29 I didn't go jogging
30 He told　　　31 Did Harry hurt
32 (1) They took a picture of the wedding
　　(2) He spent time with his family
33 (1) No, didn't, fixed the computer
　　(2) No, didn't, bought a new smartphone
34 (1) ② → Tom broke his arm yesterday.
　　(2) ④ → Sue hit the ball and I caught it.
　　(3) ⑤ → I didn't see her angry face at that time.
35 (1) rode a bike　(2) read a newspaper
　　(3) walked the dog　(4) drew a picture

01 동사 do의 과거형은 did이다.

02 동사 hit의 과거형은 hit이다.

03 ② 동사 come의 과거형은 came이고, ③ 동사 sit의 과거형은 sat 이다.

04 last night이라는 과거를 나타내는 표현이 있으므로 동사 bark의 과거형인 barked를 써야 한다.

05 yesterday라는 과거를 나타내는 표현이 있으므로 동사 give의 과 거형인 gave를 써야 한다.

06 last Monday라는 과거를 나타내는 표현이 있으므로 일반동사 과 거형의 부정문인 「주어 + didn't + 동사원형 ~.」의 형태로 써야 한다.

07 last week라는 과거를 나타내는 표현이 있으므로 일반동사 과거형 의 의문문인 「Did + 주어 + 동사원형 ~?」의 형태로 써야 한다.

08 lost는 동사 lose의 과거형이므로 빈칸에 '내일'이라는 미래를 나타 내는 tomorrow는 알맞지 않다.

09 일반동사 과거형의 부정문에서 didn't 뒤에는 동사원형이 와야 하므 로 동사 write의 과거형인 wrote는 알맞지 않다.

10 일반동사의 과거형은 주어의 인칭과 수에 의해 형태가 변하지 않으 므로 gots를 got으로 고쳐야 한다.

11 일반동사 과거형의 의문문은 「Did + 주어 + 동사원형 ~?」의 형태이 므로 saw는 see로 고쳐야 한다.

12 동사 drop의 과거형은 dropped이고, 일반동사의 과거형은 주어의 인칭이나 수에 의해 형태가 변하지 않는다.

13 일반동사 과거형의 의문문은 「Did + 주어 + 동사원형 ~?」으로 쓴다.

14 첫 번째 문장에 last year이라는 과거를 나타내는 표현이 있으므로 동사를 과거형으로 써야 한다. 동사 keep의 과거형은 kept이다. 두 번째 문장은 역사적 사실을 나타내므로 동사를 과거형으로 써야 한다. 동사 invent의 과거형은 invented이다.

15 yesterday로 보아 일반동사 과거형의 의문문이므로 「Did + 주어 + 동사원형 ~?」의 형태로 써야 하고, 이에 대한 부정의 대답은 「No, 주어 + didn't.」이다.

16 일반동사 과거형의 의문문이므로 「Did + 주어 + 동사원형 ~?」의 형 태로 써야 하고, 이에 대한 긍정의 대답은 「Yes, 주어 + did.」이다.

17 일반동사 과거형의 부정문은 「주어 + didn't + 동사원형 ~.」으로 써 야 하므로 didn't drink가 되어야 알맞다.

18 ① 일반동사 과거형의 의문문은 「Did + 주어 + 동사원형 ~?」의 형태 로 써야 하므로, eats를 eat으로 고쳐야 한다.
② 일반동사 과거형의 의문문에 대한 대답은 「Yes, 주어 + did.」 또 는 「No, 주어 + didn't.」로 해야 한다.
③ last year라는 과거를 나타내는 표현이 있으므로 일반동사 과거 형의 의문문이 되어야 하므로 Do를 Did로 고쳐야 한다.
④ 일반동사 과거형의 의문문은 「Did + 주어 + 동사원형 ~?」의 형태 로 써야 하므로, knowed를 know로 고쳐야 한다.

19 첫 번째 빈칸은 do yoga로 '~을 하다'라는 의미인 일반동사 do가 들어가야 하는데, 10 minutes ago라는 과거를 나타내는 표현이 있으므로 과거형 did가 알맞다. 두 번째 빈칸은 last night이라는 과거를 나타내는 표현이 있고, 일반동사 과거형의 부정문이므로 「주 어 + did not[didn't] + 동사원형 ~.」의 형태로 조동사 did가 들어 가야 한다. 세 번째 빈칸은 yesterday라는 과거를 나타내는 표현이 있고, 일반동사 과거형의 의문문이므로 「Did + 주어 + 동사원형 ~?」 의 형태로 조동사 Did가 들어가야 한다.

20 일반동사 과거형의 의문문에 대한 대답은 「Yes, 주어 + did.」 또는 「No, 주어 + didn't.」로 해야 한다.

21 매일 일어나는 일은 일반동사의 현재형으로 표현하므로 첫 번째 빈칸 에는 동사 have의 현재형인 has를 써야 알맞고, 두 번째 빈칸에는 yesterday morning이라는 과거를 나타내는 말이 있으므로 동사 have의 과거형인 had를 써야 알맞다.

22 항상 일어나는 습관적인 일은 일반동사의 현재형으로 표현하므로 첫 번째 빈칸에는 동사 get의 현재형인 gets를 써야 알맞다. 두 번째 빈 칸에는 yesterday라는 과거를 나타내는 말이 있으므로 동사 get의 과거형 got을 써야 알맞다.

23 일반동사 과거형의 부정문은 「주어 + didn't + 동사원형 ~.」으로 써 야 하므로 bought는 buy가 되어야 한다.

24 ⑤ '나의 남동생들이 어제 축구를 했다.'가 표의 내용과 일치한다.

25 ⓐ heared → heard, 동사 hear의 과거형은 heard이다.
ⓑ passed → pass, 일반동사 과거형의 의문문은 「Did + 주어 + 동사원형 ~?」의 형태로 써야 한다.
ⓒ don't → didn't, an hour ago라는 과거를 나타내는 표현이 있으므로 일반동사 과거형의 부정문인 「주어 + didn't + 동사원형 ~.」의 형태로 써야 한다.
ⓔ fight → fought, yesterday라는 과거를 나타내는 표현이 있 으므로 동사 fight를 과거형으로 써야 한다.

26 동사 run의 과거형은 ran이다. (run away: 도망가다)

27 일반동사 과거형의 의문문은 주어의 인칭과 수에 상관없이 「Did + 주어 + 동사원형 ~?」으로 쓴다.

28 일반동사 과거형의 의문문이므로 「Did + 주어 + 동사원형 ~?」의 어 순이 되도록 배열한다.

29 일반동사 과거형의 부정문이므로 「주어 + didn't + 동사원형 ~.」의 어순이 되도록 배열한다.

30 '그'에 해당하는 대명사 He와 동사 tell의 과거형 told를 이용하여 문 장을 완성한다.

31 일반동사 과거형의 의문문이므로 「Did + 주어 + 동사원형 ~?」으로 쓴다.

32 (1) yesterday라는 과거를 나타내는 표현이 있으므로 동사 take의 과거형 took을 써서 문장을 완성한다.
(2) yesterday라는 과거를 나타내는 표현이 있으므로 동사 spend

의 과거형 spent를 써서 문장을 완성한다.

33 (1) 지우는 일요일에 컴퓨터를 고쳤으므로 토요일에 컴퓨터를 고쳤냐는 질문에 대해서는 부정의 대답인 No, he didn't.라고 답하고, 동사 fix의 과거형 fixed를 써서 일요일에 컴퓨터를 고쳤다고 답해야 한다.
(2) 지우는 토요일에 새 스마트폰을 샀으므로 일요일에 새 스마트폰을 샀냐는 질문에 대해서는 부정의 대답인 No, he didn't.라고 답하고, 동사 buy의 과거형 bought를 써서 토요일에 새 스마트폰을 샀다고 답해야 한다.

34 (1) yesterday라는 과거를 나타내는 표현이 있으므로 동사 break의 과거형을 써야 하고, break는 불규칙 동사로 과거형은 broke이므로 breaked를 broke로 고쳐야 한다.
(2) 동사 hit는 현재형과 과거형이 같은 동사이고, 뒤의 caught로 보아 과거의 일을 나타내는 문장이므로 hitted를 hit로 고쳐야 한다.
(3) at that time이라는 과거를 나타내는 표현이 있으므로 일반동사 과거형의 부정문인 「주어 + didn't + 동사원형 ~.」의 형태가 되어야 하므로 saw를 동사원형 see로 고쳐야 한다.

35 (1) 동사 ride의 과거형 rode를 써야 한다.
(2) read는 현재형과 과거형의 형태는 같고 발음이 다른 동사이다. 동사 read의 과거형 read를 써야 한다.
(3) 동사 walk의 과거형 walked를 써야 한다.
(4) 동사 draw의 과거형 drew를 써야 한다.

Chapter 06 현재진행형과 미래형

Practice 01 현재진행형
본문 77쪽

Grammar Check Up

A 1 going 2 flying
3 having 4 coming
5 sitting 6 dying
7 beginning 8 catching

B 1 is snowing 2 are doing
3 is singing 4 is cutting
5 are practicing

C 1 My father is not[isn't] writing
2 Is the student wearing
3 He is not[isn't] jumping
4 Are the kids putting

D 1 I am[we are] 2 she is not[isn't]
3 he is not[isn't] 4 they are

Practice 02 미래형
본문 79쪽

Grammar Check Up

A 1 meet 2 be
3 bring 4 am
5 buy

B 1 I will not[won't] hide
2 Will Billy travel
3 is not[isn't] going to be
4 Are they going to plant

C 1 I will 2 we're not[we aren't]
3 she will not[won't] 4 he is

D 1 dance → to dance
2 is → be
3 going not → not going
4 see → to see
5 eats → eat

Writing Exercise
본문 80~81쪽

A 1 is studying 2 is drawing
3 am writing 4 Are you walking
5 is not[isn't] watching

B 1 Will it be
2 Are they going to help
3 Is your dad going to work
4 Are you going to move
5 Will you join

C (1) are going to have (2) am going to make
(3) is going to bake (4) are going to buy
(5) is going to make (6) is going to be

D (1) Will you wash
(2) Are you going to help
(3) Will you get

Actual Test
본문 82~86쪽

01 ③ 02 ① 03 ⑤ 04 ① 05 ②
06 ④ 07 ③ 08 ② 09 ② 10 ④
11 ③ 12 ④ 13 ④ 14 ② 15 ③
16 ⑤ 17 ③ 18 ⑤ 19 ③ 20 ④
21 ③ 22 ④ 23 ⑤ 24 ⑤ 25 ③
26 are going to move 27 is not riding his bike
28 Will your brother be 11 years old
29 is boiling
30 My dad is not[isn't] going to fix
31 Are you going to go

32 (1) He is wearing sunglasses right now.
　(2) He will[is going to] wear sunglasses tomorrow.
33 (1) No　(2) will not[won't]　(3) snowy
　(4) It will be rainy.　(5) will be sunny
34 (1) is painting → are painting　(2) rideing → riding
　(3) lieing → lying
35 (1) will go　(2) is going to visit　(3) will come

01 「자음 + e」로 끝나는 동사는 e를 삭제하고 -ing를 붙이므로 having 이 되어야 한다.

02 -ie로 끝나는 동사는 ie를 y로 바꾼 후 -ing를 붙이므로 dying이 되 어야 한다.

03 빈칸 앞의 is와 문장 끝의 now로 보아 현재진행형 문장임을 알 수 있 으므로 빈칸에는 sit의 -ing형인 sitting이 들어가야 한다.

04 soon으로 보아 미래의 일에 대해 말하고 있으므로 빈칸에는 will 또 는 are going to가 알맞다.

05 next week로 보아 미래의 일에 대해 말하고 있으므로 「be going to + 동사원형」의 형태가 되어야 하는데, 주어가 3인칭 단수이므로 be동사는 is로 쓴다.

06 next winter로 보아 미래의 일에 대해 말하고 있으므로 빈칸에는 Will이 알맞다.

07 '~하지 않을 것이다'라는 의미의 미래형의 부정형은 「will not + 동사 원형」의 형태로 쓴다.

08 「be going to + 동사원형」의 부정형은 「be + not + going to + 동사원형」의 형태로 쓴다.

09 '~하지 않을 것이다'라는 의미의 미래형의 부정형은 「be + not + going to + 동사원형」의 형태로 쓰므로 don't는 aren't가 되어야 한다.

10 현재진행형은 「be동사 + 동사원형-ing」의 형태로 써야 하므로 parking 앞에 be동사 is가 있어야 한다.

11 '~하는 중이다'라는 의미의 현재진행형은 「be동사 + 동사원형-ing」 의 형태로 쓴다.

12 '~하는 중이 아니다'라는 현재진행형의 부정형은 「be동사 + not + 동사원형-ing」의 형태로 쓴다.

13 ④는 '~하지 않을 것이다'라는 의미의 미래형의 부정형 「will not + 동사원형」의 will이 들어가야 한다. ①은 '~하는 중이다'라는 의미 의 현재진행형 「be동사 + 동사원형-ing」에 쓰이는 be동사 Are가 들어가야 하고, 나머지는 모두 '~할 것이다'라는 의미의 미래형 「be going to + 동사원형」에 쓰이는 be동사인 are[Are]가 들어가야 한다.

14 ②의 be going to는 '~로 가고 있다'라는 의미이고, 나머지는 모두 '~할 것이다'라는 의미의 미래형 be going to이다.

15 next winter라는 미래를 나타내는 표현이 있으므로 spends는 will spend나 is going to spend로 고쳐야 알맞다.

16 첫 번째 빈칸은 tomorrow라는 미래를 나타내는 표현이 있으므로 미래형 의문문인 「Will + 주어 + 동사원형 ~?」의 형태가 되어야 한 다. 두 번째 빈칸은 이에 대한 부정의 대답이므로 「No, 주어 + will not[won't]」이 되어야 한다.

17 첫 번째 빈칸은 going to로 보아 「Be동사 + 주어 + going to +

동사원형 ~?」의 미래형 의문문이 되어야 하는데, 주어가 we이므로 be동사는 Are가 알맞다. 두 번째 빈칸은 이에 대한 긍정의 대답이므 로 「Yes, 주어 + be동사.」가 되어야 하는데, 주어가 we이므로 be동 사는 are가 알맞다.

18 첫 번째 빈칸은 「be동사 + 동사원형-ing」 형태의 현재진행형 문장으 로 '나는 쇼핑몰에 가는 중이야.'라는 의미가 자연스러우므로 going 이 들어가야 알맞다. 두 번째 빈칸은 미래형 문장인 「be going to + 동사원형」의 형태가 되어야 한다. 세 번째 빈칸은 미래형 의문문인 「Be동사 + 주어 + going to + 동사원형 ~?」의 형태가 되어야 한다. 따라서 빈칸에 공통으로 들어갈 말은 going이다.

19 현재진행형 의문문에 대한 대답은 「Yes, 주어 + be동사.」 또는 「No, 주어 + be동사 + not.」으로 한다.

20 첫 번째 빈칸은 항상 일어나는 습관적인 일을 나타내고 있으므로 현재 형인 washes가 알맞다. 두 번째 빈칸은 now로 보아 지금 진행 중 인 일을 말하고 있으므로 현재진행형 「be동사 + 동사원형-ing」 형태 의 is washing이 알맞다.

21 첫 번째 빈칸은 now로 보아 지금 진행 중인 일을 말하고 있으므로 현 재진행형 「be동사 + 동사원형-ing」 형태의 is picking이 알맞다. 두 번째 빈칸은 tomorrow라는 미래를 나타내는 표현이 있으므로 「will + 동사원형」이나 「be going to + 동사원형」의 형태가 들어가 야 한다.

22 next week라는 미래를 나타내는 표현이 있고 대답이 No, she won't.인 것으로 보아, 미래형 의문문인 「Will + 주어 + 동사원형 ~?」의 형태가 되어야 하므로 Does를 Will로 고쳐야 한다.

23 ⓐ '~하고 있다'라는 의미이므로 현재진행형 「be동사 + 동사원 형-ing」의 형태인 are wearing이 알맞다.
　ⓑ '~할 것이다'라는 미래의 의미이므로 「be going to + 동사원형」 을 써야 하는데, 주어가 She이므로 be동사 is가 알맞다.
　ⓒ '~할 것이다'라는 미래의 의미이므로 「will + 동사원형」 형태인 will take가 알맞다.

24 yesterday라는 이미 지나간 일에 대한 과거 표현과 미래형을 함께 쓸 수 없으므로 yesterday를 tomorrow 등의 미래 표현으로 고치 거나 will not have를 과거형인 didn't have로 고쳐야 한다.

25 ⓑ not are feeding → are not feeding, 현재진행형 부정문이 므로 「be동사 + not + 동사원형-ing」의 형태가 되어야 한다.
　ⓒ sleeping → sleep, '~하지 않을 것이다'라는 의미의 미래형 부 정문이므로 「be not going to + 동사원형」이 되어야 한다.
　ⓔ go → going, '~할 것이다'라는 의미의 미래형 문장은 「be going to + 동사원형」이 되어야 한다.

26 next week라는 미래를 나타내는 표현을 보아 미래형 문장이므로 「be going to + 동사원형」의 순서가 되어야 한다.

27 now로 보아 지금 일어나고 있는 일을 나타내는 현재진행형 부정문 이 와야 하므로 「be동사 + not + 동사원형-ing ~.」의 순서가 되어 야 한다.

28 next year라는 미래를 나타내는 표현을 보아 미래형 의문문이므로 「Will + 주어 + 동사원형 ~?」의 순서가 되어야 한다.

29 '~하고 있다'라는 의미의 현재진행형은 「be동사 + 동사원형-ing」 의 형태로 쓰고, 주어가 3인칭 단수이므로 be동사는 is로 써서 is boiling으로 써야 한다.

30 미래형 부정문이므로 「주어 + be동사 + not going to + 동사원형 ~.」의 순서가 되어야 한다.

31 미래형 의문문이므로 「Be동사 + 주어 + going to + 동사원형 ~?」의 순서가 되어야 한다.

32 (1) right now로 보아 지금 일어나고 있는 일이므로 현재진행형 is wearing을 써서 문장을 완성한다.
(2) tomorrow로 보아 미래형 문장이므로 will wear 또는 is going to wear를 써서 문장을 완성한다.

33 (1) 금요일에는 화창한 날씨가 아니므로 No로 답한다.
(2) 미래형의 부정문으로 답해야 하므로 won't이나 will not으로 답한다.
(3) 금요일에는 눈이 온다고 하였으므로 snowy를 쓴다.
(4) 일요일에는 비가 온다고 하였으므로 비인칭 주어 It과 미래형 문장으로 써서 will be rainy로 답한다.
(5) 토요일에는 화창한 날씨이므로 미래형 문장인 will be sunny로 답한다.

34 (1) My mom and dad는 복수이므로 be동사 is를 are로 고쳐야 한다.
(2) 「자음 + e」로 끝나는 단어는 e를 삭제하고 -ing를 붙이므로 rideing을 riding으로 고쳐야 한다.
(3) -ie로 끝나는 단어는 ie를 y로 바꾼 후 -ing를 붙여야 하므로 lieing을 lying으로 고쳐야 한다.

35 (1) 6월 15일에 서울에 계시는 삼촌네로 갈 것이므로 미래형 「will + 동사원형」이나 「be going to + 동사원형」을 써야 하는데, 2단어로 쓰라고 했으므로 will go를 써서 문장을 완성한다.
(2) 그 다음 날은 박물관에 갈 것이므로 미래형 「will + 동사원형」이나 「be going to + 동사원형」을 써야 하는데, 4단어로 쓰라고 했으므로 is going to visit를 써서 문장을 완성한다.
(3) 6월 17일에 부산으로 돌아갈 것이므로 미래형 「will + 동사원형」이나 「be going to + 동사원형」을 써야 하는데, 2단어로 쓰라고 했으므로 will come을 써서 문장을 완성한다.

Chapter 07 조동사

Practice 01 조동사 can, may
본문 89쪽

Grammar Check Up

A 1 can   2 write
   3 cannot   4 Can
   5 stay   6 May I ask

B 1 cannot   2 can
   3 May[Can]   4 may

C 1 can   2 may
   3 can, cannot[can't]   4 cannot[can't]

Practice 02 조동사 must, have to
본문 91쪽

Grammar Check Up

A 1 must   2 have to
   3 doesn't   4 has
   5 not turn on

B 1 must, must not   2 must, must not
   3 must not, must   4 must, must not

C 1 have to   2 has to
   3 don't have to   4 doesn't have to

Writing Exercise
본문 92~93쪽

A 1 cannot[can't] walk   2 can speak
   3 may be   4 May[Can] I close
   5 may[can] wear

B 1 We have to wait for a long time.
   2 He can cook Chinese food very well.
   3 She doesn't have to go to school.
   4 He must pack his bag tonight.
   5 You must not open the window.

C (1) must get up   (2) must wear
   (3) must not bite   (4) must eat
   (5) must break

D (1) must get up   (2) have to leave
   (3) can I take   (4) have to pack
   (5) may rain   (6) has to go

Actual Test
본문 94~98쪽

01 ①   02 ③   03 ②   04 ③   05 ②
06 ①   07 ①   08 ①   09 ④   10 ④
11 ④   12 ④   13 ①   14 ④   15 ④
16 ⑤   17 ①   18 ①   19 ②   20 ②
21 ②, ④   22 ③   23 ④   24 ③   25 ④

26 must[have to] save our planet
27 doesn't have to bring her lunch
28 may not come here in time
29 You must not take pictures
30 May I sit here
31 Do you have to reserve
32 (1) cannot[can't] study (2) must[has to] take care of
33 (1) cannot[can't] ride a bike (2) can ride a bike
   (3) cannot[can't] play the guitar
34 (1) has to be (2) must not take
35 must be some mistake

01 '~할 수 있다'라는 의미의 조동사는 can이다.

02 '~해야 한다'라는 의미의 조동사는 must 또는 have to이다.

03 '~해도 된다'라는 의미의 허가를 나타내는 may는 can과 바꿔 쓸 수 있다.

04 '~해야 한다'라는 의무를 나타내는 must는 have to와 바꿔 쓸 수 있는데, 주어가 3인칭 단수이므로 has to가 알맞다.

05 점심을 먹지 않아서 배가 고플지도 모른다는 추측을 나타내는 may가 알맞다.

06 신호등이 초록색이면 길을 건너갈 수 있으므로 가능이나 허가를 나타내는 can이 알맞다.

07 어린이 보호 구역에서는 차를 빨리 운전해서는 안되므로 금지를 나타내는 must not이 알맞다.

08 Can you ~?에 대한 대답은 Yes, I[we] can. 또는 No, I[we] can't.로 한다.

09 Must I ~?에 대한 대답은 Yes, you must. 또는 No, you must not.(금지) / No, you don't have to.(불필요)로 한다.

10 주어가 3인칭 단수 She이므로 have to를 has to로 고쳐야 한다.

11 조동사 다음에는 동사원형이 오므로 must 뒤에 to exercise를 exercise로 고치거나, must와 같은 의미인 has to로 만들기 위해 must를 has로 바꾸어야 한다.

12 '피곤할지도 모른다'라는 추측의 의미와 '내 비옷을 입어도 된다'라는 허가의 의미를 모두 나타내는 조동사 may가 알맞다.

13 '약속을 지켜야 한다'라는 의무는 「have to + 동사원형」으로, '지금은 괜찮아서 병원에 갈 필요가 없다'라는 불필요는 「don't have to + 동사원형」으로 나타내므로 조동사 have to가 알맞다.

14 ① has to → have to, 주어가 1인칭 I이므로 동사원형인 have to로 써야 한다.
② mays → may, 조동사는 주어의 인칭이나 수에 상관없이 형태가 같다.
③ not must → must not, 조동사의 부정문은 조동사 뒤에 not을 붙인다.
⑤ makes → make, 조동사 뒤에는 동사원형이 온다.

15 ① found → find, 조동사 뒤에는 동사원형이 온다.
② fixes → fix, 조동사 뒤에는 동사원형이 온다.
③ to take → take, 조동사의 의문문은 조동사와 주어의 자리만 바꾸고, 동사는 그대로 둔다.
⑤ doesn't → don't, 주어가 2인칭 You이므로 don't have to로 써야 한다.

16 ⑤는 허가를 나타내고, 나머지는 모두 가능이나 능력을 나타낸다.

17 ①은 추측을 나타내고, 나머지는 모두 허가를 나타낸다.

18 ①은 강한 추측을 나타내고, 나머지는 모두 의무를 나타낸다.

19 ⓐ plays → play, 조동사 뒤에는 동사원형이 온다.
ⓒ must eat not → must not eat, 조동사의 부정문은 조동사 뒤에 not을 붙인다.

20 ⓑ must to do → must do 또는 have to do, 조동사 뒤에는 동사원형이 오므로 must do로 쓰거나 같은 의미인 have to로 만들기 위해 must를 have로 바꾸어야 한다.
ⓒ don't → doesn't, 주어가 3인칭 단수 She이므로 doesn't have to로 써야 한다.

21 ① Must → May 또는 Can, 허가를 나타내는 조동사인 may나 can이 와야 한다.
③ have be → have to be 또는 must be, 의무를 나타내고 있으므로 「have to + 동사원형」 또는 「must + 동사원형」의 형태가 와야 한다.
⑤ must not → don't have to, '~할 필요가 없다'라는 불필요의 의미를 나타내는 조동사는 don't have to이다.

22 '매우 피곤하다'라는 A의 말에 '쉬어야 한다'라고 답하는 것이 적절하므로 '~해야 한다'라는 의미의 조동사 have to가 알맞다.

23 이어지는 문장에 But이 나와서 '스키를 잘 타지 못한다. 하지만 스키 타는 것을 좋아한다'라는 의미가 되는 것이 자연스러우므로 cannot이 들어가야 한다.

24 ⓐ mays → may, 조동사는 주어의 인칭이나 수에 상관없이 형태가 같다.
ⓓ has → have, 주어 We는 복수 명사이므로 동사원형 have가 와야 한다.

25 ⓐ makes → make, 조동사 뒤에는 동사원형이 와야 한다.

26 '~해야 한다'라는 의미의 조동사 must 또는 have to를 이용하여 나타낸다.

27 '~할 필요가 없다'라는 의미의 조동사 don't have to로 나타내는데, 주어가 3인칭 단수 She이므로 doesn't have to로 쓴다.

28 '~가 아닐지도 모른다'는 뜻의 약한 부정의 추측은 may not을 쓴다.

29 '~해서는 안 된다'라는 강한 금지를 나타낼 때 「must not + 동사원형」의 어순으로 쓴다.

30 허가의 의미를 나타내는 may를 이용하여 「May I + 동사원형 ~?」의 어순으로 쓴다.

31 '~해야 한다'라는 의무를 나타내는 조동사 have to의 의문문은 「Do you + have to + 동사원형 ~?」의 어순으로 쓴다.

32 (1) 소라가 부모님의 출장으로 친구들과 공부할 수 없으므로 '~할 수 없다'라는 의미의 조동사 cannot[can't]을 이용하여 cannot[can't] study가 들어가야 한다.
(2) 그녀가 이틀 동안 남동생을 돌봐야 하므로 '~해야 한다'라는 의미의 조동사 must 또는 has to를 이용하여 must[has to] take care of가 들어가야 한다.

33 (1) 미나는 영어로 말할 수 있지만, 자전거는 탈 수 없으므로 cannot[can't] ride a bike로 써야 한다.
(2) 수호는 기타를 칠 수 없지만, 자전거는 탈 수 있으므로 can ride a bike로 써야 한다.
(3) 지나는 영어로 말할 수 있지만, 기타는 칠 수 없으므로 cannot[can't] play the guitar로 써야 한다.

34 (1) '~해야 한다'라는 의미의 조동사 「have to + 동사원형」의 형태로 나타내야 하고, 주어가 3인칭 단수이므로 has to로 써야 한다.
(2) 문맥상 '~해서는 안 된다'라는 금지를 나타내는 조동사 must not을 써서 나타내고, 조동사 뒤에는 동사원형이 와야 한다.

35 Jason이 호텔에서 예약을 확인하고 있는데, 그의 이름을 예약 명부에서 찾을 수 없는 상황이다. 따라서 '어떤 실수가 있음에 틀림없다!'라는 내용이 오는 것이 자연스러우므로 must be some mistake로 써야 한다.

Chapter 08 형용사와 부사

(2) fastly → fast
(3) much nuts → many[a lot of/lots of] nuts

Practice 01 형용사
본문 101쪽

Grammar Check Up

A 1 Poor, dirty　　2 exciting
　3 old, dirty　　4 special

B 1 white, green　　2 sleepy
　3 sweet　　4 tall, short

C 1 many　　2 much
　3 some　　4 any

D 1 much time　　2 many people
　3 any bread　　4 some salad

Practice 02 부사
본문 103쪽

Grammar Check Up

A 1 nicely　　2 kindly
　3 easily　　4 quickly
　5 safely　　6 fast
　7 carefully　　8 happily

B 1 Unluckily　　2 well
　3 very tall　　4 late

C 1 is often very busy on weekends
　2 always jogs in the park
　3 will never fix the broken computer
　4 usually skips breakfast

D 1 딱딱한　　2 열심인
　3 어려운　　4 열심히
　5 거의 ~ 않다

Writing Exercise
본문 104~105쪽

A 1 careful, carefully　　2 early, early
　3 good, well　　4 late, late

B 1 He doesn't have much money.
　2 There are some potatoes on the table.
　3 I want something cold.
　4 I often jump rope.
　5 Are there any eggs in the refrigerator?
　6 Many students go to school on foot.

C (1) never exercise　　(2) sometimes exercise
　(3) usually exercise　　(4) always exercise

D (1) well very → very well

Actual Test
본문 106~110쪽

01 ⑤	02 ④	03 ③	04 ②	05 ③
06 ①	07 ②	08 ③	09 ③	10 ②
11 ④	12 ⑤	13 ②	14 ②	15 ③
16 ③	17 ③	18 ①	19 ③	20 ④
21 ③	22 ③	23 ⑤	24 ②	25 ③

26 My son never eats beans.
27 We are usually at home on Sundays.
28 I saw something strange last night.
29 was quite cold today
30 Air is very important
31 It hardly rains　　32 some, many, any, much
33 We usually go to the park on weekends.
34 (1) much → many[a lot of/lots of]　(2) real → really
35 (1) always goes jogging
　(2) sometimes plays soccer with friends[plays soccer with friends sometimes]

01 -y로 끝나는 형용사는 y를 i로 바꾸고 -ly를 붙여서 부사를 만들어야 하므로 heavy의 부사형은 heavily이다.

02 명사 doll을 꾸며 주어야 하므로 형용사 lovely가 알맞다. lovely는 -ly로 끝나지만 형용사이다.

03 동사 fought를 꾸며 주어야 하므로 부사 bravely가 알맞다.

04 긍정의 평서문이자 셀 수 없는 명사 homework를 꾸며 주어야 하므로 수량 형용사 much가 알맞다.

05 '몇몇의'라는 의미로 긍정문에 쓰이는 형용사는 some이다.

06 부정문에서 '조금의 (~도 없다)'라는 의미로 쓰이는 형용사는 any이다.

07 '딱딱한'이라는 의미의 형용사와 '열심히'라는 의미의 부사 둘 다로 쓰일 수 있는 것은 hard이다.

08 '늦은'이라는 의미의 형용사와 '늦게'라는 의미의 부사 둘 다로 쓰일 수 있는 것은 late이다.

09 sometimes는 빈도부사이며, 빈도부사는 일반적으로 일반동사(play) 앞에 위치한다. 참고로 sometimes는 문장 맨 앞이나 맨 끝에 올 수도 있다.

10 always는 빈도부사이며, 빈도부사는 일반적으로 be동사(is) 뒤에 위치한다.

11 -thing으로 끝나는 대명사(something)는 형용사가 뒤에서 꾸며 준다.

12 ⑤를 제외한 나머지는 모두 형용사이다. ⑤는 '시끄럽게'라는 의미의 부사이다.

13 ②를 제외한 나머지는 모두 부사이다. ②는 '늦은'이라는 의미의 보어로 쓰인 형용사이다.

14 첫 번째 빈칸은 명사 day를 꾸며 주는 형용사 lucky가 알맞다. 두 번째 빈칸은 문장 전체를 꾸며 주는 부사 Luckily가 알맞다.

15 첫 번째 빈칸은 주어에 대해 보충 설명하는 형용사 kind가 알맞다. 두 번째 빈칸은 동사 showed를 꾸며 주는 부사 kindly가 알맞다.

16 첫 번째 빈칸은 권유문에서 '~ 좀 먹을래[마실래]?'라고 할 때 쓰이는 형용사 some이 알맞다. 두 번째 빈칸은 의문문에서 '조금의'라는 의미를 나타내는 형용사 any가 알맞다.

17 ③ 뒤에 셀 수 있는 명사(paintings)가 왔으므로 many가 알맞다. 나머지는 뒤에 모두 셀 수 없는 명사이므로 much가 알맞다.

18 부사가 형용사를 꾸밀 때는 형용사 앞에 위치해야 한다. 따라서 very는 hot 앞에 써야 한다.

19 권유문에서는 any가 아닌 some을 쓴다.

20 lemon juice는 셀 수 없는 명사이므로 셀 수 있는 명사 앞에 쓰이는 many는 적절하지 않다.

21 주어 His speech를 보충 설명하는 형용사가 와야 하므로 부사 well은 적절하지 않다.

22 '항상'은 always로 표현하며, always와 같은 빈도부사는 일반적으로 일반동사(listens) 앞에 위치한다.

23 ⓑ some → any, 부정문에서 '조금도 (~도 없다)'라는 의미로 쓰이는 형용사는 any이다.
ⓒ are many → is much, salt는 셀 수 없는 명사이므로 much를 써야 하고, be동사도 is로 고쳐야 한다.
ⓓ always is → is always, 빈도부사 always는 일반적으로 be동사(is) 뒤에 위치한다.

24 ⓐ lately → late, 문맥상 '늦게'라는 의미의 부사 late가 와야 한다. lately는 '최근에'라는 의미의 부사이다.
ⓒ plays often → often plays, 빈도부사 often은 일반적으로 일반동사(plays) 앞에 위치한다.

25 ⓐ fast very → very fast, 부사가 형용사를 꾸밀 때는 형용사 앞에 위치한다.
ⓑ some → any, 의문문에서 '조금의'의 의미를 나타낼 때는 형용사 any를 쓴다.

26 빈도부사는 일반적으로 일반동사 앞에 위치하므로 eats never를 never eats로 고쳐 써야 한다.

27 빈도부사는 일반적으로 be동사 뒤에 위치하므로 usually are를 are usually로 고쳐 써야 한다.

28 -thing으로 끝나는 대명사는 형용사가 뒤에서 꾸며 주므로 strange something을 something strange로 고쳐 써야 한다.

29 부사는 형용사 앞에서 형용사를 꾸며 주므로 quite cold의 순서로 쓴다.

30 부사는 형용사 앞에서 형용사를 꾸며 주므로 very important의 순서로 쓴다.

31 빈도부사는 일반적으로 일반동사 앞에 위치하므로 hardly rains의 순서로 쓴다. 주어가 3인칭 단수(It)이므로 동사가 rains가 되는 것에 유의한다.

32 식탁 위에 '몇몇의' 쿠키와 '많은' 캔디가 있으므로 각각 some과 many를 쓴다. 병 안에 사과 주스는 없으므로 부정문에서 '조금도 (~도 없다)'라는 의미로 쓰이는 any를 쓰고, 아침에 너무 '많은' 주스를 먹었다고 하였으므로 셀 수 없는 명사 juice 앞에는 much를 써야

한다.

33 '보통, 대개'라는 뜻의 빈도부사 usually를 사용하여 「주어(We) + 빈도부사(usually) + 일반동사(go) ~.」의 형태로 나타내며, on weekends는 '주말에, 주말마다'라는 뜻이다.

34 (1) 뒤에 셀 수 있는 명사의 복수형(friends)이 왔으므로 much를 many[a lot of/lots of]로 고쳐야 한다.
(2) 동사 love를 꾸며 주는 부사가 와야 하는 자리이므로 형용사 real을 부사 really로 고쳐야 한다.

35 (1) 인호는 매일 아침 조깅을 한다고 하였으므로 '항상'이라는 뜻의 빈도부사 always를 일반동사(goes) 앞에 사용하여 문장을 완성한다.
(2) 인호는 일주일에 한 번 친구들과 축구를 한다고 하였으므로 '때때로'라는 뜻의 빈도부사 sometimes를 일반동사(plays) 앞에 쓰거나 문장 맨 끝에 써서 문장을 완성한다.

Chapter 09 전치사

Practice 01 장소를 나타내는 전치사
본문 113쪽

Grammar Check Up

A 1 under   2 on
   3 next to   4 in front of
   5 in

B 1 at   2 in
   3 them   4 next to

C 1 in   2 behind
   3 under   4 on

Practice 02 시간을 나타내는 전치사
본문 115쪽

Grammar Check Up

A 1 at   2 on
   3 on   4 in
   5 at   6 in
   7 during   8 for

B 1 in   2 during
   3 for   4 on
   5 in, at

C 1 after   2 before
   3 before   4 after

D 1 during → for   2 in → on
   3 in → at   4 at → in

A 1 at, on   2 under, on, next to
    3 in front of, behind

B 1 reads the newspaper before breakfast
    2 will have Jenny's birthday party on Sunday
    3 turn off your cell phone during the concert
    4 plays computer games at night
    5 works for 9 hours a day

C (1) at   (2) on   (3) for   (4) in
    (5) after   (6) at   (7) during

D (1) next to   (2) behind
    (3) next to

01 ③	02 ④	03 ③	04 ①	05 ②
06 ③	07 ②	08 ①	09 ②	10 ④
11 ②	12 ③	13 ⑤	14 ④	15 ③
16 ②	17 ①	18 ④	19 ②	20 ⑤
21 ③	22 ⑤	23 ③	24 ④	25 ③

26 I will travel to Europe during the summer vacation.
27 I always have a headache before an exam.
28 is behind the movie theater
29 always comes before thunder
30 is next to the hospital
31 is in front of the park
32 It is on the bed.
33 It is under the chair.
34 (1) It is a big holiday in Korea.
    (2) We'll watch the full moon in the evening.
35 My sister's birthday is on March 15.

01 '~ 동안'의 의미로 뒤에 숫자를 포함한 구체적인 기간이 나오므로 전치사 for를 쓴다.

02 '~ 후에'라는 의미는 전치사 after로 쓴다.

03 특정한 시점을 나타내는 night 앞에는 전치사 at을 쓴다.

04 연도 앞에는 전치사 in을 쓴다.

05 어깨 위에 개미 한 마리가 있는 것으로 '(표면과 맞닿은 바로) ~ 위에'라는 의미는 전치사 on을 쓴다.

06 첫 번째 빈칸은 특정한 시점을 나타내는 noon 앞이므로 전치사 at을 써야 하고, 두 번째 빈칸은 장소의 한 지점을 나타내므로 전치사 at을 써야 한다.

07 첫 번째 빈칸은 바닥 위에서 자고 있다는 의미이므로 '(표면과 맞닿은 바로) ~위에'라는 의미의 전치사 on을 써야 하고, 두 번째 빈칸은 특정한 날 앞이므로 전치사 on을 써야 한다.

08 첫 번째 빈칸은 월 앞이므로 전치사 in을 써야 하고, 두 번째 빈칸은 도시 앞이므로 전치사 in을 써야 한다.

09 전치사 뒤에는 대명사의 목적격이 와야 하므로 me가 와야 한다.

10 문맥상 '~ 동안'이라는 의미가 와야 하고 숫자를 포함한 구체적인 기간 앞에는 전치사 during이 아니라 for를 쓴다.

11 계절 앞에는 전치사 in을 쓴다.

12 휴대전화는 침대 '아래에(under)' 있다.

13 Jennifer는 우체국 '앞에(in front of)' 있다.

14 고양이는 Green 씨의 '옆에(next to)' 있다.

15 ③ 요일 앞에는 전치사 on을 쓴다. ①, ⑤ 장소의 한 지점 앞에는 전치사 at을 쓴다. ② 구체적인 시각 앞에는 전치사 at을 쓴다. ④ 특정한 시점인 noon 앞에는 전치사 at을 쓴다.

16 ② 특정한 날 앞에는 전치사 on을 쓴다. ①,③,④,⑤ '~안에'라는 의미로 쓰거나 국가, 연도, 계절 앞에는 전치사 in을 쓴다.

17 ② at → on, 나뭇잎이 내 머리로 떨어진 것이므로 '(표면과 맞닿은 바로) ~위에'라는 의미는 전치사 on을 쓴다.
③ in → on, 날짜 앞에는 전치사 on을 쓴다.
④ in → at, 특정한 시점을 나타내는 night 앞에는 전치사 at을 쓴다.
⑤ during → for, '~ 동안'이라는 의미로 뒤에 숫자를 포함한 구체적인 기간이 올 때는 전치사 for를 쓴다.

18 ① on → in, 계절 앞에는 전치사 in을 쓴다.
② next → next to, '~옆에'라는 의미는 전치사 next to로 쓴다.
③ in → on, 요일 앞에는 전치사 on을 쓴다.
⑤ on → during, '~ 동안'이라는 의미로 뒤에 특정한 때를 나타내는 말이 올 때는 전치사 during을 쓴다.

19 '~ 동안'이라는 의미로 뒤에 특정한 때(drought)를 나타내는 말이 올 때는 전치사 for가 아닌 during을 써야 한다. (drought: 가뭄)

20 국가 앞에는 전치사 in을 써야 한다.

21 '~ 아래에'라는 의미는 전치사 under를 쓴다.

22 '~ 동안'이라는 의미로 특정한 때(math class)가 뒤에 올 때는 전치사 during을 써야 한다.

23 ⓑ in → at, 특정한 시점을 나타내는 noon 앞에는 전치사 at을 쓴다.
ⓓ on → in, 월 앞에는 전치사 in을 쓴다.

24 ⓐ in → on, 날짜 앞에는 전치사 on을 쓴다.

25 ⓑ in → on, '(표면과 맞닿은 바로) ~위에'라는 의미는 전치사 on을 쓴다.
ⓒ during → for, '~ 동안'이라는 의미로 뒤에 숫자를 포함한 구체적인 기간이 올 때는 전치사 for를 쓴다.

26 '~ 동안'의 의미로 뒤에 the summer vacation이라는 특정한 때를 나타내는 말이 올 때는 전치사 during을 써서 나타낸다.

27 '~ 전에'라는 의미의 시간을 나타내는 전치사 before를 쓴다.

28 영화관은 은행 앞에(in front of) 있다. = 은행은 영화관 뒤에(behind) 있다.

29 천둥은 항상 번개 후에(after) 친다. = 번개는 항상 천둥 전에(before) 친다.

30 우체국은 병원 '옆에(next to)' 있다.

31 빵집은 공원 '앞에(in front of)' 있다.

32 고양이는 대명사 It으로 쓰고 침대 위에 있으므로 전치사 on을 써서 on the bed로 쓴다.

33 가방은 의자 아래에 있으므로 전치사 under를 써서 under the chair로 쓴다.

34 (1) 국가 앞에는 전치사 in을 쓴다.
(2) 저녁(the evening) 앞에는 전치사 in을 쓴다.

35 날짜 앞에 쓰이는 전치사 on을 이용하여 on March 15로 나타낸다.

2 How much sugar did you buy?
3 Where did you put your pens?
4 Why is he in the hospital?
5 When did you build the house?

C (1) How long　　(2) What
(3) Who

D 1 Who　　　　2 Where
3 When, when　　4 Why

Chapter 10 의문사

Practice 01 의문사 who, what
본문 125쪽

Grammar Check Up

A 1 What 　　2 Who
3 What 　　4 Whom
5 Who 　　6 Whose

B 1 Who 　　2 What
3 Whose 　　4 Who(m)
5 What

C 1 What 　　2 Who
3 Whose 　　4 What
5 Who(m)

Practice 02 의문사 when, where, why, how
본문 127쪽

Grammar Check Up

A 1 How 　　2 When
3 Where 　　4 Why
5 How

B 1 ⓐ 　　2 ⓓ
3 ⓑ 　　4 ⓒ

C 1 When[What time] 　　2 Why
3 How fast 　　4 How often

Writing Exercise
본문 128~129쪽

A 1 Who 　　2 Who(m)
3 How 　　4 How long
5 When 　　6 Why

B 1 Who told you the answer?

Actual Test
본문 130~134쪽

01 ③　02 ④　03 ⑤　04 ③　05 ②
06 ⑤　07 ⑤　08 ③　09 ④　10 ⑤
11 ②　12 ③　13 ①　14 ④　15 ②
16 ②　17 ①　18 ②　19 ④　20 ③
21 ⑤　22 ④　23 ③　24 ④　25 ③

26 Who solved the math problem?
27 Where did you buy this hat?
28 How many cars are there in[at] the parking lot?
29 Who(m) did you meet
30 What will you make
31 How often do you visit
32 What is, cooking
33 How many, seven days
34 (1) What → Why (2) How often → How long
35 (1) What does Ben do after school?
(2) How often does Ben go to the soccer club?

01 '언제'인지 때를 묻는 의문사는 when이다.

02 '무엇'인지 사물을 묻는 의문사는 what이다.

03 '왜'인지 이유를 묻는 의문사는 why이다.

04 책을 '지난 일요일'에 빌렸다고 대답하고 있으므로 때를 묻는 의문사 when이 알맞다.

05 '셔츠'를 샀다고 대답하고 있으므로 사물을 묻는 의문사 what이 알맞다.

06 because로 대답하는 것으로 보아 이유를 묻는 의문사 why가 알맞다.

07 '여기서부터 겨우 10미터'라고 대답하는 것으로 보아 거리가 얼마나 먼지 묻는 how far가 알맞다.

08 '가장 좋아하는 선생님이 누구인지' 묻고 있으므로 사람을 묻는 의문사 who가 알맞다.

09 셀 수 없는 명사와 함께 쓰여 '얼마나 많은'이라는 의미를 나타내므로 how much가 알맞다.

10 '은행이 언제 문을 여는지' 묻고 있으므로 시간을 묻는 의문사 when이나 what time이 알맞다.

11 생일 파티에 누구를 초대할지 묻고 있으므로 '수진이와 Mike를 초대할 것'이라는 대답이 알맞다.

12 가방을 어디서 보았는지 묻고 있으므로 '침대 위에서 가방을 봤다'라는 대답이 알맞다.

13 시청에 가는 방법을 묻고 있으므로 '지하철로 갈 수 있다'라는 대답이 알맞다.

14 첫 번째 빈칸은 '너의 직업이 무엇인지' 묻고 있으므로 사람의 직업을 물을 때 사용할 수 있는 의문사 what이 알맞다. 두 번째 빈칸은 '너는 파티에 무엇을 입을 것인지' 묻고 있으므로 사물을 묻는 의문사 what이 알맞다.

15 첫 번째 빈칸은 '콘서트는 어땠는지' 묻고 있으므로 상태를 묻는 의문사 how가 알맞다. 두 번째 빈칸은 '너는 한국에 얼마나 오래 머무를 것인지' 묻고 있으므로 '얼마나 오래'라는 의미를 나타내는 how long이 와야 하므로 how가 알맞다.

16 의문사가 쓰인 일반동사 의문문은 「의문사 + do동사 + 주어 + 동사원형 ~?」으로 나타내는데, 주어가 3인칭 단수(the movie)이므로 is를 does로 고쳐야 한다.

17 '일주일에 한 번' 부모님댁을 방문한다는 B의 대답으로 보아 How long(얼마나 오래)을 How often(얼마나 자주)으로 고쳐야 한다.

18 샤워를 '저녁에' 한다는 대답으로 보아 '언제 샤워를 하는지' 묻는 질문이 알맞으므로 의문사 when이 쓰인 질문이 와야 한다.

19 '고열이 있었기 때문'이라고 이유를 말하는 대답으로 보아 '왜 집에 일찍 갔는지'를 묻는 질문이 알맞으므로 의문사 why가 쓰인 질문이 와야 한다.

20 주어가 없으므로 주어를 넣어서 '너는 언제 집을 청소했니?(When did you clean the house?)'나 '누가 집을 청소했니?(Who cleaned the house?)'와 같은 질문으로 고쳐야 한다.

21 '누가 너에게 그 그림을 보여주었니?'라고 묻고 있으므로 소유격 Whose를 주격 Who로 고쳐야 한다.

22 '무엇을 기다리고 있는지' 묻는 A의 말에 '버스가 5분 전에 떠났다'라는 B의 대답은 자연스럽지 않다.

23 ⓒ lives → live, 의문사가 쓰인 일반동사 의문문은 「의문사 + do동사 + 주어 + 동사원형 ~?」의 형태로 쓴다.
ⓓ many → much, 셀 수 없는 명사(water)와 함께 쓰여 '얼마나 많은'이라는 의미를 나타내므로 How much가 알맞다.

24 ⓐ Who → Whose, '그것이 누구의 아이디어인지' 묻고 있으므로 소유격 Whose를 써야 한다.

25 ⓐ Whom → Who, '누가 선생님인지' 묻고 있으므로 주격 Who를 써야 한다.
ⓓ invented → invent, 의문사가 쓰인 일반동사 과거형 의문문은 「의문사 + did + 주어 + 동사원형 ~?」의 형태로 쓴다.

26 의문사가 주어인 의문문으로 '누가 그 수학 문제를 풀었는지' 묻고 있으므로 「의문사(Who) + 동사 ~?」의 어순으로 나타낸다.

27 의문사가 쓰인 일반동사 과거형 의문문으로 '어디서 샀는지'를 묻고 있으므로 장소를 묻는 의문사 where를 사용하여 「의문사(Where) + did + 주어 + 동사원형 ~?」의 어순으로 나타낸다.

28 '주차장에 얼마나 많은 자동차가 있는지' 묻고 있고, 셀 수 있는 명사(car)이므로 '얼마나 많은'이라는 의미의 수를 묻는 how many를 쓴다. '~(들)이 있다'라는 의미의 「there is[are] ~」의 구조를 사용하여 「How many cars + are there ~?」의 어순으로 나타낸다.

29 어제 'Jim'을 만났다고 대답하고 있으므로 어제 '누구를' 만났는지 묻

는 의문문이 와야 한다. 의문사 who(m)과 일반동사(meet)를 사용하여 「의문사(who(m)) + did + 주어 + 동사원형 ~?」의 어순으로 나타낸다.

30 점심으로 '스파게티'를 만들 것이라고 대답하고 있으므로 점심으로 '무엇을' 만들지 묻는 의문문이 와야 한다. 의문사 what을 사용하여 「의문사(what) + 조동사 + 주어 + 동사원형 ~?」의 어순으로 나타낸다.

31 '한 달에 두 번'이라는 빈도로 답하고 있으므로 빈도를 묻는 의문사 how often과 일반동사(visit)를 사용하여 「의문사(how often) + do동사 + 주어 + 동사원형 ~?」의 어순으로 나타낸다.

32 Tom이 '무엇을 하고 있는지'를 묻는 의문문이 되어야 자연스러우므로 의문사 what을 사용한다. 또한, 현재진행형 시제가 쓰였고, Tom은 3인칭 주어이므로 동사 자리에 is를 쓴다. 대답도 「be동사 + 동사원형-ing」 형태의 현재진행형으로 cooking을 써야 알맞다.

33 셀 수 있는 명사(days)와 함께 '얼마나 많은'이라는 의미를 나타내는 how many를 쓴다. 대답으로는 7일(seven days)이라고 써야 한다.

34 (1) '숙제를 해야 하기 때문에'라고 도서관에 가는 이유를 말하는 B의 대답으로 보아 의문사 What을 Why로 고쳐야 한다.
(2) '3시간 동안'이라는 B의 대답으로 보아 '얼마나 오래' 있을지 묻는 말이 와야 하므로 How often(얼마나 자주)을 How long(얼마나 오래)으로 고쳐야 한다.

35 (1) 방과 후에 보통 '축구를 한다'고 했으므로 Ben이 방과 후에 무엇을 하는지 묻는 질문이 되도록 의문사 what을 사용하여 「What + do동사 + 주어 + 동사원형 ~?」의 형태로 써야 알맞다.
(2) '일주일에 두 번'이라고 했으므로 얼마나 자주 축구 클럽에 가는지 묻는 질문이 되도록 how often(얼마나 자주)을 사용하여 「How often + do동사 + 주어 + 동사원형 ~?」의 형태로 써야 알맞다.

Chapter 11 접속사

Practice 01 접속사 and, but, or, so 본문 137쪽

Grammar Check Up

A
1 and	2 or
3 but	4 so
5 or	

B
1 and	2 so
3 or	4 but

C
1 I can drive a car, but I can't ride a bike.
2 I went to the window, and I looked out.
3 It was Jenny's birthday, so we phoned her.
4 Will you fix the computer or will you buy a new computer?

접속사 when, because

Grammar Check Up

A 1 when
2 Because of
3 when
4 because
5 get

B 1 because
2 When
3 because
4 when
5 when

C 1 There were many people in the station when we arrived there.
2 Because I was very tired, I stayed home all day long.
3 I couldn't arrive at the airport on time because I missed the train.
4 When she was six years old, she wrote her first story.

Writing Exercise   본문 140~141쪽

A 1 but it is difficult
2 so she didn't say a word all day long
3 and they study a lot of things
4 or you can go to a hotel
5 so he won first prize in the math contest

B 1 when she reads books
2 Because she was sick
3 because it is old
4 When the crosswalk light is green
5 because of a stomachache

C (1) and   (2) because
(3) When   (4) and
(5) and   (6) and
(7) so

D (1) and a scarf
(2) but we don't have any rings
(3) or the blue one

Actual Test   본문 142~146쪽

01 ①	02 ④	03 ②	04 ③	05 ⑤
06 ④	07 ②	08 ②	09 ⑤	10 ①
11 ③	12 ②	13 ③	14 ④	15 ⑤
16 ⑤	17 ①	18 ②	19 ⑤	20 ④
21 ④	22 ③	23 ②	24 ③	25 ③

26 eat noodles or rice for dinner
27 very tired because I walked for an hour
28 be careful when you use a knife
29 He took a look at the red car, and he bought it right

away.
30 The test was very difficult, but she passed it.
31 I drank too much coffee, so I'm not sleepy.
32 (1) and (2) but (3) or
33 When she cooks in the kitchen, she listens to music.
34 Because she missed the bus,
35 (1) so (2) grow up

01 '~와', '그리고'의 의미는 접속사 and로 나타낸다.

02 빈칸 다음에 컴퓨터를 새로 산 이유가 이어지고 있으므로 '~ 때문에'라는 이유를 나타내는 접속사 because가 알맞다.

03 서로 반대되는 내용이 연결되고 있으므로 '그러나'라는 의미의 접속사 but이 알맞다.

04 '쉬거나 약을 먹어야 한다'라는 선택 사항에 대해 말하고 있으므로 접속사 or가 알맞다.

05 '동물원에 갔지만 얼룩말을 보지 못했다'라는 의미가 되어야 자연스러우므로 서로 반대되는 내용을 연결하는 접속사 but이 알맞다.

06 '그 소식을 들었을 때 그녀는 울었다'라는 의미가 되어야 자연스러우므로 접속사 When이 알맞다.

07 '바빠서 점심을 먹지 않았다'라는 의미가 되어야 자연스러우므로 because를 so로 고쳐야 한다.

08 '긴장할 때[긴장하기 때문에] 다리를 떤다'라는 의미가 되어야 자연스러우므로 So를 When 또는 Because로 고쳐야 한다.

09 첫 번째 빈칸은 '컴퓨터를 사용하지 않을 때 그것을 꺼야 한다'라는 의미가 자연스러우므로 '~할 때'의 의미를 나타내는 접속사 when이 알맞다. 두 번째 빈칸은 '음식을 먹을 때 포크를 사용한다'라는 의미가 자연스러우므로 접속사 when이 와야 한다.

10 첫 번째 빈칸은 '나는 컵, 그릇과 병이 필요하다'라는 의미가 자연스러우므로 '~와', '그리고'의 의미를 나타내는 접속사 and가 알맞다. 두 번째 빈칸은 '스테이크와 양파 수프를 주문했다'라는 의미가 자연스러우므로 접속사 and가 와야 한다.

11 첫 번째 빈칸은 '네 혹은 아니요 중 하나로 대답하라'라는 의미가 자연스러우므로 '또는', '혹은'의 의미를 나타내는 접속사 or가 알맞다. 두 번째 빈칸은 '내일 또는 다음 주 월요일에 부산으로 떠난다'라는 의미가 자연스러우므로 접속사 or가 와야 한다.

12 ②는 '언제'라는 의미의 의문사 when이 쓰였고, ①,③,④,⑤는 '~할 때'라는 의미의 접속사 when이 쓰였다.

13 '너무 더웠기 때문에 나는 땀을 많이 흘렸다'라는 접속사 because가 쓰인 문장은 '너무 더워서 나는 땀을 많이 흘렸다'라는 접속사 so를 사용한 문장과 의미가 같다.

14 '나는 저녁 식사 후에 개를 데리고 산책한다'라는 접속사 after가 쓰인 문장은 '나는 개를 데리고 산책하기 전에 저녁 식사를 한다'라는 접속사 before를 쓴 문장과 의미가 같다.

15 첫 번째 빈칸은 '내 차가 고장났기 때문에 나는 버스를 탔다'라는 의미가 자연스러우므로 '~ 때문에'라는 이유를 나타내는 접속사 because가 와야 한다. 두 번째 빈칸은 '안개 때문에 잘 보이지 않는다'라는 의미가 자연스럽고, 뒤에 명사(구)가 이어지고 있으므로 because of가 와야 알맞다.

16 첫 번째 빈칸은 미래의 일을 나타내는 문장으로, 시간의 부사절에서는

현재형으로 미래의 의미를 나타내지만 주절은 미래형을 써야 하므로 will go가 와야 한다. 두 번째 빈칸은 시간의 부사절이므로 미래의 일을 현재형으로 나타내어 comes가 와야 알맞다.

17 because 뒤에 명사구 his confidence가 왔으므로 because를 because of로 고쳐야 한다.

18 when이 이끄는 시간의 부사절에서는 미래형 대신 현재형으로 미래를 나타내므로 will graduate를 graduates로 고쳐야 한다.

19 ⑤ 서로 반대되는 내용이 연결되고 있으므로 접속사 but이 들어가야 한다. ①,②,③,④ 비슷하거나 연결되는 내용이 이어지고 있으므로 접속사 and가 들어가야 한다.

20 ③ '그가 오늘 바빠서 그곳에 가지 못했다'라는 내용이므로 접속사 because가 들어가야 한다. ①,②,④,⑤ '~할 때'라는 의미의 접속사 when이 들어가야 한다.

21 두 개의 문장이 서로 반대되는 내용이므로 접속사 but으로 연결한다.

22 '~하면'의 의미로 접속사 when을 써야 하고, when이 이끄는 시간의 부사절에서는 주절이 미래형일지라도 부사절은 현재형으로 써야 하므로 주절은 will have, when절은 comes가 알맞다.

23 ⓑ so → because, '비가 많이 와서 일찍 돌아왔다'라는 의미가 되어야 자연스러우므로 '~ 때문에'의 의미를 나타내는 접속사 because를 쓴다.
ⓓ but → so, '1년 동안 아파서 직업을 잃었다'라는 의미가 되어야 자연스러우므로 '그래서'라는 의미의 접속사 so를 쓴다.

24 ⓐ because → because of, 뒤에 명사구(the snow)가 이어지므로 because of가 와야 한다.
ⓒ has to → have to, or로 연결된 단어가 주어로 쓰인 경우, 동사는 or 뒤의 단어(I)에 수를 일치시킨다.

25 ⓒ will be → are, when이 이끄는 시간의 부사절이므로 미래형을 현재형을 써야 한다.
ⓓ because of → because, 뒤에 「주어 + 동사」 형태의 절이 이어지므로 because를 써야 한다.

26 '또는'이라는 의미의 접속사 or를 사용하여 문장을 완성한다.

27 '~ 때문에'라는 의미의 이유를 나타내는 접속사 because를 사용하여 문장을 완성한다.

28 '~할 때'라는 의미의 시간을 나타내는 접속사 when을 사용하여 문장을 완성한다.

29 '그는 빨간 차를 한 번 보고 바로 샀다.'라는 의미가 되도록 '그리고'의 의미를 나타내는 접속사 and를 사용하여 한 문장으로 연결한다.

30 '그 시험은 매우 어려웠지만, 그녀는 그것을 통과했다.'라는 의미가 되도록 '그러나'의 의미를 나타내는 접속사 but을 사용하여 한 문장으로 연결한다.

31 '나는 커피를 너무 많이 마셔서, 잠이 오지 않는다.'라는 의미가 되도록 '그래서'라는 의미를 나타내는 접속사 so를 사용하여 한 문장으로 연결한다.

32 (1) '텐트, 음식과 침낭을 살 필요가 있다'라는 의미가 자연스러우므로 '~와', '그리고'의 의미를 나타내는 접속사 and가 와야 자연스럽다.
(2) '알고 있지만, 충분한 돈이 없다'는 내용이므로 '그러나'라는 의미의 접속사 but이 와야 한다.
(3) '부모님께 돈을 요청하거나 캠핑을 가지 않는 것으로 결정해야 한다'는 내용이므로 '또는', '혹은'의 의미를 나타내는 접속사 or가 와야 한다.

33 '~할 때'라는 의미의 시간을 나타내는 접속사 when을 써야 한다. 접속사 when이 쓰인 부사절로 시작하라고 하였으므로 문장 뒤에 콤마를 넣고, 주절 she listens to music을 이어서 쓴다.

34 '~ 때문에'라는 의미의 이유를 나타내는 접속사 because를 사용하여 나타내고 부사절이 주절 앞에 있으므로 콤마를 문장 뒤에 쓴다.

35 (1) 문맥상 '그녀를 존경해서 선생님이 될 것이다'라는 의미가 되어야 자연스러우므로 but을 so로 고쳐야 한다.
(2) 시간을 나타내는 부사절에서는 미래에 일어날 일을 현재형으로 나타내므로 grow up이 알맞다.

Chapter 12 명령문, 청유문, 감탄문

Practice 01 명령문, 청유문
본문 149쪽

Grammar Check Up

A 1 Eat   2 Don't
3 Be   4 don't be
5 Let's

B 1 Don't ride   2 Turn off
3 Let's play   4 Don't cross

C 1 Let's wait in line.
2 Don't cut your fingernails too short.
3 Let's not fight again.
4 Brush your teeth after eating.
5 Don't sit on the table.

Practice 02 감탄문
본문 151쪽

Grammar Check Up

A 1 How   2 What
3 How   4 a long
5 tall

B 1 How handsome   2 What an old building
3 How exciting   4 How hard
5 What fresh juice

C 1 What a wonderful world it is!
2 How lucky the man is!
3 What an expensive sweater this is!
4 What a cheap watch it is!
5 What good students they are!

Writing **Exercise**

A 1 Do exercise   2 Don't tell a lie
   3 How brave   4 Let's not throw
   5 What surprising news

B 1 What a good singer she is!
   2 Do your homework after dinner.
   3 Don't come home too late.
   4 Let's make a model airplane together.
   5 How hard this work was!

C (1) Don't surf   (2) Go, get
   (3) Don't eat   (4) Don't skip
   (5) Don't use   (6) Be careful

D (1) How beautiful   (2) What a tall tower
   (3) What an old tower   (4) Let's take pictures

Actual Test

01 ⑤	02 ⑤	03 ②	04 ②	05 ③
06 ①	07 ②	08 ①	09 ⑤	10 ④
11 ①	12 ⑤	13 ②	14 ⑤	15 ②
16 ⑤	17 ①	18 ③	19 ④	20 ③
21 ④	22 ②	23 ④	24 ③	25 ④

26 Let's go on a picnic this weekend.
27 How narrow the road is!
28 What a brave soldier he is!
29 Listen to the teacher in class.
30 Don't play computer games too long.
31 What a cute cat it is!
32 (1) mix the ingredients together[mix together ingredients]
     (2) don't touch the hot apple pie
33 Let's play soccer after school.
34 (1) ②, Let's clean the room.
     (2) ④, How dirty they are![What dirty socks they are!]
35 Don't be late again.

01 '~하지 마라.'라는 의미의 부정 명령문이므로 「Don't + 동사원형 ~.」으로 나타낸다.

02 '~하자.'라는 의미의 청유문이므로 「Let's + 동사원형 ~.」으로 나타낸다.

03 명사를 강조하는 감탄문은 「What + a[an] + 형용사 + 명사 + 주어 + 동사!」의 형태로 쓴다.

04 일반동사의 부정 명령문은 「Don't + 동사원형 ~.」으로 나타내므로 Don't cry.로 고쳐야 한다.

05 명령문은 동사원형으로 시작하므로 Study로 고쳐야 한다.

06 첫 번째 빈칸은 '내가 저녁을 요리할 것이니 외식하지 말자'라는 내용이 되어야 자연스러우므로 부정 청유문 「Let's not + 동사원형 ~.」의 형태가 와야 한다. 두 번째 빈칸은 '방 안이 너무 더우니 창문을 열자'라는 내용이 되어야 하므로 긍정 청유문 「Let's + 동사원형 ~.」의

07 첫 번째 빈칸은 주소가 무엇인지 묻고 있으므로 의문사 What이 알맞다. 두 번째 빈칸은 명사를 강조하는 감탄문이므로 「What + a[an] + 형용사 + 명사 + 주어 + 동사!」의 형태로 써야 한다.

08 첫 번째 빈칸은 형용사를 강조하는 감탄문이므로 「How + 형용사/부사 + 주어 + 동사!」의 형태가 와야 한다. 두 번째 빈칸은 '운동을 얼마나 자주 하는지' 묻는 문장이므로 의문사 How often이 적절하다.

09 must not은 '~해서는 안 된다'라는 의미로 금지를 나타낸다. 따라서 금지의 의미를 나타내는 부정 명령문 「Don't + 동사원형 ~.」으로 바꿔 쓸 수 있다.

10 「Shall we + 동사원형 ~?」은 '우리 ~할까?'라는 청유의 의미를 나타내므로 긍정 청유문 「Let's + 동사원형 ~.」으로 바꿔 쓸 수 있다.

11 명령문은 동사원형으로 시작하므로 be동사인 경우에는 Be ~.로 나타내야 한다. 따라서 Do를 Be로 고쳐야 한다.

12 '~하지 말자.'라는 부정 청유문은 「Let's not + 동사원형 ~.」으로 나타내므로 go not을 not go로 고쳐야 한다.

13 강조하는 명사가 복수형으로 형용사 앞에 a가 필요하지 않으므로 a huge를 huge로 고쳐야 한다.

14 ⑤는 형용사 noisy를 강조하는 감탄문이므로 How가 와야 하고, ①, ②, ③, ④는 명사를 강조하는 감탄문이므로 What이 와야 한다.

15 ②는 명사 nice cars를 강조하는 감탄문이므로 What이 와야 하고, ①, ③, ④, ⑤는 형용사나 부사를 강조하는 감탄문이므로 How가 와야 한다.

16 영화 시작 5분 전이라는 내용으로 보아 빨리 가자는 내용이 이어지는 것이 자연스러우므로 ⑤ '뛰자.'가 적절하다.

17 비가 많이 내리고 있다는 내용으로 보아 집에 있으라는 내용이 이어지는 것이 자연스러우므로 ① '집에 머물러라.'가 알맞다.

18 ① Do → Be, be동사의 긍정 명령문은 원형인 Be를 사용한다.
② an → a, 형용사 poor 앞에 쓰인 관사이므로 a가 와야 한다.
④ Be watch → Watch, 일반동사의 긍정 명령문은 「동사원형 ~.」의 형태로 나타낸다.
⑤ What → How, 형용사 colorful을 강조하는 감탄문이므로 How를 써야 한다.

19 ① Does not → Don't, 일반동사의 부정 명령문은 「Don't + 동사원형 ~.」의 형태로 나타낸다.
② How → What, 명사 soft scarves를 강조하는 감탄문이므로 What을 써야 한다.
③ What → How, 형용사 clean을 강조하는 감탄문이므로 How를 써야 한다.
⑤ watches → watch, 부정 명령문은 「Don't + 동사원형 ~.」의 형태로 나타낸다.

20 형용사 lovely를 강조하는 how 감탄문으로 「How + 형용사/부사 + 주어 + 동사!」의 형태로 나타낸다.

21 '~하지 말자.'라는 부정 청유문은 「Let's not + 동사원형 ~.」의 형태로 나타낸다.

22 ⓐ How → What, 명사 a beautiful park를 강조하는 감탄문이므로 What을 써야 한다.
ⓓ runs → run, 부정 명령문은 「Don't + 동사원형 ~.」의 형태로 나타낸다.

23 ⓐ Do → Be, be동사의 긍정 명령문은 원형인 Be를 사용한다.
ⓒ Lets → Let's, '~하지 말자.'라는 부정 청유문의 형태는 「Let's
not + 동사원형 ~.」이다.
ⓓ is it → it is, 명사를 강조하는 what 감탄문은 「What + a[an]
+ 형용사 + 명사 + 주어 + 동사!」의 형태로 쓴다.

24 ⓑ Not → Don't, 일반동사의 부정 명령문은 「Don't + 동사원형
~.」의 형태로 나타낸다.
ⓒ How → What, 명사 a tiny puppy를 강조하는 감탄문이므로
What을 써야 한다.

25 ⓐ Finishes → Finish, 일반동사의 긍정 명령문은 「동사원형 ~.」의
형태로 나타낸다.

26 '~하자.'라는 의미의 청유문이므로 「Let's + 동사원형 ~.」으로 나타낸
다.

27 형용사 narrow를 강조하는 감탄문이므로 「How + 형용사/부사 +
주어 + 동사!」로 나타낸다.

28 명사 a brave soldier를 강조하는 감탄문이므로 「What + a[an]
+ 형용사 + 명사 + 주어 + 동사!」로 나타낸다.

29 '수업 시간에 선생님 말씀에 귀 기울여라.'라는 의미가 되어야 자연스
러우므로 동사원형으로 시작하는 명령문으로 나타낸다.

30 '너무 오래 컴퓨터 게임을 하지 마라.'라는 의미가 되어야 자연스러우
므로 부정 명령문 「Don't + 동사원형 ~.」의 형태로 나타낸다.

31 '정말 귀여운 고양이구나!'라는 의미가 되어야 자연스러우므로 명사를
강조하는 what 감탄문 「What + a[an] + 형용사 + 명사 + 주어 +
동사!」의 형태로 나타낸다.

32 (1) '~해라.'라는 의미를 나타내는 「동사원형 ~.」 형태의 긍정 명령문
이므로 mix the ingredients together 또는 mix together
ingredients의 어순으로 쓴다.
(2) '~하지 마라.'라는 의미를 나타내는 「Don't + 동사원형 ~.」 형태
의 부정 명령문이므로 don't touch the hot apple pie의 어순
으로 쓴다.

33 '방과 후에 축구하자.'라는 의미가 되어야 자연스러우므로 「Let's +
동사원형 ~.」 형태의 청유문으로 나타낸다.

34 (1) 「Let's + 동사원형 ~.」 형태의 청유문이므로 Lets를 Let's로 고
쳐야 한다.
(2) 형용사 dirty를 강조하는 감탄문이므로 What을 How로 고치
거나, 명사 socks를 강조하는 What dirty socks they are!로
고쳐야 한다.

35 문맥상 '다시는 늦지 마라.'라는 의미가 되어야 자연스러우므로 부정
명령문 「Don't + 동사원형 ~.」의 형태로 나타낸다.

Chapter 01 명사

Practice 01 셀 수 있는 명사
워크북 2~3쪽

01-1
1	notebooks	2	knives
3	puppies	4	teeth
5	days	6	men
7	dishes	8	roofs
9	cities	10	buses
11	pianos	12	stories

01-2
1	a	2	an
3	a	4	A
5	an	6	a
7	a	8	An
9	An	10	a
11	an	12	a

01-3
1	pigs	2	potato
3	piggy banks	4	sheep
5	teeth	6	mice
7	leaves		

01-4
1	children	2	fish
3	feet	4	scissors
5	shelves	6	classes
7	women	8	deer

01-5
1	an egg	2	three mice
3	Many deer	4	a good idea
5	three watches	6	a pair of sneakers
7	Four sweet potatoes		
8	fresh air		

Practice 02 셀 수 없는 명사
워크북 4~5쪽

02-1
1	×	2	A
3	×	4	×
5	×	6	×
7	×	8	an
9	a	10	×
11	a	12	an

02-2
1	glasses of juice	2	sheets of paper
3	cans of soda	4	slice of cheese
5	cup of tea	6	bottles of water
7	bowl of soup	8	loaves of bread
9	pieces of pizza	10	cartons of milk
11	bars of soap		

02-3
1	cola	2	happiness
3	sugar	4	Busan
5	two cups of cocoa	6	an English
7	a piece of meat		

02-4
1	slices of cake	2	time

3	Paris	4	pieces of paper
5	soda	6	friends
7	pair of glasses		

02-5
1	pork	2	a pair of pants
3	a lot of love	4	some money
5	two spoonfuls of sugar		
6	three bowls of rice		
7	two glasses of carrot juice		

Chapter Test
워크북 6~7쪽

01 ③, ④ 02 ④ 03 ②, ⑤ 04 ①, ③ 05 ⑤
06 ④ 07 ⑤ 08 ② 09 ④ 10 ②
11 an English → English 12 piece → pieces
13 a cup of coffee 14 a bottle of orange juice
15 (1) the France → France
　 (2) childs → children
　 (3) slice → bowl

01 ① potato의 복수형은 potatoes이다.
　 ② knife의 복수형은 knives이다.
　 ⑤ city의 복수형은 cities이다.

02 apple은 첫소리가 모음이므로 앞에 an이 들어가야 하고, 나머지는 모두 a가 들어가야 한다.

03 ② eraser는 첫소리가 모음이므로 a 다음에 올 수 없다.
　 ⑤ water는 셀 수 없는 명사이므로 앞에 a/an을 쓸 수 없다.

04 ① woman의 복수형 women이 되어야 적절하다.
　 ③ deer는 단수형과 복수형이 같으므로 deer가 되어야 적절하다.

05 (A) love는 셀 수 없는 명사이므로 앞에 a를 쓸 수 없다.
　 (B) glass(안경)와 같이 한 쌍을 이루는 명사는 항상 복수형 (glasses)으로 써야 한다.
　 (C) chocolate은 셀 수 없는 명사이므로 단위 표현 bar에 복수 표시하여 수량을 나타낸다.

06 salt는 셀 수 없는 명사이므로 복수형으로 쓸 수 없고, 단위 표현 a spoonful of를 사용하여 수량을 나타내야 한다. '소금 두 스푼'이므로 two spoonfuls of salt가 적절하다.

07 '장갑 한 켤레'는 a pair of gloves라고 쓰므로, 완전한 문장은 Buy a pair of gloves.의 순서가 된다. 따라서 세 번째 오는 단어는 pair이다.

08 house는 앞에 a를 쓰지만, 형용사 old의 첫소리가 모음이므로 앞에 an을 써야 한다.

09 ⓐ new bag → a[the] new bag / new bags, 셀 수 있는 명사 new bag 앞에는 a/an, the 또는 소유격을 쓰거나 복수형으로 써야 한다.
　 ⓓ bottle of ketchups → bottles of ketchup, ketchup은 셀 수 없는 명사이므로 단위 표현 bottle에 복수 표시를 해야 한다.

10 cheese는 셀 수 없는 명사로 복수형으로 쓸 수 없고, 단위 표현 a

slice of를 사용하여 복수를 나타내야 하므로 '치즈 두 장'은 two slices of cheese가 되어야 한다.

11 English(영어)는 셀 수 없는 명사이므로 앞에 an을 쓸 수 없다.

12 '피자 두 조각'은 셀 수 없는 명사 pizza 대신 단위 표현 piece에 복수 표시하여 two pieces of pizza로 써야 한다.

13 '커피 한 잔'은 a cup of coffee로 나타낸다.

14 '오렌지 주스 한 병'은 a bottle of orange juice로 나타낸다.

15 (1) 국가명 앞에 a/an, the를 쓸 수 없으므로 the를 빼고 France 라고 써야 한다.
(2) child의 복수형은 children이다.
(3) 셀 수 없는 명사 salad의 수량은 slice가 아니라 bowl을 써서 나타내므로 a bowl of salad라고 써야 한다.

Chapter 02 대명사

Practice 01 인칭대명사
워크북 8~9쪽

01-1
1 He　　　2 She
3 It　　　4 We
5 They　　6 You
7 her　　　8 her
9 them　　10 him
11 It　　　12 them

01-2
1 our　　　2 My
3 It　　　4 his
5 Its　　　6 your
7 them

01-3
1 him　　　2 me
3 her　　　4 his
5 our　　　6 you
7 He　　　8 their
9 your　　　10 Its
11 us　　　12 my

01-4
1 It is[It's] very interesting.
2 His father is a firefighter.
3 My grandparents visit us every Saturday.
4 She often calls them.
5 This is your computer.
6 I like their long ears.
7 I listen to her songs sometimes.

01-5
1 I miss them　　2 Our homework
3 its tail　　　4 We love you
5 My, help me　　6 like her paintings
7 They wear their

Practice 02 this, that, it
워크북 10~11쪽

02-1
1 These　　　2 That
3 It　　　4 This
5 Those　　　6 It

02-2
1 This　　　2 That
3 It　　　4 These
5 Those　　　6 It
7 This　　　8 Those
9 these　　　10 That

02-3
1 This　　　2 That
3 These　　　4 It
5 those　　　6 These
7 that

02-4
1 This watch is wrong. /
　These watches are wrong.
2 That[She] is my grandmother.
3 It is 5 km from here to the bank.
4 I need that bike. / I need those bikes.
5 These are her cats. / This is her cat.
6 Those boxes are very heavy. /
　That box is very heavy.
7 It is stormy here in Boston.

02-5
1 This boy is my son.
2 Those flowers are for you.
3 That is an easy problem.
4 It is dark outside.
5 Many children like these books.
6 Those are my old toys.
7 Those are brave soldiers.

Chapter Test
워크북 12~13쪽

01 ①　　02 ③　　03 ⑤　　04 ②　　05 ⑤
06 ②　　07 ①, ③　　08 ③　　09 ⑤　　10 ②
11 it[It]　　12 me　　13 Their
14 (1) Jenny's (2) my
15 (1) these → this (2) his → him

---

01 빈칸이 명사 앞에 위치하므로 소유격이 들어가야 하는데, us는 목적격이므로 알맞지 않다.

02 Those 다음에는 복수 명사가 와야 하므로 단수 명사인 camera는 알맞지 않다.

03 단수 명사 The rabbit의 소유격을 대신할 수 있는 인칭대명사는 Its 가 적절하다.

04 This는 '이 사람'의 의미로 사람을 가리킬 때도 쓸 수 있으므로 주어 진 우리말을 영작하면 This is my cousin.이 적절하다.

05 ⑤는 목적격으로 쓰인 her이다. 밑줄 친 her와 나머지는 모두 소유격으로 쓰인 her이다.

06 첫 번째 빈칸에는 앞 문장에서 언급한 Julia를 대신하는 목적격 her

가 들어가야 하고, 두 번째 빈칸에는 Julia와 I를 포함하는 주격 We 가 들어가야 한다.

07 ① this → these, socks가 복수 명사이므로 복수형 these를 써야 한다.
③ he → him, 동사 love의 목적어 자리이므로 목적격 him을 써야 한다.

08 ⓑ,ⓔ의 It은 '그것'을 나타내는 인칭대명사이다. ⓐ,ⓒ,ⓓ의 It은 날씨, 거리, 날짜 등을 나타내는 비인칭 주어이다.

09 glasses(안경)는 항상 복수형으로 쓰는 명사이므로 지시대명사로 복수형 those가 적절하고, 'Anna의'라는 소유격은 Anna's로 써서 Are those Anna's glasses?가 알맞다.

10 ⓐ This → It, 요일을 나타낼 때는 비인칭 주어 It을 주어로 쓴다.
ⓑ this → these, shoes가 복수 명사이므로 복수형인 these를 써야 한다.
ⓔ these → this 혹은 watch → waches, watch가 단수 명사이므로 단수형 지시형용사 this를 쓰거나 지시형용사 these가 왔으므로 복수 명사인 watches로 써야 한다.

11 시간, 명암을 나타낼 때는 비인칭 주어 it[It]을 쓴다.

12 I를 대신하는 대명사이고 remember의 목적어 자리이므로 I의 목적격 me를 쓴다.

13 Sophie and David를 대신하는 3인칭 복수 대명사이고 명사 앞이므로 they의 소유격 Their를 쓴다.

14 (1) 명사의 소유격은 명사 뒤에 's를 붙여서 나타내므로 Jenny's라고 쓴다.
(2) '나'의 소유격은 my로 쓴다.

15 (1) These → this, 단수 명사 picture 앞이므로 these의 단수형 this를 써야 한다.
(2) his → him, 전치사의 목적어 자리에는 목적격 him을 써야 한다.

Chapter
03 **be동사**

Practice 01 **be동사의 현재형** 워크북 14~15쪽

01-1
1	am	2	are
3	are	4	is
5	is	6	is
7	are	8	is
9	are	10	are
11	is	12	are

01-2
1 is, She's sad.
2 are, They're in the living room.
3 am, I'm thirsty.

4 is, It's hot and cloudy.
5 are, We're proud of you.
6 are, You're a kind teacher.
7 is, He's always late for school.
8 am, I'm 13 years old.
9 is, That's a good idea.
10 are, They're my best friends.

01-3
1	This	2	are
3	It	4	am
5	is	6	are
7	My grandmother		

01-4
1	is	2	is
3	are	4	are
5	is	6	are
7	are	8	are

01-5
1 This smartphone is
2 Those sneakers are
3 Juliet is
4 Many cookies are
5 Some turtles are
6 The pharmacy is
7 A piano is
8 Tom and his friends are

Practice 02 **be동사의 부정문과 의문문** 워크북 16~17쪽

02-1
1 He is not smart and wise.
2 You are not in our club.
3 Julie is not from Canada.
4 Daniel is not a genius.
5 Ella and I are not in the garden.
6 She is not a top ballerina.
7 They are not in the same class.
8 The cake is not in the refrigerator.

02-2
1 She's not my favorite singer. /
She isn't my favorite singer.
2 I'm not hungry now.
3 They're not good for our health. /
They aren't good for our health.
4 You're not honest. / You aren't honest.
5 We're not late for school. /
We aren't late for school.

02-3
1 Are they in Paris, France?, they aren't
2 Is he angry at me?, he isn't
3 Is it far from here?, it is
4 Are you good at math?, I am[we are]
5 Is her hair long and black?, it is

02-4
1	is not	2	Is
3	isn't	4	Is
5	aren't	6	Are
7	Are	8	am not

02-5
1	Billy is not	2	Are these

3 The book is not   4 Are the students

5 The water is not   6 Are the actors

02-6
1 This towel is not dirty.
2 Is he a magician?
3 She is not in the classroom.
4 Is this dish very spicy?
5 Are they at the movie theater?
6 The pool is not large.
7 Is your cell phone under the bed?
8 I am not busy this week.

Practice 03   be동사의 과거형   워크북 18~19쪽

03-1
1 She was in New Zealand
2 He was 150 cm tall
3 They were college students
4 Christmas was wonderful
5 We were baseball players
6 Brad was 12 years old
7 Jane and I were classmates

03-2
1 I wasn't eight years old last year.
2 Jenny and I weren't cheerleaders two years ago.
3 The vegetables weren't fresh an hour ago.
4 It wasn't snowy and stormy yesterday.
5 The bus wasn't crowded this morning.

03-3
1 Were they at the movie theater?, they weren't
2 Was his dad tired last night?, he was
3 Was the park very clean?, it wasn't
4 Were the caps on sale?, they were
5 Were you upset yesterday?, I wasn't[we weren't]

03-4
1 was   2 was not
3 Were   4 weren't
5 Was   6 were
7 Was

03-5
1 wasn't   2 was
3 were   4 weren't
5 wasn't   6 Were

03-6
1 Her backpack was not expensive.
2 Were Jessy and you in the cafeteria?
3 The books were not boring.
4 Were you free yesterday?
5 Was the market far from here?
6 The monkeys were not in the cage.
7 Was your father upstairs?

Practice 04   There is[are]   워크북 20~21쪽

04-1
1 There are   2 There are
3 There is   4 There are
5 There is   6 There are
7 There is

04-2
1 There are not[aren't] many onions in the basket.
2 There was a cat on the roof.
3 There were not[weren't] many mountains in our village.
4 There is not[isn't] a shirt on the bed.
5 There was not[wasn't] a pencil in the pencil case.

04-3
1 Are there many people on the bus?, there aren't
2 Was there an egg in the basket?, there was
3 Is there a picture on the wall?, there isn't
4 Were there two birds in the cage?, there were
5 Were there lots of books on the shelf?, there weren't

04-4
1 There are[were]   2 There isn't[wasn't]
3 There was   4 There is[was]
5 Was there   6 There are[were]
7 Was there

04-5
1 There is a pharmacy
2 There are two scientists
3 There were many ants
4 Are there five players
5 There was not[wasn't] any money

04-6
1 There was a big pond in our yard.
2 There are about 230 countries in the world.
3 There are not any fish in the fishbowl.
4 Were there many people at the party?
5 There were not any restaurants here last year.

Chapter Test   워크북 22~23쪽

01 ③   02 ④   03 ②   04 ④   05 ④
06 ⑤   07 ①, ⑤   08 ④   09 ⑤   10 ③
11 There were some pictures
12 are not[aren't] interesting
13 (1) Were   (2) wasn't   14 It's → Its
15 parents

---

01   주어인 His eye color가 단수이므로 are가 아닌 is가 와야 한다.

02   첫 번째 빈칸은 Kevin and I가 복수이므로 are가 알맞고, 두 번째

빈칸은 His name이 3인칭 단수이므로 is, 세 번째 빈칸은 1인칭 주어 I이므로 am이 알맞다.

03 첫 번째 빈칸은 Dorothy가 런던에 있는지 묻는 질문에 No라고 대답했으므로 isn't가 알맞다. 두 번째 빈칸은 Dorothy가 지금 로마에 있다고 했으므로 is가 알맞다.

04 '~가 있었다'는 There was[were]로 나타내는데, 주어가 a bench로 단수이므로 There was a bench under the tree.로 써야 한다.

05 Are you 다음에 복수 명사가 왔으므로 you가 '너희들'의 의미이다. 따라서 대답으로는 Yes, we are. 또는 No, we aren't.가 적절하다.

06 [보기]의 주어는 3인칭 단수이고, three years ago라는 과거를 나타내는 부사구가 있으므로 was가 와야 한다. ⑤ 주어가 I이고 과거를 나타내고 있으므로 was가 와야 한다. ②,③,④는 주어가 모두 복수 명사이므로 are[were]가 들어가야 알맞다.

07 ① Were → Was, the movie가 단수 명사이므로 Was를 써야 한다.
⑤ aren't → isn't, 셀 수 없는 명사인 ice는 항상 단수 취급하므로 isn't를 써야 한다.

08 ④는 '거기에'라는 의미로 쓰인 부사이다. ①,②,③,⑤의 There [there]는 「There + be동사」로 쓰여 '~에 있(었)다'는 의미로 쓰였다.

09 Were you ~?로 질문했고 부정의 대답이므로 No, I wasn't. 또는 No, we weren't.로 대답하는 것이 알맞다.

10 주어가 3인칭 단수인 He이고 과거의 일이므로 were를 was로 고쳐야 한다.

11 '~가 있었다'는 There was[were]로 나타내는데, 주어가 복수 명사이므로 There were some pictures로 써야 한다.

12 주어가 These books인 복수 명사이고, 부정문이므로 are not[aren't] interesting으로 써야 한다.

13 첫 번째 빈칸은 의문문의 주어가 you이고 과거의 일이므로 Were를 써야 하고, 두 번째 빈칸은 No로 대답하였고 주어가 I이므로 wasn't를 써야 한다.

14 문장의 주어는 '그것의 다리들'이라는 의미가 되어야 하므로 It is의 줄임말인 It's가 아니라 소유격 Its로 고쳐야 한다.

15 B의 대답으로 보아 A는 be동사로 시작하는 의문문이며, they로 대답했으므로 주어로는 복수 명사가 와야 하므로 Are your parents in the living room?으로 물어보는 것이 알맞다. 따라서 세 번째 오는 단어는 parents이다.

Chapter 04 일반동사 1

Practice 01 일반동사의 현재형
워크북 24~25쪽

01-1
1 does	2 pays
3 has	4 eats
5 takes	6 fries
7 misses	8 climbs
9 makes	10 mixes
11 studies	12 catches

01-2
1 drinks	2 goes
3 watch	4 fly
5 wear	6 plays
7 fight	8 fixes
9 opens	10 jumps
11 finishes	12 reads

01-3
1 takes	2 eat
3 They	4 starts
5 has	6 Jessy
7 gets	8 The men

01-4
1 play	2 has
3 goes	4 comes
5 cries	6 swim
7 opens	8 teach

01-5
1 Anne lives
2 My dad jogs
3 The earth goes around
4 It rains
5 My sister washes
6 David speaks
7 My cats sleep
8 My parents want

Practice 02 일반동사 현재형의 부정문과 의문문
워크북 26~27쪽

02-1
1 don't have	2 doesn't like
3 don't know	4 doesn't love
5 don't do	6 don't listen
7 doesn't seem	8 doesn't write

02-2
1 Does water boil at 100°C?, it does
2 Do David and his brother do their homework after dinner?, they don't
3 Does the sun set in the west?, it does
4 Does her dad work at the bank?, he does
5 Does Mrs. Park have enough money?, she doesn't
6 Do you buy clothes on the Internet?, I [we] don't

Workbook Answers

7 Do Sue and her sister walk to school?,
   they do
8 Does he wash the dishes after a meal?, he
   doesn't

02-3
1	does not	2	Do
3	remember	4	don't
5	Does	6	read
7	Do	8	doesn't

02-4
1 doesn't → don't
2 snows → snow
3 Do → Does
4 don't → doesn't
5 Does → Do
6 has → have
7 loves → love
8 Do → Does

02-5
1 My sons don't like
2 My dad doesn't skip
3 Does the moon go around
4 Do you exercise
5 I don't keep
6 My sister doesn't wear
7 Does he go for a walk

Chapter Test

01 ①, ⑤	02 ④	03 ②	04 ④	05 ③
06 ①	07 ④	08 ④	09 ⑤	10 ②

11 Do, don't, practice
12 (1) go (2) play (3) flies (4) takes
13 (1) likes, doesn't like (2) don't like
14 Does your uncle live in Seoul?
15 comes from Canada, doesn't speak Korean well,
   has many Korean friends

01 ① 「자음 + y」로 끝나는 동사의 3인칭 단수형은 y를 i로 바꾸고 -es
   를 붙이므로 cry의 3인칭 단수형은 cries이다.
   ⑤ -ch로 끝나는 동사는 -es를 붙이므로 watch의 3인칭 단수 현재
   형은 watches이다.

02 문맥상 '나는 여자 형제가 없다'라는 내용이 되어야 하고, 주어가 1인
   칭 I이므로 빈칸에는 don't have가 알맞다.

03 주어가 3인칭 단수인 일반동사 현재형의 의문문은 「Does + 주어 +
   동사원형 ~?」의 형태이므로 enjoys를 동사원형 enjoy로 고쳐야
   한다.

04 동사가 doesn't like이므로 빈칸에 3인칭 단수만 올 수 있다.

05 뒤에 이어지는 말을 보아 긍정의 대답이 와야 하며, 의문문의 주어가
   you and your sister이므로 대답은 Yes, we do.로 해야 한다.

06 우리말을 바르게 영작하면 The bookstore does not open
   on Sundays.이므로 do는 필요하지 않다.

07 주어가 복수 명사(her parents)인 일반동사 현재형의 의문문은
   「Do + 주어 + 동사원형 ~?」으로 써야 하므로 Does를 Do로 고쳐야
   한다.

08 ④의 does는 '~을 하다'의 의미인 일반동사이고, 나머지는 의문문,
   부정문을 만드는 데 사용된 조동사 do[does]이다.

09 첫 번째 빈칸은 주어가 1인칭 I이므로 don't가 들어가야 하고, 두 번
   째 빈칸과 세 번째 빈칸은 주어가 3인칭 단수이므로 각각 Does와
   carries가 들어가야 한다.

10 ⓑ like → likes, 주어가 3인칭 단수이므로 likes로 써야 한다.
   ⓒ lives → live, 주어가 They로 복수이므로 일반동사를 원형 그대
   로 써야 한다.
   ⓓ goes → go, 주어가 you로 2인칭인 일반동사 현재형의 의문문
   은 「Do + 주어 + 동사원형 ~?」의 형태로 쓴다.

11 일반동사 현재형의 의문문의 주어가 복수 명사(the players)이므로
   주어 앞에는 Do를 쓰며, 부정의 대답은 No, they don't.로 한다.
   이어지는 문장에서도 주어가 복수이므로 일반동사 원형인 practice
   로 쓴다.

12 문맥상 주어 We와 My mom and I는 복수이므로 일반동사를 원
   형 그대로 써서 (1) go, (2) play가 각각 들어가야 알맞다. (3)과 (4)
   에는 my sister와 My dad가 3인칭 단수 주어이므로 일반동사 3
   인칭 단수 현재형인 flies, takes가 각각 들어가야 알맞다.

13 (1) 유나와 민호는 각각 3인칭 단수이므로 likes, doesn't like로
   써야 한다.
   (2) '민호와 유나'는 복수이므로 don't like로 써야 한다.

14 주어가 3인칭 단수이므로 일반동사 현재형의 의문문인 「Does + 주
   어 + 동사원형 ~?」의 형태로 쓴다. 주어는 your uncle이고, 동사는
   live이므로 Does your uncle live in Seoul?이 되어야 한다.

15 주어 I를 3인칭 단수 주어인 Lily로 바꾸면 come은 comes,
   don't speak은 doesn't speak, have는 has로 써서 문장을
   완성해야 한다.

Chapter
05 일반동사 2

Practice **01 일반동사의 과거형**

01-1
1	did	2	ran
3	visited	4	dropped
5	gave	6	tried
7	wrote	8	tied
9	used	10	made
11	studied	12	got

01-2
1	went	2	took

3	sent	4	watched
5	bought	6	felt
7	looked	8	joined
9	won	10	ate
11	fought	12	broke

01-3

1	liked	2	visited
3	knew	4	talked
5	played	6	started
7	met	8	ran

01-4

1	swimed → swam	2	raineds → rained
3	wears → wore	4	teaches → taught
5	hitted → hit	6	reads → read
7	works → worked	8	stoped → stopped

01-5

1 Our team lost 2 My puppy slept
3 He cut the cake 4 I drew the picture
5 She used my cell phone
6 I put together
7 They heard the news
8 He gave

Practice 02 **일반동사 과거형의 부정문과 의문문** 워크북 32~33쪽

02-1

1	didn't break	2	didn't know
3	didn't answer	4	didn't sit
5	didn't do	6	didn't drive
7	didn't find	8	didn't build

02-2

1 Did you read a comic book yesterday?, I [we] did
2 Did Karl buy a cap for his brother?, he didn't
3 Did they search for information on the Internet?, they didn't
4 Did your dad make a cake for your mom?, he did
5 Did the cat jump over the fence last night?, it did
6 Did many birds sing this morning?, they didn't
7 Did they live in Chicago last year?, they did
8 Did she take a rest last night?, she didn't

02-3

1	said → say	2	Do → Did
3	meets → meet	4	rides → ride
5	don't → didn't	6	Does → Did

02-4

1 Cathy didn't go
2 I didn't walk
3 Did you exercise
4 My sister didn't pass
5 Did Daniel borrow
6 Did you take

02-5

1 Did the train arrive on time?
2 He did not wash his car yesterday.

---

3 My dad did not fix the computer.
4 Did you lose the keys yesterday?
5 We did not do our best.
6 She did not need your help.

Chapter Test 워크북 34~35쪽

01 ②, ④	02 ③	03 ④	04 ③	05 ⑤
06 ⑤	07 ②	08 ②	09 ①	10 ④

11 He taught English 12 The rain stopped
13 Did you take these photos?
14 went, rode, ate, saw, had
15 Jack did not[didn't] tell his secret to me.

---

01 동사 read와 put은 현재형과 과거형이 같다. 나머지 동사의 현재형과 과거형은 ① run – ran, ③ know – knew, ⑤ hear – heard이다.

02 drop과 chat은 「단모음 + 단자음」으로 끝나는 동사로, 자음을 한 번 더 쓰고 -ed를 붙여서 dropped, chatted와 같이 과거형을 만든다.

03 과거에 일어난 일에 대해 말하고 있으므로 meet과 become의 과거형인 met와 became이 알맞다.

04 우리말을 영작하면 Sophia did not write the letter.이므로 wrote는 필요하지 않다.

05 yesterday라는 과거를 나타내는 표현이 있으므로 과거형 동사가 와야 하고, 동사 buy의 과거형은 bought이다.

06 Did로 시작하는 과거형 의문문이고, 이어지는 말로 보아 부정의 대답이 와야 하므로 No, she didn't.가 알맞다.

07 last week라는 과거를 나타내는 표현이 있으므로 동사의 현재형인 reads는 알맞지 않다.

08 ① slept → sleep, 일반동사 과거형의 부정문은 「did not[didn't] + 동사원형」의 형태로 써야 한다.
③ had → have, 일반동사 과거형의 의문문은 「Did + 주어 + 동사원형 ~?」의 형태로 써야 한다.
④ knew → know, 일반동사 과거형의 부정문은 「did not[didn't] + 동사원형」의 형태로 써야 한다.
⑤ go → went, last weekend라는 과거를 나타내는 표현이 있으므로 일반동사 과거형이 와야 하고, 동사 go는 불규칙 동사이므로 과거형은 went이다.

09 첫 번째 빈칸은 일반동사 과거형의 의문문인 「Did + 주어 + 동사원형 ~?」의 형태이므로 동사원형 snow가 알맞다. 두 번째 빈칸은 문맥상 긍정의 대답이 와야 하므로 「Yes, 주어 + did.」의 형태로 쓴다.

10 ⓐ sang → sing, 일반동사 과거형의 의문문은 「Did + 주어 + 동사원형 ~?」의 형태로 써야 한다.
ⓒ visited → visit, 일반동사 과거형의 부정문은 「did not[didn't] + 동사원형 ~.」의 형태로 써야 한다.
ⓓ drank → drink, 현재의 반복적인 습관을 나타내므로 현재형으로 써야 한다.

11 last year라는 과거를 나타내는 표현이 있으므로 teach의 과거형 taught를 써야 한다.

12 this morning이라는 과거를 나타내는 표현이 있으므로 stop의 과거형 stopped를 써야 한다.

13 일반동사 과거형의 의문문이므로 「Did + 주어 + 동사원형 ~?」의 형태로 쓴다. 주어는 you이고 '이 사진들을 찍다'는 take these photos이므로 Did you take these photos?가 되어야 한다.

14 지난 달에 있었던 일이므로 동사의 과거형을 써서 go의 과거형 went, ride의 과거형 rode, eat의 과거형 ate, see의 과거형 saw, have의 과거형 had를 순서대로 쓴다.

15 '말해 주지 않았다'는 일반동사 과거형의 부정문으로 나타내야 하므로 「did not[didn't] + 동사원형」의 형태로 고쳐 쓴다.

Chapter 06 현재진행형과 미래형

Practice 01 현재진행형

워크북 36~37쪽

01-1
1 is eating
2 are cleaning
3 is running
4 is raining
5 are moving
6 is learning
7 are holding

01-2
1 My mom isn't reading a magazine.
2 He isn't peeling apples.
3 The kids aren't making noise.
4 My dad isn't smiling at me.
5 Two puppies aren't sitting on the sofa.

01-3
1 Is she writing a letter?, she is not[isn't]
2 Are they hiding under the bed?, they not[aren't]
3 Is Tommy riding a bike?, he is not[isn't]
4 Are the farmers sleeping under the tree?, they are
5 Is Minhee looking out the window?, she is

01-4
1 playing
2 tying
3 is not
4 Is
5 know
6 Are
7 waiting

01-5
1 fixing
2 is not driving
3 reading
4 Are
5 planning
6 touching
7 is drawing

01-6
1 He is lying
2 We are not[aren't] doing

3 Are they solving
4 My kid is not[isn't] swimming
5 Is Anne drinking
6 The key is hanging
7 I am not reading

Practice 02 미래형

워크북 38~39쪽

02-1
1 will have
2 is going to rain
3 will call
4 am going to wash
5 are going to travel
6 is going to order

02-2
1 won't study
2 am not going to watch
3 won't visit
4 isn't going to cook
5 aren't going to join
6 aren't going to plant

02-3
1 Will he be a great pianist?, he will
2 Is Tommy going to have lunch at 1:00?, he isn't
3 Will they buy a gift for their mom?, they won't
4 Are the young men going to work here?, they are
5 Is Jessica going to see a dentist?, she is
6 Will he change his plans for summer vacation?, he won't

02-4
1 will
2 Are
3 will water
4 take
5 will not wash
6 are not going
7 am going to

02-5
1 dance
2 not going to
3 will help / are going to help
4 going to bake
5 not drive
6 run
7 be

02-6
1 I am[I'm] going to send
2 The store will open
3 She is not[isn't] going to take
4 Will you be
5 Are they going to go
6 Jake will not[won't] cut
7 I am not going to answer

Chapter Test

워크북 40~41쪽

01 ①, ⑤　02 ④　03 ⑤　04 ②　05 ②
06 ③　07 ③　08 ⑤　09 ③　10 ①
11 it will not[won't]　12 We are not going to wait
13 ⓐ are traveling　ⓑ are going
14 are not speaking
15 Are you going to buy this cap?

01 ① 「자음 + e」로 끝나는 동사는 e를 삭제하고 -ing를 붙이므로 living이 되어야 한다.
⑤ 「단모음 + 단자음」으로 끝나는 동사는 자음을 한 번 더 쓰고 -ing를 붙이므로 swimming이 되어야 한다.

02 now로 보아 지금 진행 중인 일을 나타내는 현재진행형 「be동사 + 동사원형-ing」를 쓰는 것이 알맞다. 주어가 3인칭 단수이므로 is looking으로 써야 한다.

03 tomorrow로 보아 미래의 일을 나타내는 문장이고 주어가 복수이므로 빈칸에는 will이나 are going to가 와야 알맞다.

04 첫 번째 빈칸은 next year로 보아 미래형으로 써야 하므로 will try가 알맞고, 두 번째 빈칸의 want는 '원하다'라는 의미의 감정을 나타내는 동사로 진행형으로 쓸 수 없으므로 want가 알맞다.

05 ① jogging → am jogging, '~하고 있다'라는 의미의 현재진행형은 「be동사 + 동사원형-ing」의 형태로 나타낸다.
③ travels → travel, will 다음에는 동사원형을 써야 한다.
④ He is going to go to the airport. → He is going to the airport, '그는 공항에 가는 중이다.'라는 의미는 현재진행형 문장이므로 「be동사 + 동사원형-ing」의 형태로 나타낸다.
⑤ are going not to → are not going to, 「be going to + 동사원형」의 부정형은 「be동사 + not + going to + 동사원형」으로 써야 한다.

06 ③은 '~에 가는 중이다'라는 의미인 현재진행형 문장이고, 나머지는 미래형 「be going to + 동사원형」이 쓰인 문장이다.

07 B의 대답으로 보아 A에는 be동사로 시작하는 현재진행형 의문문이 와야 한다. I로 대답하고 있으므로 의문문의 주어는 you가 되어 Are you reading으로 써야 한다.

08 will not의 축약형인 won't 다음에는 동사원형을 써야 하므로 watching은 watch로 고쳐야 한다.

09 「Are you going to + 동사원형 ~?」의 미래형 의문문에 대한 긍정의 대답은 Yes, I am.이 되어야 한다.

10 ⓐ work → to work, 미래형 문장은 「Are you going to + 동사원형 ~?」의 형태로 써야 한다.
ⓑ am having → have, '가지다'의 의미로 쓰인 have는 진행형으로 쓸 수 없다.
ⓒ changes → change, will not의 축약형인 won't 다음에는 동사원형을 써야 한다.
ⓔ are → is, 주어가 3인칭 단수이므로 be동사 is를 써야 한다.

11 「Will + 주어 + 동사원형 ~?」의 의문문에 대한 부정의 대답은 「No, 주어 + will not[won't].」이다.

12 주어가 '우리'인 미래형의 부정문이므로 We 다음에 「be동사 + not + going to + 동사원형」의 순서가 되도록 배열한다.

13 ⓐ now로 보아 지금 일어나고 있는 일을 나타내므로 현재진행형 「be동사 + 동사원형-ing」의 형태인 are traveling으로 고쳐야 한다.
ⓑ tomorrow로 보아 미래의 일을 나타내는 「be going to + 동사원형」을 써야 하고, 주어가 We이므로 going을 are going으로 고쳐야 한다.

14 현재진행형의 부정문은 「be동사 + not + 동사원형-ing」이다. 주어가 They이므로 be동사는 are가 와야 한다.

15 미래의 계획을 나타내는 미래형 의문문 중에서 be동사를 포함하는 것은 「Be동사 + 주어 + going to + 동사원형 ~?」이다. 주어가 you이고, 7단어이므로 Are you going to buy this cap?으로 써야 한다.

Chapter 07 조동사

Practice 01 조동사 can, may

워크북 42~43쪽

01-1 1 can live　2 can't swim
3 Can, use　4 can't fly
5 Can, pass　6 can't move

01-2 1 may use　2 may wear
3 May, open　4 May, stay
5 may be　6 May, leave

01-3 1 Yes, I can.
2 May I
3 No, she may not.
4 No, you cannot[can't].
5 No, you may not.

01-4 1 can　2 be
3 cannot play　4 may
5 May　6 read
7 dance　8 not remember

01-5 1 허가　2 가능
3 허가　4 추측
5 가능　6 허가
7 추측　8 허가

01-6 1 make　2 go
3 Can he play　4 May I ask
5 may be　6 cannot[can't] eat
7 Can we have　8 may not be

02 -1

1	must	2	must
3	must not	4	must not
5	must	6	must not

02 -2

1	has to wash	2	have to pick up
3	have to cook	4	has to study
5	has to go	6	have to wash

02 -3

1	doesn't have to	2	has to
3	don't have to	4	have to
5	have to	6	doesn't have to

02 -4

1	clean	2	has to
3	must	4	doesn't have to
5	has	6	don't have to

02 -5

1 He must be polite
2 She doesn't have to finish
3 They must not park
4 She has to follow
5 You don't have to worry
6 We have to make

02 -6

1 He must not drink too much coffee.
2 You don't have to take your umbrella.
3 We have to wear seat belts.
4 Do they have to deliver it within a week?
5 Amy must send an email to him.
6 She has to return some books to the library.

---

01 ②	02 ③	03 ④	04 ②	05 ④
06 ④	07 ②	08 ③	09 ④	10 ③

11 has to   12 Must   13 has → have
14 (1) can drive a car   (2) cannot[can't] drive a car
15 You don't have to listen to their words carefully.

01 날씨가 화창하고 따뜻하다고 했으므로 소풍을 가도 된다는 허가의 의미를 나타내는 may가 알맞다.

02 시력이 나쁘다고 했으므로 안경을 써야 한다는 의무의 의미를 나타내는 must가 알맞다.

03 [보기]와 ④의 Can[can]은 '~해도 된다'라는 허가의 의미를 나타내고, ①,②,③,⑤의 can[Can]은 '~할 수 있다'라는 가능이나 능력의 의미를 나타낸다.

04 [보기]와 ②의 may는 '~일지도 모른다'라는 추측의 의미를 나타내고, ①,③,④,⑤의 May[may]는 '~해도 된다'라는 허가의 의미를 나타낸다.

05 첫 번째 빈칸은 '~임에 틀림없다'라는 강한 추측을 나타내는 의미이고, 두 번째 빈칸은 '~해야 한다'라는 의무의 의미를 나타내고 있으므로 공통으로 들어갈 말은 must가 알맞다.

06 허가의 의미를 나타내는 의문문 「May I ~?」에 대한 대답은 Yes, you may. 또는 No, you may not.으로 한다.

07 주어가 3인칭 단수 He이므로 have to를 has to로 고쳐야 한다.

08 조동사 can 의문문은 「Can + 주어 + 동사원형 ~?」의 형태이므로 speaks를 speak으로 고쳐야 한다.

09 '~해서는 안 된다'라는 의미의 강한 금지는 must not으로 나타낸다.

10 ⓑ is → be, 조동사 뒤에는 주어의 인칭이나 수에 상관없이 동사원형이 와야 한다.
ⓒ don't has to → doesn't have to, 주어가 3인칭 단수 He이므로 조동사 have to의 부정형은 doesn't have to로 써야 한다.

11 '~해야 한다'라는 의무를 나타내는 must는 have to로 바꿔 쓸 수 있는데, 주어가 3인칭 단수이므로 has to로 써야 한다.

12 '주말에는 학교에 갈 필요가 없다'라는 B의 대답으로 보아 '매일 학교에 가야 하는지'를 묻는 말이 되어야 자연스러우므로 '~해야 한다'라는 의무의 의미를 나타내는 조동사 must가 와야 적절하다.

13 주어가 We로 복수형이므로 has to를 have to로 고쳐야 한다.

14 (1) 민수는 차를 운전할 수 있지만, 쿠키는 만들 수 없으므로 can drive a car로 써야 한다.
(2) Judy는 테니스를 칠 수 있지만, 차는 운전할 수 없으므로 cannot[can't] drive a car로 써야 한다.

15 '~할 필요가 없다'라는 불필요의 의미를 나타내는 조동사 don't have to를 이용하여 나타낸다. (carefully: 주의 깊게)

Chapter 08   형용사와 부사

01 -1

1	hungry, thirsty	2	green
3	famous	4	brown, blue
5	fast	6	cold
7	kind	8	black

01 -2

1	much	2	many
3	many	4	much
5	much	6	many
7	much	8	many

01 -3

1	some	2	some
3	any	4	some
5	some	6	any
7	any	8	some

01 -4

1	new car	2	a great book

3 something rare   4 some
5 many   6 any
7 much

01-5
1 the sharp knife   2 some bread
3 many toys   4 much homework
5 any time   6 something new
7 sounds beautiful

01-6
1 The students look tired.
2 This is an old temple.
3 I bought some flowers.
4 Do you have anything cheap?
5 We do something special for Children's Day.
6 I saw many students at the bookstore.
7 There isn't any hospital on this street.

Practice 02 부사

02-1
1 wisely   2 healthily
3 strangely   4 warmly
5 quietly   6 well
7 really   8 politely
9 happily   10 luckily

02-2
1 hard, hardly   2 late, lately
3 high, highly   4 near, nearly

02-3
1 I usually eat apple pie for dessert.
2 My father is often busy.
3 Ava is never selfish.
4 They must always get up at 6:00.
5 We often see her there.

02-4
1 brightly   2 very fast
3 often tells   4 well
5 Sadly   6 quietly
7 will never

02-5
1 clearly   2 heavily
3 late   4 very well
5 never make   6 can always
7 high

02-6
1 am sometimes late
2 Luckily, I passed
3 always drinks some milk
4 are usually kind to us
5 will never forget you
6 is very important to me

Chapter Test

01 ③ 02 ② 03 ④ 04 ② 05 ①
06 ② 07 ② 08 ⑤ 09 ② 10 ③
11 was hardly a cloud in the sky
12 nearly fell asleep in class
13 (1) always goes to school
   (2) never goes to school
   (3) usually goes to school
14 hard meets → hardly meets
15 Too much stress is not good for

01 ③ '혼자의, 쓸쓸한'이라는 의미의 형용사 lone과 '외로운'이라는 의미의 형용사 lonely의 관계이다. ①,②,④,⑤ 형용사와 부사의 관계이다.

02 '몇몇의, 조금의'라는 의미의 수량 형용사로 긍정문에는 some을 쓴다.

03 명사 students를 수식하는 형용사가 와야 하는데, well은 부사이다.

04 빈칸 뒤에 셀 수 있는 명사의 복수형 birds가 왔으므로 셀 수 없는 명사 앞에 쓰는 수량 형용사 much는 올 수 없다.

05 동사 speak을 꾸며 주는 '빨리'라는 뜻의 부사 fast로 고쳐야 알맞다. fast는 형용사와 부사의 형태가 같다.

06 빈도부사는 일반적으로 일반동사 앞에 오므로 sometimes writes로 고쳐야 한다. 참고로 빈도부사 sometimes는 문장 맨 앞이나 맨 끝에 오기도 한다.

07 첫 번째 빈칸은 문맥상 '늦게'라는 의미의 부사 late가 와야 한다. 두 번째 빈칸은 '최근에'라는 의미가 와야 자연스러우므로 부사 lately가 와야 한다.

08 ⑤ '이른'이라는 의미의 형용사로 쓰였다. ①,②,③,④ '일찍'이라는 의미의 부사로 쓰였다.

09 ⓐ easy → easily, 동사 mix를 꾸며 주는 '쉽게'라는 의미의 부사가 와야 한다.
ⓓ goes often → often goes, 빈도부사 often은 일반적으로 일반동사 앞에 위치한다.

10 ⓑ always is → is always, 빈도부사 always는 일반적으로 be동사 뒤에 위치한다.
ⓒ much → many, 셀 수 있는 명사의 복수형 trees를 수식하는 수량 형용사 many가 와야 한다.

11 과거형 문장으로 '거의 ~ 않다'라는 의미의 부사 hardly가 be동사 was 뒤에 위치한다.

12 과거형 문장으로 '거의'라는 의미의 부사 nearly가 일반동사 fell 앞에서 동사를 꾸며 준다.

13 (1) 미나는 항상 버스를 타고 등교하므로 빈도부사 always를 일반동사(goes) 앞에 써서 나타낸다.
(2) 미나는 절대 지하철을 타고 등교하지 않으므로 빈도부사 never를 일반동사(goes) 앞에 써서 나타낸다.
(3) Tom은 대개 지하철을 타고 등교하므로 빈도부사 usually를 일반동사(goes) 앞에 써서 나타낸다.

14 '친구들을 거의 만나지 못한다'라는 의미가 되어야 자연스러우므로

'열심히'라는 뜻의 부사 hard를 '거의 ~ 않다'라는 뜻의 부사 hardly로 고쳐야 한다.

15 stress는 셀 수 없는 명사이므로 수량 형용사 much를 써서 too much stress로 나타내고, 이어서 is not good for를 쓴다. (be good for: ~에 좋다)

Chapter 09 전치사

Practice 01 장소를 나타내는 전치사
워크북 54~55쪽

01-1
1	in	2	on
3	in front of	4	under
5	behind	6	next to
7	over		

01-2
1	next to	2	on
3	at	4	in
5	behind	6	under
7	in front of		

01-3
1	at	2	in
3	me	4	on
5	in front of	6	next to
7	under	8	over

01-4
1 on the floor
2 at the bus stop
3 in front of the church
4 under the sea
5 behind the sofa
6 next to the bed
7 in Korea

01-5
1 stood in front of the students
2 many vegetables in the box
3 slept under the tree
4 the one next to the school
5 heard footsteps behind her
6 get a taxi at the airport
7 a mark on your shirt

Practice 02 시간을 나타내는 전치사
워크북 56~57쪽

02-1
1	in	2	at
3	at	4	in
5	on	6	in
7	on		

02-2
1	after	2	before
3	before	4	before
5	after	6	after
7	before		

02-3
1	for	2	for
3	during	4	during
5	during	6	for
7	during		

02-4
1	during	2	on
3	in	4	at
5	for	6	in

02-5
1	at	2	during
3	on	4	for
5	in		

02-6
1 ends at 3 p.m.
2 go to the movies on Friday
3 drinks water before meals
4 drew the picture for two weeks
5 change color in autumn
6 goes to the gym after lunch

Chapter Test
워크북 58~59쪽

01 ③	02 ②	03 ③	04 ④	05 ③
06 ②	07 ①	08 ③	09 ④	10 ③

11 for two hours
12 meet at my house before the show
13 next to the post office
14 in → on
15 Don't park in front of the store.

01 요일 앞에는 전치사 on을 쓴다.

02 '신호등에서'라는 장소의 한 지점을 나타내므로 전치사 at이 알맞다.

03 첫 번째 빈칸은 도시 이름 앞이므로 전치사 in을 쓴다. 두 번째 빈칸은 연도 앞이므로 전치사 in을 쓴다.

04 뒤에 숫자를 포함한 구체적인 기간인 an hour가 나오므로 전치사 during을 for로 고쳐야 한다.

05 '도로의 끝에서'라는 장소의 한 지점을 나타내므로 전치사 in을 at으로 고쳐야 한다.

06 첫 번째 빈칸은 장소의 한 지점을 나타내므로 전치사 at을 써야 하고, 두 번째 빈칸은 오후를 나타내므로 전치사 in을 써야 한다.

07 첫 번째 빈칸은 도시 앞이므로 전치사 in을 써야 하고, 두 번째 빈칸은 구체적인 시각 앞이므로 전치사 at을 써야 한다.

08 축구공은 의자 '아래에(under)' 있다.

09 '~ 후에'라는 의미는 전치사 after로 나타낸다.

10 ⓒ in → at, 6 o'clock이라는 구체적인 시각 앞에는 전치사 at을 쓴다.

ⓓ at → in, 국가 앞에는 전치사 in을 쓴다.

11 '~ 동안'이라는 의미로 숫자를 포함한 구체적인 기간인 two hours 가 있으므로 전치사 for를 사용한다.

12 '~에'라는 의미로 장소의 한 지점을 나타내는 전치사 at과 '~ 전에'라 는 의미로 시간을 나타내는 전치사 before를 사용하여 나타낸다.

13 병원은 우체국 '옆에(next to)' 있다.

14 벤치 위에 앉은 것으로 '(표면과 맞닿은 바로) ~ 위에'라는 의미는 전치 사 on을 써야 하므로 in을 on으로 고쳐야 한다.

15 '~ 앞에'라는 의미는 전치사 in front of를 써야 하고, '~하지 마라.'라 는 의미는 부정 명령문인 「Don't + 동사원형 ~.」의 형태로 나타낸다.

Chapter 10 의문사

Practice 01 의문사 who, what
워크북 60~61쪽

01-1
1	Who	2	Who
3	Whose	4	Who[What]
5	What	6	Whose
7	Who	8	What
9	Whose	10	What

01-2
1	Whose	2	Who(m)
3	Whose	4	What
5	Who	6	What
7	Who(m)		

01-3
1	What	2	Whose
3	What	4	Who
5	What	6	Who
7	What		

01-4
1	What	2	Who
3	Whose	4	What
5	Who	6	Who
7	Whose		

01-5
1	Who is	2	What is
3	What exercise do	4	Whose backpack
5	Who told		
6	Who(m) did you meet		

Practice 02 의문사 when, where, why, how
워크북 62~63쪽

02-1
1	Why	2	When
3	Where	4	How
5	Why	6	Where

02-2
1	When	2	How
3	Why	4	How many
5	Where	6	When[What time]

02-3
1	Why	2	Where
3	When	4	How far
5	How often	6	Where

02-4
1 Why did your mom make
2 When will you return
3 Where did he buy
4 How did you know
5 Why must we sleep
6 Where does she study
7 What time do they have

02-5
1 Where did you meet yesterday?
2 How did the accident happen?
3 Why did you tease Tim?
4 When do you feel happy?
5 Why does a dog wag its tail?
6 When do you usually get up?
7 How did you solve the difficult problem?

Chapter Test
워크북 64~65쪽

01 ⑤		02 ③		03 ②		04 ⑤		05 ②	
06 ②		07 ④		08 ②		09 ④		10 ⑤	

11 What time
12 (1) Who (2) what
13 What color do you like
14 When → Where
15 How much water do you drink every day?

01 '길 건너편에 있다'라고 대답하고 있으므로 장소를 묻는 의문사 where가 알맞다.

02 '저녁 식사 후에' 숙제를 한다고 대답하고 있으므로 시간을 묻는 의문 사 when이 알맞다.

03 '날씨가 어떤지' 묻는 말이므로 의문사 What을 상태를 묻는 의문사 How로 고쳐야 한다.

04 뒤에 셀 수 있는 명사의 복수형 tickets가 이어지므로 How much 를 How many로 고쳐야 한다.

05 ②는 사물을 묻는 의문사 what이 들어가야 하고 ①,③,④,⑤는 장소 를 묻는 의문사 where가 들어가야 알맞다.

06 첫 번째 빈칸은 '오늘 시험이 어땠는지' 묻고 있으므로 의문사 how가 알맞다. 두 번째 빈칸은 '여기서 공원까지 거리가 얼마나 먼지' 묻고 있 으므로 how far가 되어야 알맞다.

07 '자동차로 여기 온다'라고 말하는 B의 대답으로 보아 '언제'라는 시간 을 묻는 의문사 When을 '어떻게'라는 뜻의 수단·방법을 묻는 의문사 How로 고쳐야 한다.

08 이유를 묻는 의문사 why를 사용하여 학교에 결석한 이유를 묻고 있 으므로 '왜냐하면'이라는 뜻의 because를 써서 대답한다.

09 '일주일에 두 번 컴퓨터 게임을 한다'라고 하였으므로 '얼마나 자주'라는 의미의 횟수를 묻는 how often을 써서 질문해야 한다.

10 '얼마나 오래'라는 의미는 how long으로 나타낸다.

11 '언제 빵집이 문을 여는지'를 묻는 말이다. when이 시각을 물을 때는 what time으로 바꿔 쓸 수 있다.

12 (1) '그는 나의 삼촌 David야.'라는 B의 대답으로 보아 그 남자가 누구인지 묻는 말이 와야 하므로 의문사 who가 알맞다.
(2) '그는 컴퓨터 기술자야.'라는 B의 대답으로 보아 그의 직업을 묻는 말이 와야 하므로 의문사 what이 알맞다.

13 셔츠를 찾고 있다는 A의 말에 대해 어떤 색을 좋아하는지 물을 때 「What + 명사 + do동사 + 주어 + 동사원형 ~?」의 형태로 나타낸다.

14 '학교 옆 가게에서'라는 장소를 대답하고 있으므로 시간을 묻는 의문사 When을 장소를 묻는 의문사 Where로 고쳐야 한다.

15 '얼마나 많은'이라는 의미의 '양'을 묻고 있으므로 how much를 써서 「How much water + do동사 + 주어 + 동사원형 ~?」의 어순으로 나타낸다.

Chapter 11 접속사

Practice 01 접속사 and, but, or, so
워크북 66~67쪽

01-1
1	and	2	but
3	or	4	so
5	but	6	or

01-2
1 so she gained weight
2 and (we) collected seashells
3 but (it) will rain soon
4 and my sister bought blue jeans
5 or on foot

01-3
1	and	2	so
3	or	4	and
5	but	6	or

01-4
1	but	2	or
3	or	4	and
5	so		

01-5
1 wash the dishes or clean the living room
2 are delicious, but too much sugar is bad
3 so I feel tired
4 a fork, a knife, and a plate
5 so he beat the other competitors

Practice 02 접속사 when, because
워크북 68~69쪽

02-1
1	because	2	when
3	When	4	Because
5	when	6	because

02-2
1 because her sister drew on her report
2 when I was an elementary school student
3 When I arrived at the bus stop
4 Because I don't have enough money
5 When my dog barked loudly
6 because of a bad cold

02-3
1	because	2	because
3	When	4	Because of
5	Because	6	When

02-4
1 When we heard the news
2 Because it was too hot
3 Because I have two decayed teeth
4 When he is angry
5 because of the typhoon

02-5
1 when we take medicine
2 because he is rude
3 when I saw the accident
4 because of the bad weather
5 Because the box is very heavy

Chapter Test
워크북 70~71쪽

01 ②	02 ⑤	03 ③	04 ⑤	05 ②
06 ④	07 ④	08 ⑤	09 ①	10 ④

11 some money, so she bought a bike
12 warm water when he has a cold
13 because it's broken
14 will see → see
15 Many people grow plants or keep pets at home.

01 '나의 아버지는 일찍 일어나서 아침 식사를 준비하신다'라는 의미가 되어야 자연스러우므로 '~와', '그리고'라는 의미의 접속사 and가 알맞다.

02 '나는 어제 너무 많이 먹었기 때문에 배가 아팠다'라는 의미가 되어야 자연스러우므로 '~ 때문에'라는 의미의 접속사 because가 알맞다.

03 '그녀는 노래는 잘 부르지만, 춤은 못 춘다'라는 의미가 되어야 자연스러우므로 접속사 so를 but으로 고쳐야 한다.

04 '네가 나에게 전화했을 때 나는 자고 있었다'라는 의미가 되어야 자연스러우므로 접속사 because를 when으로 고쳐야 한다.

05 첫 번째 빈칸은 '탁자 한 개, 의자 두 개, 그리고 책상 한 개가 필요하다'라는 의미가 되어야 자연스러우므로 '~와', '그리고'라는 의미를 나타내는 접속사 and가 알맞다. 두 번째 빈칸은 '후식으로 커피와 케이크를 먹었다'라는 의미가 되어야 자연스러우므로 접속사 and가 와야 한다.

06 첫 번째 빈칸은 '네 학교는 언제 개학하니?'라는 의미가 되어야 자연스러우므로 '언제'를 묻는 의문사 when이 알맞다. 두 번째 빈칸은 '내 남동생은 기분이 좋을 때 기타를 친다'라는 의미이거나 '내 남동생은 기분이 좋아서 기타를 친다'라는 의미가 되어야 자연스러우므로 '~할 때'라는 의미를 나타내는 접속사 when이나 '~때문에'라는 의미를 나타내는 접속사 because가 올 수 있다.

07 시간의 부사절에서 미래의 일을 나타낼 때 주절이 미래형일지라도 부사절은 현재형으로 써야 하므로 will finish를 finish로 고쳐야 한다.

08 ⑤는 뒤에 명사구(heavy snow)가 오므로 전치사구 because of가 알맞다. ①,②,③,④는 뒤에 주어와 동사가 있는 절이 오므로 접속사 because가 알맞다.

09 첫 번째 빈칸은 '바람이 너무 세서, 나는 오늘 밤에 외출하지 않을 것이다'라는 의미가 되어야 자연스러우므로 '그래서'라는 의미의 접속사 so가 와야 한다. 두 번째 빈칸은 '내가 그녀를 만났을 때 그녀는 행복해 보였다'라는 의미가 되어야 자연스러우므로 '~할 때'라는 의미의 접속사 when이 알맞다.

10 ⓓ because → because of, '~때문에'라는 의미이고, 뒤에 명사구(the traffic jam)가 오므로 because of가 와야 한다.

11 '돈이 좀 있어서 자전거를 샀다'라는 내용은 원인과 결과의 관계이므로 '그래서'라는 의미의 접속사 so를 사용하여 나타낸다.

12 '감기에 걸리면'이라는 때를 나타내므로 '~할 때, ~하면'이라는 의미의 접속사 when을 사용하여 나타낸다.

13 빈칸에는 Tom이 미나의 휴대전화가 고장이 나서 그것을 사용할 수 없다는 말이 와야 하므로 이유의 접속사 because를 사용하여 나타낸다.

14 시간의 부사절에서 미래의 일을 나타낼 때 주절이 미래형일지라도 부사절은 현재형으로 써야 하므로 will see를 see로 고쳐야 한다.

15 많은 사람들이 집에서 '식물을 기르거나 반려동물을 키운다'라는 선택 사항을 나타내므로 '또는', '혹은'이라는 의미의 접속사 or를 사용한다. or를 사용하여 9단어로 써야 하므로 Many people grow plants or keep pets at home.으로 연결하는 것이 알맞다.

Chapter 12 · 명령문, 청유문, 감탄문

Practice 01 명령문, 청유문
워크북 72~73쪽

01-1
1	Close	2	Let's be
3	Let's turn	4	Save
5	Be	6	Turn

01-2
1	Don't drink	2	Don't add
3	Let's not report	4	Don't take pictures
5	Let's not wash	6	Let's not go

01-3
1	Let's	2	not waste
3	Do	4	be
5	Be	6	Don't

01-4
1	Be	2	Don't wake
3	Let's sell	4	Take off
5	Let's not talk	6	Don't be angry

01-5
1	Let's not take	2	Don't make
3	Give	4	Let's put
5	Don't give up	6	Pat

Practice 02 감탄문
워크북 74~75쪽

02-1
1	What	2	How
3	What	4	How
5	What	6	What
7	How	8	How
9	What	10	How

02-2
1 What noisy kids
2 How skinny
3 What a beautiful rainbow
4 How slowly
5 What happy news
6 How crowded
7 What a lovely day
8 How elegant

02-3
1	How	2	How
3	What	4	How
5	What a		

02-4
1 How healthy
2 How humorous
3 What a useful tool
4 What hard bread
5 What a polite girl
6 How handsome

02-5
1 How sweet this chocolate is!
2 What a big mushroom it is!
3 What neat handwriting it is!
4 How rough the waves are!
5 What nice pictures they are!
6 How heavy your backpack is!

Chapter Test
워크북 76~77쪽

01 ③	02 ④	03 ①	04 ②	05 ③
06 ②	07 ①	08 ④	09 ⑤	10 ②

11 How diligent she is   12 to eat → eat
13 Don't swim   14 be careful
15 What a pretty doll this is!

01 '~하지 마라.'라는 의미의 부정 명령문은 「Don't + 동사원형 ~.」의 형태로 나타낸다.

02 부사 high를 강조하는 how 감탄문으로 「How + 형용사/부사 + 주어 + 동사!」의 형태로 나타낸다.

03 명사 big elephants를 강조하는 감탄문이므로 How를 What으로 고쳐야 한다.

04 '~하지 말자.'라는 의미의 부정 청유문은 「Let's not + 동사원형 ~.」의 형태로 나타내므로 Let's don't를 Let's not으로 고쳐야 한다.

05 ③은 부사 hard를 강조하는 감탄문이므로 How가 와야 한다. ①,②,④,⑤는 명사를 강조하는 감탄문이므로 What을 써야 한다.

06 첫 번째 빈칸은 '그녀는 어떻게 출근하니?'라는 의미가 되어야 자연스러우므로 '어떻게'라는 의미로 수단을 묻는 의문사 how가 알맞다. 두 번째 빈칸은 '그 돌은 정말 무겁구나!'라는 의미가 되어야 자연스러우므로 형용사 heavy를 강조하는 how 감탄문을 쓴다.

07 '~하지 마라.'라는 의미의 부정 명령문은 「Don't + 동사원형 ~.」의 형태로 나타내므로 No는 Don't로 고쳐야 한다.

08 ① Not → Don't, 일반동사 부정 명령문은 「Don't + 동사원형 ~.」의 형태로 나타낸다.
    ② Lets → Let's, '~하자.'라고 상대에게 권유하는 청유문은 「Let's + 동사원형 ~.」의 형태로 쓴다.
    ③ Comes → Come, 일반동사의 긍정 명령문은 「동사원형 ~.」의 형태로 나타낸다.
    ⑤ Let's talk not → Let's not talk, '~하지 말자.'라는 의미의 부정 청유문은 「Let's not + 동사원형 ~.」의 형태로 쓴다.

09 '그것은 정말 재미있는 책이구나!'라는 의미의 명사를 강조하는 what 감탄문은 「What + a[an] + 형용사 + 명사 + 주어 + 동사!」의 형태로 나타낸다. 관사를 빠뜨리지 않도록 유의한다.

10 ⓑ is the party → the party is, 형용사나 부사를 강조하는 how 감탄문은 「How + 형용사/부사 + 주어 + 동사!」의 형태로 나타낸다.
    ⓓ these are → this is 또는 a dry desert → dry deserts, 감탄문 내 명사, 주어, 동사의 수를 일치시켜야 한다.

11 '그녀는 정말 부지런하구나!'라는 의미가 되도록 「How + 형용사/부사 + 주어 + 동사!」의 형태로 형용사를 강조하는 how 감탄문으로 나타낸다.

12 '~하자.'라는 의미의 긍정 청유문은 「Let's + 동사원형 ~.」의 형태로 나타내므로 to eat을 eat으로 고쳐야 한다.

13 '강에서 수영하지 마라.'라는 의미가 되도록 「Don't + 동사원형 ~.」의 형태인 부정 명령문으로 나타낸다.

14 형용사 careful을 이용하여 문맥상 '조심하라'라는 명령문이 와야 하므로 be로 시작하여 be careful로 쓴다.

15 '이것은 정말 예쁜 인형이구나!'라는 의미가 되도록 명사를 강조하는 what 감탄문인 「What + a[an] + 형용사 + 명사 + 주어 + 동사!」의 형태로 나타낸다.

MEMO

GRAMMAR
MASTER

절취선